BUT WHERE IS GOD?
PSYCHOTHERAPY AND THE RELIGIOUS SEARCH

BUT WHERE IS GOD?

PSYCHOTHERAPY AND THE RELIGIOUS SEARCH

JOHN C. ROBINSON

Troitsa Books
Huntington, New York

Editorial Production:	Susan Boriotti
Office Manager:	Annette Hellinger
Graphics:	Frank Grucci and Jennifer Lucas
Information Editor:	Tatiana Shohov
Book Production:	Donna Dennis, Patrick Davin, Christine Mathosian and Tammy Sauter
Circulation:	Maryanne Schmidt
Marketing/Sales:	Cathy DeGregory

Library of Congress Cataloging-in-Publication Data
Robinson, John C., 1946-
  But where is God?: psychotherapy and the religious search / by John C. Robinson.
    p. cm.
  ISBN 1-56072-504-X
  1. Psychotherapy -- Religious aspects. 2. Psychotherapy patients -- Religious life. 3. Psychology and religion. 4. Spirituality. I. Title.
RC489.R46R6   1998   98-49097
616.89'41--dc21   CIP

Copyright © 1999 by John C. Robinson
  Troitsa Books, a division of
  Nova Science Publishers, Inc.
  6080 Jericho Turnpike, Suite 207
  Commack, New York 11725
  Tele. 516-499-3103   Fax 516-499-3146
  e-mail: Novascience@earthlink.net
  e-mail: Novascil@aol.com
  Web Site: http://www.nexusworld.com/nova

Printed in the United States of America

CONTENTS

PREFACE

Religion, and its wellspring, mystical spirituality, have been abiding and passionate interests for me since childhood. I have always felt a natural, indwelling affinity with the sacred. Religious dogma, on the other hand, confused me terribly. Growing up I could not figure out what its real purpose and teachings were, and always had many more questions than answers:

* "Is there a God?"
* "What is God?"
* "Can we know God directly?"
* "What does God want from us?"
* "Is there one deity or many?"
* "Why are there so many different religions and so many sects of each religion?"
* "Why do some people believe they have the right to tell me what religion I should practice?"
* "How can people be so certain about things like heaven, hell, and eternal souls?"
* "How can a religion believe that a person is inherently evil, sinful, or bad?"
* "How do I discover what I believe?"
* "Why do some people have profound religious experiences and not others?"
* "What really happens in these experiences?"
* "How can respected religious leaders or supposedly enlightened gurus get in trouble for sexual or financial improprieties?"
* "Are such people frauds?"
* "What is a spiritually enlightened teacher?"
* "How can devoutly religious people harm others with prejudice, ethnic hatred, or religiously rationalized punishment?"
* "Why do some religions justify warfare?"
* "When is religion, spirituality, or mystical experience simply an expression of psychological problems?"
* "Does religion have anything to offer in psychological healing?"
* "How do we understand the psychology of religion and the religion of psychology?"

Eventually, I realized that nearly everyone asks these kinds of questions some time in their life, that psychology and the social sciences actually hold some of the answers, and that only a well thought out integration of psychological, religious, spiritual, and mystical experience could fully grasp the diverse and complex phenomena of the religious search.

I grew up without formal religious instruction. My parents were products of their times, times in which the heady achievements of science seemed ready to supplant the "superstitious" foundations of religion altogether. I remember the day Time Magazine's cover shocked the world with the question, "Is God dead?" Skeptical (and critical) of formal religion, my parents turned to psychoanalysis and science in its place. "People seek religious answers because they are neurotic,"

I was told, "or because they cannot understand the laws of science." Unable to unfold my still callow religious longing in this discrediting atmosphere, I accepted the twentieth century's "enlightened" worldview (which I eventually discovered was also a religion).

Despite this inauspicious beginning, I never surrendered my spiritual yearning, and for years, religion remained a fascinating and compelling mystery for me. In high school, I would ask my friends all sorts of questions about their religions and what they believed about heaven, hell, souls, and death. "Why don't baby sparrows go to heaven?" "How do you know God loves you?" As a guest at their religious services, I felt like an anthropologist witnessing strange, indecipherable, yet intriguing rituals. Encountering smugly confidant religious professionals, on the other hand, I smoldered angrily, wanting to confront their arrogant certainty. I could see that there was also something unhealthy about religion, that it could be used to control, manipulate, shame, or disempower people. I needed to figure out how the religious sentiment, so potentially beautiful, loving, and exalted, could also become so mean.

For years there were no definitive answers and no one really willing to openly discuss these apparently heretical questions. Eventually I bunkered my native mysticism underground and turned to psychology. Here, at least, were answers to questions like, "Why do people act the way they do?" or "What are the causes of human unhappiness?" Settling into psychology as a profession, it also seemed natural to adopt its "scientific" disinterest in religion. So I made a life and raised a family in much the same way my parents did. Still, a subtle but gnawing awareness kept urging me beyond this tight little world. It was as if I had two lives: one in conventional psychology, the other a relentless, seditious, and wide ranging religious search propelled, as Wordsworth described, by "A presence that disturbs me with the joy of elevated thoughts; a sense sublime of something far more deeply interfused..." And always, in the back of my consciousness, was my grandmother's wise counsel issued at the completion my doctoral degree shortly before her death. She exhorted me in my new found science to "Let man keep his soul." I thought how sweet it was for her to say that, how quaint! Only now, twenty-five years later, am I beginning to grasp what she was trying to say.

Over the intervening years of early adulthood, I explored eastern and western religions, the richly symbolic world of mythology, and the increasing ranks of the New Age, transpersonal, and Native American spiritual writers. Rather than simplifying matters, this exhaustive search usually left me with additional (albeit more sophisticated) questions. Gradually, however, a new comprehension began to grow inside and a larger sense of what humanity's religious longing was all about. But I needed the long journey through psychology, enriched by years of first hand psychotherapeutic experience, before I could return to the matter of religion and its contradictions with mature, objective, and yet loving eyes.

Then, at midlife, my sequestered passion erupted anew and I became intensely interested in the religious and spiritual challenges of life's second half. No amount of cleverness, money, knowledge, or fame can solve the unconquerable realities of aging, suffering, loss, illness, and death that confront the heroic ego after midlife. I understood then that there is a religious depth to the psyche that calls to us in the later years and I needed to comprehend its nature and teaching. What I learned about the psychological and spiritual nature of the midlife passage can be found in my first book, *Death of a Hero, Birth of the Soul*.

My religious search now flowered fully. Ironically, the absence of personal religious indoctrination in childhood gave me the opportunity to freely explore and contrast religious models without pre-existing bias or loyalty. Spiritual understanding and maturity grew steadily, leading me into deeply personal confrontations with the sacred through prayer, spiritual direction, meditation, vision quests, and the mythopoetic language of soul expressed in the men's movement. Then one day I realized I wanted to bring this new consciousness into my practice as a clinical psychologist. Could I do it? Would it be professionally appropriate and practical? Though many peers shared a general interest in spirituality, I was advised not to identify myself as a spiritually oriented psychotherapist or even speak of it too often. I would lose my credibility, they said. People might think I was some kind of religious fanatic and I would attract all kinds of weird clients. Over the past ten years, however, I slowly began to integrate spiritual principles and intuitions into my clinical practice. With the increased confidence born of age and experience, I now feel it is time to bring what I have learned out of the consulting room.

Most people who write about spiritual psychotherapy do so within a specific psychological or religious tradition (e.g., Jungian psychology, Christian psychotherapy, Buddhist mindfulness), and several recent edited works have arrayed this diversity of spiritual approaches to psychological treatment (e.g., Boorstein, 1996; Scotton et. al., 1996; Shafranske, 1996). Each orientation offers something unique and wonderful. There have been few if any works, however, that integrate this spectrum of religious meaning and experience into a single, inclusive, and clinically sophisticated paradigm blending psychological theory and practice with the theologies and practices of the major and indigenous world religions, recent discoveries about "Near Death," mystical, and non-ordinary experiences, and the multiplying themes of New Age, transpersonal, and Recovery movements. I believe that working therapists need this organizing and universalizing perspective to deal with the multiplicity of psychological, religious, spiritual, and mystical phenomena that find their way into the consulting room.

I write this book hoping to restore the once vital relationship between psychology and spirituality, for as surprising as it may seem in today's scientific and economic materialism, psychology at one time embraced the spirit. The psychospirituality I write about flows from countless sources, including the shamanism and mythologies of pre-industrial peoples (and those perceptive enough to understand their secret wisdom such as Jung, Campbell, and Eliade), the great saints, mystics, and religious teachers across time and traditions (e.g., Buddha, Moses, Jesus, Lao Tzu, Confucius, Mohammed, Ramana Maharshi), the giants of western philosophy who struggled mightily with soul and spirit (e.g., Plato, Plotinus, Kant, Augustine, Berkeley), the legions of poets across time who have plumbed the ineffable mysteries of life with their inspired intuitions, our own intellectual and spiritual ancestors here in America (e.g., Emerson, Whitman, and James), the new and emerging spiritual fruit of Jungian theorists, and the numerous contemporary psychotherapists now bold enough to discuss the relevance of spirituality and altered states of consciousness to their clinical work. As all these strands proclaim, there is a religious orientation to the living cosmos natural to humankind. It existed before scientific psychology lost the soul, and it still exists today.

My convictions are these: I believe that psychology has much to teach us about the nature of religious and spiritual dysfunction, that the religious psyche has much to teach us about our spiritual longing and the highest goals of psychotherapy, and that the sacred, in all its variations, contributes ubiquitously to the problems and meaning of life. This work seeks to restore a healthy, balanced, and mature religious perspective to the transformative journey of therapy. As the title denotes, it strives for a professional and interdisciplinary synthesis of psychotherapy and the religious search, a goal that is as ultimately unreachable as it is worth reaching toward.

One might ask what kind of religious credentials I have that could justify writing a work so far out of my own field of clinical psychology. My reply is that I have been pursuing this path all my life. This is not the dabbling of a dilettante or recent religious convert. Moreover, I have been doing the kind of work described in this book for several years, integrating psychotherapy and spirituality with appropriate and interested clients, in men's gatherings and workshops, in formal talks, and in my previous book. I have thought hard and dug deep. There is virtually nothing that I discuss in this book that I have not known, seen, or experienced first hand. As Jung observed years ago, each man's psychology is actually a personal confession. This is mine.

INTRODUCTION

James enters the psychotherapist's office. He has psychologically worked on himself before, solving various important emotional and life problems. But now he is looking for something else. He wants to talk about God. In church, and often in the wilderness, he senses the holy, but it goes no further. Is he imagining this "Presence"? James has tried to talk to his clergy, but abstract or doctrinaire answers seemed to predominate, and no one he talked with had much direct experience with God. Still he keeps asking, "How do I know God? Where is God's presence and purpose in my life? What is real and what is imagined on the spiritual path?" Good questions.

Over the years, James pursued a variety of spiritual practices and teachers. He had a number of unusual experiences, some of which seemed pretty spiritual, but they invariably faded. He wondered if he was fooling himself. James found people who talked convincingly about God, who even said they were "God-realized" or enlightened, and implied that he could be also if he practiced with them long enough. Whenever he reached an impasse with their particular techniques, he was told to practice more. In time James recognized that most of these masters were no more realized than he was. Others had hidden emotional, sexual, or financial problems. No one he personally knew had ever been "enlightened" by these teachers.

James is also reluctant to discuss his spiritual feelings in therapy, afraid they will be discounted or reduced to a psychiatric condition. His previous therapists had squirmed uncomfortably around the topic of religion. One declared that religion was not the province of psychotherapy and directed him back to his clergy. Another began sharing her own highly personal spiritual beliefs to the extent that James no longer felt heard. Embarrassment and futility won out, and James simply learned not to mention his spiritual needs any longer in psychotherapy. This man's legitimate questions, well earned skepticism, and healthy spiritual yearning have been betrayed by the very people who could have supported and guided his religious search.

Mary comes into therapy in crisis. She is overwhelmed by an unexpected grief following a "routine" abortion. She knows something big has happened, something almost unbearable. Mary realizes that her decision may have been a terrible mistake. But she is also surprised by her profound and unanticipated need to know if God hates her for this action, if the baby could ever forgive her, if she can ever forgive herself. Grief, guilt, and depression shroud her inner life. Where does she turn? Mary's doctor has given her the facts and a prescription for Prozac, her clergy the biblical doctrine and an admonition to seek God's forgiveness, her friends and parents have provided emotional support, one therapist helped her face the psychological reality of this loss, another tried to convince her to accept an amalgam of New Age reincarnation beliefs, but no one has helped her fully sort out *for herself* the interwoven emotional and spiritual dimensions of this great sorrow, or experience God's healing love and forgiveness in a personal, tangible, and truly meaningful way. The therapist who does undertake these goals will need to be equipped with skills never even conceived of in graduate training.

Charles has a teenage daughter in a convalescent facility. She has been brain dead since a severe asthma reaction occurred over a year ago. He visits her everyday. Charles cannot believe his beautiful little girl is gone. The neurologist has told him that his daughter will never recover. Charles can't let go of his hope. The facility social worker referred him for psychotherapy to help him deal with this terrible loss. Over and over Charles asks, "Why is God letting my child linger like this? What does He want from me?" He never hears an answer and his depression is deepening. Can a psychotherapist engage these kinds of questions?

All through high school and college, Paula was involved in Christian youth groups. The leaders provided a warm and safe haven from the stresses of adolescence but actively discouraged dating and she had never even "made out." Following college she became very involved in a church that discouraged any involvement with non-Christians. You were said to be "slimed" by contact with them. As time went by, Paula heard more and more talk about the devil and "spiritual warfare." Dark forces were said to be at work. One day, she felt Satan had taken her soul and shook uncontrollably for hours until an exorcism was performed. Thereafter she became deathly afraid to go to sleep, and grew ever more exhausted from her nighttime battles. The church's warfare against the devil became increasingly rancorous and frightening. One women in particular seemed capable of seeing into the minds of others. Finally, fearing she was losing her sanity and her soul, Paula fled the church.

In desperation, Paula finally consulted a therapist, an equally frightening step in light of the extremely negative ways mental health professionals had been characterized in her religious community. Can a secular psychotherapist help Paula? The one she chose did. Everyone, she learned, has a "dark side" of unrecognized (and usually "unchristian") feelings and needs (e.g., jealousy, envy, competition, greed, and sexuality). Gradually Paula came to recognize how her pastors, trying to be unrealistically and perfectly holy, had projected their own human shadow (symbolized conveniently as the devil) onto their parishioners. Paula further learned that she, in turn, had been "possessed" by her own shadow: the rage she felt at their terrifying intimidation tactics. Childhood experiences with a controlling and rageful father had also left her vulnerable to such authority manipulation. After a year and a half of therapy, Paula overcame her fear of being possessed, joined a healthier church, and found her relationship to God renewing itself naturally.

Margaret is approaching 60. She was rejected by her mother at three, placed in boarding school at five, and a year later learned her mother had been killed in a car accident. Her father never came to pick her up. Forty-five years later, Margaret fell into her unfinished childhood depression. As therapists know, feelings may be buried, but they are buried alive. So Margaret's profound loss had to be faced one day and indeed she has been working it through steadily and productively over the past several years of therapy. Now, as she feels herself growing older, Margaret longs for the additional healing of a religious life. But she is stuck. She can't trust God. She understands now that this distrust is related to her mother's abandonment; still she is deeply ambivalent. She never wants to be dependent again, ever, even on God. Margaret needs help separating her mother wound from her experience of God. Her profound distrust is a complex entanglement of psychological and spiritual themes. This will be the final issue of her psychotherapy, if she can resolve it.

Jerry is 25 years old. He has been carrying a secret for years. As an alter boy, he was molested by the parish priest for three years. Fondled, kissed, then raped. He couldn't tell his parents or church authorities. It would have been outrageously disrespectful. And who'd believe him? In adolescence, Jerry refused to attend church, began abusing drugs to numb his pain and degradation, yet still found himself the object of sexual advances by older men. And sometimes he couldn't seem to resist. A cycle of seduction and self-hatred took him ever deeper into depression. Unable to sustain any kind of healthy and respectful love relationships, Jerry turned against himself. He overdosed and nearly died. After all, his needs didn't count to anyone. God hadn't protected him. All he was good for was to be a sexual object. As far as Jerry is concerned, religion had damaged him irreparably.

Other people come into therapy asking similar questions, like "Why has God abandoned me in this time of illness?" "Does life have any real meaning?" "Can anyone help me with my secret fear of hell?" "Why did my husband have to die?" "What makes me start crying when I hear hymns in church?" "I nearly drowned in a boating accident and had this experience of passing into heaven. Am I crazy?" "My daughter just joined this strange religious group and she won't discuss it with me. Do you suppose it's one of those cults? What should I do?" I could describe examples like these for pages.

The struggles these people bring into therapy illustrate the complex intersection of religious, spiritual, and psychological problems. Many of these people have searched widely through multiple religions, spiritualities, teachers and therapists. They know a lot but don't have any answers. A few have been deeply hurt by insensitive or misguided psychological and spiritual practitioners, others have spent years in practices that left them with many skills but no closer to their goal. Yet they know there is a transcendent reality just beyond the veil of experience, they hunger for its guidance and healing, they know their very lives are built on this sacred order, but their search repeatedly comes up short. Some were successfully treated, some were not, and some never came in for help.

For most psychotherapists, this intersection of religion, spirituality, and psychology has been professionally impoverished as a result of decades of sterile clinical training, lack of educational exposure to normal religious and spiritual experience, excessive psychologizing and pathologizing, rigid taboos against discussing religion or the experience of God in psychotherapy, and the externally prescribed treatment formulae of "modern" psychological practice (e.g., managed care rules, pre-established treatment protocols, over reliance on psychopharmacology, and a myopic concern for symptoms over soul). Until recently, psychology had offered little to those therapists wishing to respond to their client's existential religious hunger.

It is time for psychology to address these struggles directly. Ninety-four percent of Americans report a belief in God, ranking America as one of the most religious countries in the world (Gallup, 1989). Indeed, religious issues, concerns, and experiences arise frequently in psychotherapeutic practice, often confusing client and therapist alike and raising questions rarely if ever addressed in our formal training. Feeling unprepared and self-conscious in this realm, therapists are often reluctant to address their client's spiritual concerns or even discuss such issues among themselves. Historically they have resorted to pathologizing the religious experience or simply referring their religiously motivated clients to the clergy. Like its predecessors alcoholism, sexuality, and child abuse, religion and spirituality have too long been taboo subjects in psychology and psychotherapy.

The vast majority of well trained counselors and psychotherapists routinely fail to inquire about their client's religious and spiritual lives, much less formally assess it or invite the sacred into the hour as a healing resource. Yet religious feelings, beliefs, and needs are central to the human experience the world over and often hold deep meaning to both therapists and clients alike. When this universal human longing is ignored or devalued in therapy, material invaluable to the goals of healing is neglected, resulting in a tremendous but unrecognized betrayal of the client's ultimate well-being and healthy spiritual development. Confusing matters further, therapists correctly realize that religious interests and practices are not always what they appear and may instead be disguises for psychopathology. But how do therapists know the difference and how should they respond when a client brings up a religious problem?

Unfortunately, therapists still receive little or no training enabling them to distinguish between psychological, religious, spiritual, and mystical phenomena or integrate them positively into the psychotherapeutic endeavor. *But Where is God?* argues that a mature integration of psychotherapy and spirituality is now culturally and scientifically possible, practical, responsible, and enormously important. Everything in life has both psychological and spiritual meaning; but more to the point, we are fundamentally spiritual beings surrounded and nourished by the sacred. A psychotherapy that fails to understand this misses its clients' yearning for a healing relationship to the divine. Leaving the spiritual domain entirely to religion, on the other hand, overlooks the numerous psychological problems hidden along the spiritual path, including religious addiction and abuse, the dark side of religious teachers and gurus, spiritual self-deception, and the failure to recognize the powerful obstructions to spiritual growth hidden in complex personality problems.

In *Death of a Hero, Birth of the Soul*, I examined the universal developmental process of a man's life with all its interpenetrating personal, psychological, mythic, poetic, therapeutic, spiritual, and mystical dimensions, and its overriding religious meaning. I discovered midlife to be a profound developmental stage freeing the compulsive hero from his Sisyphian life sentence to recover the true self and its inherent mystical consciousness. *But Where Is God?* continues the description of the phases, methods, and meaning of this great journey, and explores the role spirituality can (and already does) play in our lives and in our work as healers.

As the subtitle alludes, *But Where Is God?* is a primer. Originally, a primer was a prayer book or manual for teaching children how to spell or read. Now a primer refers to a textbook that gives the first principles of any subject. As a modern primer, my goal is to provide a short textbook-like summary of the basic principles and practices for integrating psychotherapy and spirituality. But this integration is so new that we are indeed like children just learning its alphabet and words, hungry for learning but also ignorant, impressionable, and gullible. Like an old fashioned educational primer, therefore, this book's intent is also to provide such very basic teachings. Finally, this is also a "prayer book" honoring and calling forth our relationship with the divine, and the way psychotherapy can support that alliance. It is, furthermore, a prayer that our work can be guided by a healthy and mature mixture of science and spirituality that serves our shared commitment to alleviating human suffering.

To some, the effort to find a synthesis capable of supporting a spiritually oriented psychotherapy will seem an extravagant, grandiose, and naively simplistic enterprise; to others, the conclusions presented in this book will be entirely natural, obvious, timely and self-evident. My purpose, however, is simply to introduce new ideas and possibilities into our professional awareness and start us thinking about the emergent questions and issues. But this book is also about taking risks. Its content is unconventional, unorthodox, and possibly even heretical by psychiatric and religious standards. Its goal is to open new horizons of healing and, in the process, to question those paradigms that still limit our contact with the most important questions and forces fueling the psychotherapeutic journey.

At a time when psychiatry, clinical psychology, and science are racing headlong toward biochemical explanations and treatments for human emotional distress, this modest work moves toward the opposite pole, to the workings of spirit and soul in everyday life, human suffering, and healing. Such an endeavor is intrinsically respectable, emphasized as it has been in mankind's eternal enterprises of philosophy and religion. The only difference here is that we now explicitly desire to bring it back into psychology and psychotherapy, where its long absence has fostered to increasingly arid forms of theory and practice.

This book is for therapists and clients of all orientations as well as related medical, mental health and clergy professionals. It is about our common religious search and how the tools of psychology, religion, spirituality, and mysticism can help us along the way. Specifically, *But Where Is God?* comprises three interdependent works in one: It is 1. a general introduction to the field of spiritual psychotherapy, 2. a fresh theoretical paradigm integrating the realms of psychology, spirituality, religion, and mysticism, and 3. a practical synthesis of psychotherapy and spiritual direction. As such, it combines basic information (i.e., psychology, psychopathology, spirituality) with a unique theoretical stance, years of psychotherapeutic experience, and an enlightened model of psychotherapy. Because the topic of spirituality is only now resurfacing in the professional world, clients and practitioners alike need a conceptualization that combines clear psychological thinking and objectivity with an awareness of sacred consciousness, its many manifestations, and the value of religious community in healthy functioning.

As I watch with interest the new books coming out in this field, I realize that *But Where Is God?* is a actually a third generation work. The first generation consisted of very occasional early works on psychotherapy and spirituality (e.g., Assagioli, 1971; Peck, 1978, Watts, 1961) and works on religious or pastoral counseling within specific traditions. The second generation, representing the beginning of modern thought in spiritual psychotherapy, were edited works (e.g., Boorstein, 1996; Scotton et. al., 1996; Shafranske, 1996) or textbooks (e.g., Genia, 1995; Kelly, 1995; Steere, 1997). They introduce and survey a wide breadth and diversity of psychological, religious, and transpersonal material without a spiritually coherent paradigm or synthesis.

Technically and scientifically solid, they also lack a well defined and passionate vision of the spiritual experience and its potential. The present third generation work, on the other hand, reaches this edge with a radical orientation to enlightened consciousness, psychological growth, and personality transformation. It grows not only from a reasoned overview of the field, buttressed by a quarter century of clinical experience, but also from the author's own first hand experience with mystical consciousness and its influence in psychotherapy and personality evolution. It leaves the reader free to remain primarily with the scientific and clinical aspects of the topic or use them as foundational springboards into a spiritually informed and inspired metaphysical understanding of psychotherapy.

Finally, I want to offer four brief caveats to avoid offending or disappointing too many people. This is one man's viewpoint. Spirituality is a very personal matter and no one can legislate its content or proper place in another person's life. Secondly, psychotherapy and spirituality comprise a vast subject area and by necessity this work must be selective in its choice of topics. Third, this is not a book about simple or feel-good "cure-alls" to life problems. The difficulties we confront in psychotherapy and in life are often complex and deeply rooted. What is offered here is an invitation to include another dimension in the work of psychological healing, and to include it in a way that does not fall prey to the temptations of magical thinking and self-deception that often occur on both the religious and the scientific paths. Lastly, it is important for the reader to test this material against personal experience, beliefs, and training. Without such grounding, these ideas can be misleading at best and destructive at worst. Think everything through carefully, measure it against your own experience and reading, and then, when you are ready, trust yourself to walk through this extraordinary doorway of possibilities.

SOME COMMENTS ON CONTENT AND ORGANIZATION

Reviewing the Table of Contents for *But Where Is God?*, one can readily discern its order and trajectory. Part I presents an "Argument for a Mature Integration of Psychotherapy and Spirituality." The goal of Part II is "Building a Model for a Spiritual Psychotherapy," challenging readers to appreciate the range of religious, spiritual and mystical phenomena that any theory of personality, psychopathology, and psychotherapy must understand, integrate, and embrace. Part III, "Sacred Journeys: Experiences in Spiritual Psychotherapy," presents the author's personal views and treatment experiences in order to move from theory to real people. Part IV, "Professional Issues," examines a wide range practical and applied problems encountered in a spiritually oriented psychotherapy, and Part V, "Sacred Psychology: Summary and Implications," concludes with reflections on the religious nature and functioning of the psyche. The reader is encouraged to explore this material sequentially and then use the Table of Contents as a reference for returning to specific themes and issues. Finally, supplementary material intended to broaden, clarify, or enrich specific Chapter topics is included in several appendices.

Every effort has been made to structure this material in simple, reader friendly, and easily accessible fashion. In addition to section and Chapter headings, the contents of each Chapter are listed beneath the title so the reader can know what to expect and later find specific information when the need arises. Though this is partly a textbook, I have tried to avoid heavy or overly detailed academic discourse. At bottom, *But Where Is God?* is much more than that. It is meant to provide guidance, explanation, encouragement, and inspiration to anyone sincerely interested in the spiritual dimensions of personality, suffering, and healing.

PART ONE

ARGUMENT FOR A MATURE INTEGRATION OF PSYCHOTHERAPY AND SPIRITUALITY

The synthesis of psychotherapy and spirituality is no small challenge. On one side is a choir of fervent believers who need no convincing, on the other, a secular chorus of critics convinced spirituality has nothing to do with the science of psychology. Part I seeks a balanced hearing of this matter, arguing first for a mature integration psyche and soul, reviewing the history of their artificial bifurcation, and then carefully considering both the benefits and the liabilities attending the renewal of this ancient unity.

CHAPTER ONE

WHY IS THE INTEGRATION OF PSYCHOTHERAPY AND SPIRITUALITY IMPORTANT?

Contents: Argument for a Mature Integration
             Objections and Replies

ARGUMENT FOR A MATURE INTEGRATION

Bringing spirituality into psychotherapy is a complex and controversial goal fraught with risks, confusion, boundary conflicts, professional taboos, and all the irrationality that attends the religious quest. The question that naturally arises, therefore, is why pursue this goal at all? I believe there are four very important reasons.

The first reason is simply that spirituality is increasingly important to psychotherapists of all persuasions. As early as 1986, in a survey of 425 mental health professionals across the country, psychologist Allan Bergin found that "even though some therapists remain actively hostile to organized religion, a sizable majority are deeply interested in a vaguely defined non-institutional spirituality. Sixty-eight percent of the family therapists, clinical psychologists, social workers, and psychiatrists surveyed said they sought 'a spiritual understanding of the universe and one's place in it'" Only 5 percent, however, received any training in dealing with such religious issues in therapy (Bergin, 1990).

The second reason for exploring the psychotherapy-spirituality interface is that psychotherapy clients want and need to talk about the spiritual meaning and experiences of their lives. The majority of the people who come into psychotherapy are religious (often more religious in fact than their therapists according to surveys) and their religious questions and concerns are important to them. Moreover, a 1992 Gallup Poll found that two thirds of the adult population preferred a professional counselor with spiritual values and beliefs, and 81 percent preferred to have their own values and beliefs integrated into the counseling process. Unfortunately, clients frequently feel their spiritual needs are not recognized, valued, or sensitively handled in therapy. Scott Peck summarized this problem succinctly. Speaking as Distinguished Psychiatric Lecturer to the American Psychiatric Association in 1992, he pointed out, "The single most common complaint I hear from psychotherapy patients about their therapists...has been that they did not or would not listen to the spiritual aspects of their lives." Echoing Bergin, he also observed, "The traditional lack of training in the realm of spirituality, however, assures that most well-trained, astute practitioners will often flounder destructively in these matters." (Peck, 1993)

The third reason spirituality is important to psychotherapy is that many personal questions are really religious ones "Who am I?" "Why am I here?" "What is the purpose of my life?" or "Why have I or my loved ones been allowed to suffer so much?" While therapists may focus productively on the personal and psychological significance of such questions, probing their unconscious and symbolic significance, we have to realize that our clients are also reaching for higher levels of meaning and orientation. They are asking, "What is my spiritual nature?" "What is the ultimate purpose of life?" "Why are we here?" "Is there a God?" "What is the meaning of suffering and why does God allow it?" These questions address the spiritual journey of life and its universal events, stages, and struggles. They are not trivial questions; rather they are questions of profound personal, moral, and spiritual significance that everyone encounters in the struggle of life.

Finally, a cross-fertilization of religious and psychological thinking is sorely needed. With all the abuses and misunderstandings we have seen in religious circles in all traditions, applying a psychotherapeutic model to the spiritual journey is as important as applying a spiritual model to psychological one. We need the concepts and tools of each to find a healthy balance in both, for without such integration, psychological practitioners ignore the whole realm of the spirit (and spiritual pathology) and spiritual practitioners ignore the whole realm of the psyche (and psychopathology).

OBJECTIONS AND REPLIES

No matter how reasonable the argument may be for including spirituality in psychotherapy, therapists can anticipate considerable resistance. It would be wise, therefore, to address the probable objections and criticisms that will arise, including the following:

- **Psychotherapy is only meant for psychological problems; it is not intended for or relevant to spiritual ones.**

Response: Just because we have not traditionally included spiritual matters in clinical practice does not mean they should be ignored. Moreover, it is not an easy task to separate psychological and spiritual phenomena. The psychological aspects of spiritual experience and the spiritual aspects of psychological experience are both important but typically overlooked. Common psychological problems on the spiritual road include hidden emotional problems of teachers and religious groups, psychological complications of the spiritual quest, religiously rationalized child abuse, and the importance of distinguishing between psychopathology and non-ordinary states of consciousness. Spiritual aspects of psychological problems include the ultimate meaning or purpose of emotional problems or tragedies, the underlying religious nature of the psyche, and the influence of the divine in a client's presenting problems.

- **Spiritual concerns are not scientific and psychology is a science.**

Response: Spiritual concerns and events pervade everyday life and they can be studied scientifically. In fact, there is a growing scientific literature on such spiritual topics as prayer, non-ordinary states of consciousness, and Near-Death and mystical experience. Secondly, medicine and psychotherapy often deal with conditions not yet fully understood, and we would not turn away those in need simply because science has yet investigated their complaints. It should also be acknowledged that psychotherapy is not as scientific as we like to imagine, for it involves intuition, experimentation, self-analysis, and faith. It is not a mechanical endeavor like engineering nor is it as clearly defined as the practice of medicine. As we will see, the interface between psychology and spirituality increasingly blurs the more closely we examine it.

- **Psychotherapists are not trained in religion and spirituality.**

Response: This objection is unfortunately true but it is also correctable, and should be rectified, for therapy has missed the importance of religion and spirituality from its inception. Psychotherapists can and should receive training in spiritual matters, especially topics such as the higher states of consciousness, the role of transference in cult and religious abuse, the fundamental tenants of the great religious traditions, stages of spiritual growth, and the working relationship between therapeutic and religious practitioners. Without such training, psychotherapists will indeed ignore or overlook a wide range of legitimate treatment needs and problems, many of which the client may be unconscious of or afraid to bring up.

It should also be pointed out that clergy, pastoral counselors, spiritual directors, and spiritual teachers are under trained and under experienced in the field of psychopathology and the unconscious dynamics of client-professional relationship (known in psychotherapy as transference and discussed in Chapter 10). It would be equally valuable for them to receive additional training in these complex, powerful, and often unconscious psychological processes.

- **How can a psychotherapist help a client explore his relationship to the divine without a theological frame of reference?**

Response: This is a proper and important question. Doing spiritual work without some kind of theology is like doing psychotherapy without a theory of personality, psychopathology, and healing. Or like driving from Sacramento to Mexico City without a map. Or building a house without a plan. Good intentions are not enough.

To do this work, a psychotherapist does need to have a personal spirituality and a basic theology of some kind, which he has lived, tested, and forged from the spiritual fires of his own life. This is part of the preparatory work required of any psychotherapist entering this field. Most therapists will have already done much of this preparation naturally, for the same interest that now calls them into this work will have been pulling them toward religious reading, practice, prayer, and reflection for years. The one additional personal requirement is putting this lifetime of experience into order. If a therapist plans to incorporate the spiritual realm into his psychotherapeutic work, he should be able to clearly formulate and discuss his spiritual assumptions and metaphysics, for this is the "informed consent" condition ethically and legally required in medical and psychological treatment. Equally clear, however, is the absolute dictum of not imposing one's own theology on another.

- **How can a psychotherapist provide spiritual guidance to a client if he is not well established in that client's religious tradition?**

Response: This objection is similar to the last one and it too is valid. Certainly if a client's primary need is to explore his faith with an expert in that faith, he should find such an expert. If the client is unsure what he believes, or whether he believes in his own tradition, and if he fears censure or disapproval asking questions of his own tradition, he may wish to examine his questions in a therapeutic context, especially if he has already found that milieu to be safe and trustworthy. Just as a therapist needs to formulate his own basic spirituality and theology, our clients have the same need. If, on the other hand, a client's unfolding theology poses questions beyond the experience or formal knowledge of the therapist, and beyond his own internal resources, then it is proper for him to seek answers from whatever religious tradition calls him.

- **Psychotherapists cannot and should not replace clergy, spiritual directors, spiritual teachers, or religious institutions.**

Response: This objection is valid. Integrating spirituality into psychotherapy is not intended to replace these experts, religious practitioners, or organized faith communities. Religious expertise has its own inherent value and legitimacy, and individual spiritual discussion in the psychotherapy context certainly cannot replace a healthy religious community. But this objection should not prevent psychotherapists from receiving additional training and working in the spiritual realm to the extent of their knowledge and specialization. Actually, the goal of a psychotherapy-spirituality integration is to encourage practitioners from both sides to work more closely together, for we are all really interested the same goals: healing, growth, transformation, and human harmony.

Moreover, if psychotherapy can help restore an individual's religious faith and spiritual experience, he will be empowered to search for the religious guidance and community central to his path.

- **Where do you draw the line, then, between psychotherapists and religious professionals?**

Response: In most traditional settings, each professional performs the tasks for which he is trained and qualified. Ideally, each should also receive training in related areas and know when to consult and refer. Along the boundaries between professions are those who have an interest in both disciplines, and they often form a hybrid specialization. This certainly occurs within medicine, psychology, and religion, and there is no reason it should not occur between them. As always, the cardinal criteria for functioning in new or developing area are: maintaining the same high standards of one's profession (i.e., training, experience, ethics), consulting actively with others in the field, keeping abreast of the literature, and holding the highest respect for one's clients and peers. For those who specialize in a spiritually oriented psychotherapy, the line between the mental health and religious professional is still observed, though with such common interest and concerns, more communication and collaboration may take place between them in bridging this gap. We all become, in a sense, better neighbors and friends.

- **Won't psychotherapists become religious proselytizers and ignore the real work of treatment?**

Response: Proselytizing occurs in both religious and psychological areas, probably with equal frequency, for it is human nature to sell or impose convictions that have been personally meaningful on those we are trying to help. Religious and psychological professionals alike must be sensitive to this problem. Psychotherapists, for example, are ethically bound to respect their client's belief systems. But more importantly, it is the sophisticated psychological understanding of the therapist-client relationship (i.e., the dynamics of transference and counter transference discussed later) that ultimately minimizes and prevents such distraction and abuse. The therapist is always silently asking himself questions like, "What is really happening in this discussion? Is it constructive or defensive? Does it truly serve the client's growth?" Given the foibles of human nature, there is really no way to eliminate the problem of proselytization altogether in either discipline. For psychology, however, it is assumed that therapists will not abandon their ethical and clinical training when they include spiritual concepts and methods in their work, and instead maintain the same high professional standards while at the same time utilizing spiritual concepts and tools to enlarge the meaning and scope of their work.

- **Won't psychology's emphasis on individuality and individuation simply lead to an autonomous, self-centered spiritual materialism, missing the entire purpose of the spiritual journey, that is, serving others and surrendering the self to the divine?**

Response: Real spirituality begins with the unique, highly personal, and first-hand experience of the sacred. It often occurs in the heart of crisis, when skill, identity, affluence, and power fail and one stands alone, stripped of individual resources and self-importance. Anyone who falls into the universal trap of believing that a spiritual practice will automatically fix, protect, or improve them, will find this delusion shattered. A psychology that falls into this trap will indeed fall prey to egocentricity and spiritual materialism, and miss the whole point of the religious path. The ego most often finds God when it is humbled, bypassed, or defeated. This objection, therefore, is valid for all seekers, therapists, and clergy, and each must come to terms with it.

- **Psychology lacks the religious tradition to guide clients in their spiritual journey. It is not a religion.**

Response: Psychotherapy cannot replace religion, religious institutions, religious communities and practices, or religious practitioners. A therapist cannot answer questions outside his training and experience, and knowing when to refer is always a sign of professional maturity. But a therapist can be familiar with the universal religious themes, problems, and experiences that arise in the sacred journey of life and assist his client in understanding and responding to them. As we will see, such assistance may at times include the thoughtful use of selected spiritual readings and practices in the service of the client's psychospiritual growth and transformation.

CHAPTER TWO

HISTORY, POLITICS, AND CONTEMPORARY CULTURE: HOW PSYCHOTHERAPY LOST ITS SOUL AND WHERE THINGS ARE HEADING

Contents: History and Politics
             Contemporary Forces and Questions
             Things to Come: Moving from a Psychological to a Spiritual Age

Why has the religious experience been so long ignored or discounted by psychotherapists? The answers are historical, political, and cultural, and involve the competition of worldviews and the splintering of religious life. Although these forces cleaved psychology from its sacred origins, the tide of change has turned powerfully. Psychology has begun to recover its soul and a radical paradigm shift, virtually a new psychospiritual myth, is in the making.

HISTORY AND POLITICS

Worldviews are belief systems about the nature of reality that shape human perception, expectation, and opinion. Individuals, families, groups, and cultures all have world views that define their beliefs about morality, politics, race, economics, gender, sexuality, child-rearing, the good life, and anything else felt to be important. Worldviews similarly exist among the trades and professions, defining the goals and methods permitted in each specialty. Conflict among worldviews is common and typically driven by culture, economics, and ego. Some worldviews focus on the secular; others, like religion, address the sacred order and its place in everyday life. Secular and religious world views often conflict.

For the earliest peoples of earth, illness and misfortune were spiritual and religious problems derived from a wrong alignment with the sacred world. Myths presented the spiritual worldview, telling stories of the cause and cure of man's problems. The first physician was the tribal shaman who practiced a mixture of natural, psychological, and spiritual arts in the maintenance of health and the relief of human suffering. This fundamentally spiritual orientation to all life's problems accompanied mankind through its six or seven million years of evolution, and has only recently (and thinly) been covered by the current scientific and material worldview. Despite the rapid advances of science and technology, the ancient religious psyche has probably changed little over the millennia. It still predominates among pre-industrial peoples and those less enculturated in the prevailing scientific paradigm. For "modern" people, the inborn religious perspective tends to be obscure on a daily basis, but can arises powerfully whenever survival is threatened.

In the early Christian era, physicians were priests. The church granted their licenses and medicine still considered illness an act of God. Counseling was a spiritual endeavor focusing on "cure of the soul." This intimate relationship between medicine and religion continued for hundreds of years, further buttressed by the venerable enterprise of philosophy. In fact, psychological questions were originally the province of philosophy, which merged with theological speculation in the Middle Ages. A vestige of this relationship is evident in our academic degrees: psychologists still receive the Doctor of Philosophy degree though it is possible to graduate with virtually no training in philosophy. Philosophical analysis, with its great and weighty questions about reality and knowledge, complemented by theology's intellectual and mystical inquiry into the nature of God, produced centuries of intellectual and religious thought that still influences western culture.

This Judeo-Christian worldview, built on centuries of theological and philosophical discussion, continued until the seventeenth century when it came under attack from the scientific revolution (beginning in the late 1500's and early 1600's) and age of enlightenment (the late 1600's and 1700's). A volatile time, new scientific discoveries clashed with the religious order, leading to extensive political repression (e.g., the Spanish Inquisition). Rather quickly by historical standards, the religious paradigm was displaced by scientific empiricism, now the dominant and collective western world view in literally all matters except God. Empirical studies rather than philosophical, theological, or spiritual inquiry now answer psychological questions.

The political conflicts described above bring up two important distinctions. The first is between the religious psyche and the ego. The religious psyche is the original and deepest strata of the unconscious in the human personality. It is a great indwelling storehouse of universal and ultimate meanings that yields mythic and mystical apprehensions of our place in the living, divine cosmos. The ego's interests, on the other hand, revolve around survival, mastery, and preservation, usually focused in the material world. Without proper alignment to the religious psyche, the ego may be tempted to use the rich and numinous symbols of the religious psyche to garner personal power (Edinger, 1972). Many who became powerful religious leaders in the middle ages, for example, were not very spiritual but had acquired tremendous authority from their presumed religious expertise and their identification in the mind of the masses with the sacred. Through ceremonial garments, rituals, and their status as official representatives of God and divine knowledge, the clergy appeared to embody the numinous power of the religious psyche itself. Those motivated by self-serving interests defended their authority and its economic advantages with threats, oppression, incarceration, torture, and interrogation. As repeatedly witnessed in the history of man, all manner of atrocities and war can be rationalized in the name of God when the inflated ego is worshipped instead of the sacred.

The second distinction contrasts science and the religious psyche. While the religious psyche may offer profound spiritual meanings and practices, the scientific study of the natural world offers equally powerful methods of understanding and healing. Science derives from the rational, objective, analytic capacities of the mind, and it discovers relationships in the phenomena of the world that the religious psyche often overlooks or dismisses. With the remarkable discoveries of medical science in recent decades, many westerners almost dismissed religion altogether, asking in the 1950's whether God was indeed dead. We seemed to feel science and medicine would solve all our problems and the scientific ego became inflated. Ironically, it is currently being deflated by the host of problems science has not solved: pollution, population, mutating viruses, failing antibiotics, warfare, and the personal inevitability of death and suffering. Faced once again with the reality of human helplessness and insignificance, people have begun to return again to religion. Collective consciousness, too far removed from the spirit, is swinging back again.

Government has been a third force in the history of religion and spirituality over the centuries. When government is in hands of a monarchy, it often seeks the allegiance and blessing of religion to legitimize its power, as if God were presumed to give his personal approval. When government denies the validity of religion or the existence of God, it surreptitiously seeks to become the religion it replaced, disguised cleverly in popular or patriotic rhetoric. When government is a theocracy, its use of absolute power is justified because the ruler is presumed to be divine. Finally, when government and religion agree to operate independently and without interference, secular and divine laws are divided. Religion then speaks to man's relationship with the sacred, constitutional law to his relationship to the state and citizenry. Conflicts between government and religious beliefs may continue but tend to be separated and compartmentalized.

In the history of western civilization, religion, science, and government eventually parted ways. To avoid further conflict of their world views, they implicitly agreed to divide up the world: science would study the observable or natural world, the church maintained its authority over the supernatural, and the government agreed to leave each alone as long as they did not interfere with the running of state. Today, religion, science, and government consult, converse, and occasionally coerce each other, but none have final jurisdiction, though laws usually take precedence over religious beliefs. Government becomes the primary funder of science and in this role sometimes exceeds its proper influence and priorities. While separation of science, church, and state does reduce large-scale religious oppression, it does not guarantee that the ego's relationship with the religious psyche will be a healthy one in any particular religious institution.

The political separation of religious and scientific domains allowed the sciences, including psychology, to grow at unparalleled and exponentially increasing rates. The field of psychology is only a little over one hundred years old. The sub field of psychotherapy took root around the turn of the nineteenth century with the work of Sigmund Freud and the new science of psychoanalysis. Suddenly, the phenomena of mind, emotion, and behavior were taken from the religious sphere into the powerful scientific paradigm. Unconscious conflicts between instinct and socialization became the cause of disturbed behavior, replacing supernatural causes such as spirits and demons. In time, the fascination with the psychological causes of behavior permeated all levels of western society: popular magazines, doctors' offices, and family conversations. More remarkably, psychotherapists became the new "priests" of popular culture. People began turning to their shrinks instead of their clergy for advice on everything from child rearing to the purpose of life itself. Equally fascinated by this new paradigm, the clergy also began studying psychology, bringing it into their sermons and pastoral counseling.

The implications of these historical and political developments for psychological healing were profound. Forgetting its spiritual origins, psychotherapy became a stepchild of science whose material world view was imbued with the implicit message: "Don't talk about religion because the clergy owns that territory and anyway it cannot be proven scientifically so we're not interested." As a consequence of this prohibition, mental health practitioners developed a profoundly one-sided perspective. Science not religion defines their requisite training and little guidance is provided about what to do when religious and spiritual themes do emerge. This split has meant that religion and spirituality have been officially off limits to psychotherapists from the start.

For professional psychology, this distrust and skepticism toward religion and spirituality has actively continued for numerous reasons. First, there is the recognition that the "spiritual healing" practiced down through the ages was not always spiritual or healing, and worse, that terrible abuse and injustice can be justified in the name of religion. Not a good track record. Second, with virtually no training in religious or spiritual phenomena, most therapists feel they do not know enough to serve a client's transpersonal needs and do not, as a result, inquire deeply about such matters during treatment. Many therapists also feel that spirituality and religion are private concerns and not the business of psychotherapy. Third, any careful thinker reflecting on the diversity, inconsistencies, and conflict among the many religious and spiritual paradigms would have to wonder whether there is any objective "truth" in this field, and hence whether it is professionally sound to bring spirituality into the practice of psychotherapy at all. Faced with such doubts, and fearing censure from their peers and professional regulatory boards, most psychotherapists have chosen to avoid the spiritual realm in their work. Finally, given the dominant scientific and economic worldview, there is virtually no way to explain the value of prayer, spiritual guidance, or spiritual growth to an insurance carrier, malpractice lawyer, or licensing board. In this time of rampant litigation and governmental regulation with insufficient safeguards, the official schism between psychology and spirituality remains wide and deep.

The formal distrust and distance between psychology and religion is seen all too clearly in surveys indicating that therapists as a whole tend to be critical of formal religion, attend church less often than their clients, rarely if ever refer clients for pastoral counseling or spiritual direction, and get few if any referrals from religious professions. Moreover, meaningful dialogue between clergy and therapists is largely absent for professionals in both fields. Religion also distrusts psychology's interest in the spiritual. They fear therapists, untrained in theology, will treat religious matters incorrectly and superficially. Not only has "the cure of souls" has been practiced for centuries by the clergy, but many fear that therapy tends to "psychologize" the spirit, reducing it to a belief system and missing the great and purposeful mystery of the spiritual world.

Despite this historical climate of distrust, psychology has begun to look for its spiritual roots, that is, its original connection to the sacred and the deep religious psyche. Hidden behind their professional distrust and disavowal, many psychotherapists have been exploring spirituality anew. Their interest is evident in proliferating transpersonal and religious professional associations (e.g., Division 36 of the American Psychological Association, the Association for Transpersonal Psychology, International Association of Transpersonal Psychology, countless local study groups), psychospiritual books and journals (e.g., Common Boundary, Noetic Sciences Review, Yoga Journal), institutes for spiritual studies and direction (e.g., Shalem, Institute for Transpersonal Psychology), conferences on spirituality and healing, and clinical applications of religious and transpersonal paradigms (e.g., Boorstein, 1996). The idea of soul, so long missing from psychological theory and practice, has also found its way back onto the practitioners bookshelf (e.g., Hillman, 1996; Moore, 1992). Similarly, the search for a new scientific paradigm that includes a mystical understanding of the universe is intense. For psychology, this is a time of change, reconciliation, and spiritual renewal.

CONTEMPORARY FORCES AND QUESTIONS

Institutional religion has splintered increasingly in the last century spawning the rapid proliferation of new religious forms and movements. In America alone, there are over 500 different sects of Christianity (Cox, 1993) along with a host of recurring issues such as fundamentalism versus liberalism, rigidity versus freedom of expression, mysticism versus dogmatism, literal versus metaphoric, one interpretation versus another. Beginning with the Puritans' revolt against the Church of England, America has also been home to an incredible proliferation of new or imported religious movements, including Transcendentalists, Mormons, Millerites, Christian Scientists, Theosophists and Anthroposophists, Hare Krishnas, Scientologists, Unification Church "Moonies," Jim Jones' People's Temple, the Shree Rajneesh Ashram in Oregon, Zen retreats, Transcendental Meditation, and countless New Age practitioners.

Religious experience has also been further splintered within established traditions because of increasing specialization: theologians analyze, preachers illuminate broad-scale principles, evangelists convert, pastoral counselors treat personal emotional and spiritual problems, and clerics with large administrative and fund-raising concerns rarely have time for the individual amidst the myriad of problems affecting their institution. Such complex institutional organization often means a growing distance between the parishioner and cleric. Western religions have also tended to emphasize institutional authority and obedience over first hand, personal mystical experience. With mystical theology and practices largely removed from everyday institutional religion in recent decades, and disillusioned with traditional religious authority, spiritual seekers fled organized religion in droves to Eastern or non-traditional religions in search of direct religious experience. Sadly, most did not find it and many were fooled by gurus who promised nirvana but delivered sexual or financial exploitation.

Contemporary cultural trends further contribute to this splintering of the religious life. For example, the search for individuality and spirituality in the west has become obsessive and highly materialistic. In this trendy consumer atmosphere, even the divine can become a commodity to purchase in the supermarket of spirituality classes, teachers, techniques, and tours. We have similarly forgotten that experienced spirituality and personal morality are inescapably intertwined in a healthy culture. Our contemporary legal system now defines morality by statutory law, allowing most people to bypass the spiritual growth inherent in tough moral decisions. In criminal trials, winning takes precedence over truth, justice, and spiritual meaning. Law has replaced religious morality in our evaluation of life.

The breakdown of formal religion has lead to the search for a new spirituality. The culture itself has virtually exploded with spiritual viewpoints and techniques, mixing east and west, modern and ancient, and introducing all manner of esoteric and hybrid beliefs and practices, including witchcraft, Native American religions, psychic arts, fundamentalism, divination, lucid dreaming, traditional religion, and past lives. We are, most certainly, in a "New Age" if for no other reason than this incredible proliferation of spiritual seeking, cross-cultural experimentation, and diversity of spiritual paradigms. This search has also embraced psychology and the hunger to blend spirituality and psychological healing has grown rapidly in the past few years. Psychologists have taken to scientifically studying mystical phenomena, exploring the transpersonal bases of psychotherapy, and writing about therapy as a spiritual journey.

The emerging psychological and spiritual questions at the end of the twentieth century are as interesting as they are legion and important: Can science and religion formulate a truly healthy and non-competitive relationship? Can science study religious phenomena? Can medical practitioners open themselves to the spirit as they work? Can religious healers contribute to western medicine? Can religious practices, such as prayer and meditation, contribute concretely to health and wellness? Can psychotherapy be both a scientific and a spiritual process? Can therapists safely and meaningfully invite spirituality into the consulting room? Can religious professionals bring the insights of psychotherapy to bear on relationships with parishioners and their understanding of themselves as caregivers? Will such an integration bring us closer to God and to health or simply create more self-centeredness? For these questions, an altogether new scientific paradigm is essential.

THINGS TO COME: MOVING FROM A PSYCHOLOGICAL TO A PSYCHOSPIRITUAL AGE

Up until the mid twentieth century, the consciousness of the average individual tended to be indistinguishable from the surrounding cultural and religious worldview. Rituals and ceremonies existed for every important life event (e.g., birth, marriage, death, seasonal change, yearly harvests), and religious symbols structured consciousness and culture so completely that few knew they were actually in a religious myth. While conflict may have existed, it always existed within the myth, for so pervasive was the over-riding model that no one questioned its validity. In fact, most people never even needed to think about it; they just lived it.

In the past 50 years, however, western culture has entered the psychological age. "Baby boomers" were the first to grow up in this revolutionary time, with post-war parents being spoon fed child development theories by family doctors, educators, psychoanalysts, and the media. At no other time in history have we asked so many psychological questions - about feelings, emotional health and illness, criminal behavior, social problems - and spent so much time and money exploring answers. As a result of the psychological age, large numbers of people have fallen outside their religious mythology, captivated instead by science, materialism, and individualism. Formal religious life has been pushed to the margins by a competitive and highly stimulating consumer society. Nonetheless, the archetypal religious psyche still dwells beneath the surface of consciousness, and most clients come to psychotherapists unconsciously searching for more than psychological answers. As Jung pointed out, they hunger for religious renewal and a personal reorientation to the sacred origin of their lives (1933). Theirs is both a psychological and a religious search.

The psychological age is an age of the individual and of the individuation process. Since simple collective answers no longer hold our diverse human community in any single religious myth, spiritual truths must increasingly be found and tested individually. The psychological age shifts the emphasis from external and hierarchical religious authority to a more conscious, internal, and individualistic one. Now each person is responsible for confronting the religious questions previously reserved only for religious authorities. The psychotherapist in this era understands that he or she is a midwife to the individuation process in both its psychological and spiritual aspects.

It has been argued, too, that the psychological age is more than a cultural fad, representing instead an evolution of myth and consciousness. In pre-historic times, tribal man lived closer to a mystical perception of the world where everything was alive, had souls, and the gods were many. With Greek and Roman civilization, the gods became distant and disinterested. With Judaism, only one god existed but he made a personal pact with a single people. The Christian myth said that this God chose to enter the human experience to teach humankind how to live a truly spiritual life. Then, with the splintering of the religious life, the religious quest became the individual's responsibility and the spiritual journey of individuation was born. This argument goes one more step. It states that a psychospiritual age is approaching which equates individuation with incarnation. Each will be called not only to individuate psychologically but, more profoundly, to do what Jesus did: incarnate God's consciousness as the center of human life (Edinger, 1987).

Western man's focus has thus sequentially moved from the original mystical experience to a dualistic religious model involving a dialogue between man and the outer God, and then to a psychological model where the dialogue takes place within between the ego and the religious unconscious with its indwelling divine consciousness. The coming psychospiritual age, so the argument goes, will be a time of spiritual immanence in which everything is known and experienced as the divine itself. Symbolized in the west as the coming "Kingdom of God," it is a time where "heaven on earth" is realized. Many have described this as simply a shift in consciousness (Campbell, 1988, May, 1994, Robinson, 1995). Whether one understands this evolution as mythic, literal, or involving a transformation of consciousness will depend on the individual's degree of personal mystical awareness.

In the psychological age, we are called not to permanently discard or transcend the ego, but rather to grow its capacity to hold or encounter the divine mystery until we can personally experience divine consciousness and move into a truly psychospiritual era. It may be argued that the ego evolved in order to access, realize, and manifest such holiness. This extraordinary developmental task requires us to expand consciousness until it can commingle with the divine mind. Experiences of enlightenment are examples of the breakthrough of this "cosmic consciousness." It is the personal task of twenty-first century man to experience unitive consciousness and live according to its revelations. What happened only to mystics and religious prophets must now happen to everyday people, for as human beings carry and open this ultimate consciousness, they participate in the sacred transformation of life. One of the highest purposes of a spiritual psychotherapy is to assist this process at the individual level.

In essence, the psychospiritual age is about individual consciousness awakening to the eternal and ever present mystical reality. The psyche (and its executive, the ego) is the mediator, the channel, and the translator for this divine consciousness. Such a revolutionary evolution of consciousness often comes in the midst of considerable social and world turmoil. It is only as old forms crumble that the divine breaks into reality again, allowing society to reorganize its institutions around sacred principles rather than the secular forces of power, economics, and ego. In the context of this powerfully unfolding evolutionary advance, the central question of this book assumes it highest significance. "But Where is God?" asks, in effect, can psychotherapy contribute to this profound evolution of consciousness, and if so, how can we integrate spirituality and psychotherapy in a mature and constructive fashion. Chapter 3 examines the potential benefits and liabilities of this core project.

CHAPTER THREE

INTEGRATION OF PSYCHOTHERAPY AND SPIRITUALITY: BENEFITS AND LIABILITIES

A psychology that ignores the religious literature is spiritually empty, a religion that ignores the psychological literature is naive.

Contents: Potential Benefits of Integrating Psychotherapy and Spirituality
Potential Liabilities of Integrating Psychotherapy and Spirituality

It is time now to move to the question of whether a therapist should invite religious, spiritual, or mystical issues into psychotherapy. Below is a review of the benefits and the liabilities of integrating spirituality and psychotherapy. A case is made for the value of this endeavor; at the same time, the reader is warned of the potential risks involved. Each point is, in effect, an argument pro or con. Though not every point will speak to you personally, observe your reactions, for the ones that do touch you will reflect something of your own feelings and views. In the end, see how it adds up and reach your own conclusions. In a way, this review is an opportunity for self-assessment, measuring your own personal position on this topic. We start with the potential benefits.

POTENTIAL BENEFITS OF INTEGRATING PSYCHOTHERAPY AND SPIRITUALITY

SPIRITUAL ASSESSMENT

Asking a client to explore their personal views of spirituality, religion and the sacred allows a therapist to determine whether some portion of the presenting problem is related to negative religious beliefs or traumatic experiences (e.g., ideas about guilt, sin, or hell, or memories of religious abuse).

As noted earlier, healing for the vast majority of the world is viewed as a spiritual process. Even when scientific medicine supplants aboriginal healing methods, the religious strata of the psyche continues to experience illness as somehow related to spirits, divine law, or the spiritual intentions of the cosmos. Understanding our client's religious attitudes (latent, unformulated, or simply unspoken) permits the therapist to enter a belief system central to both the presenting problems and the healing process. This system, structured with religious symbols and themes, is accessible through psychological methods (e.g., dream analysis, biographical review, sand play) and its activation can facilitate the healing process. If ignored, however, deep religious assumptions can undermine or retard even the most skillful clinical psychotherapeutic interventions.

Put another way, if we understand that everyone formulates some ideas about ultimate issues (e.g., why we are here, the purpose of life, what happens at death, etc.), then we must conclude that everyone has some kind of religious beliefs that mediate their view of the world and their personal problems. Scott Peck points out, "It is essential that therapists arrive at this knowledge, for the world view of the patients is always an essential part of their problems, and a correction in their world view is necessary for their cure. So I say to those I supervise: 'Find out your patients' religions even if they say they don't have any.'" (Peck, 1978). Opening up the topic of spirituality, therefore, invites our clients to explore their personal and subjective spiritual beliefs as a source of meaning, ultimate values, guidance, and inspiration.

This exploration is, in effect, a form of "spiritual assessment" that seeks to establish whether the client's relationship to the divine is healthy, positive and supportive, or mired by 1. parental transference, in which the client imbues the God image with negative parental attributes, rendering it frightening, cruel, or punitive, 2. historical resentment or distrust, involving feelings of abandonment or betrayal by God, or 3. actual religious abuse (e.g., religious teaching or methods that were frightening, guilt inducing, cruel, or otherwise traumatizing). Pathology of the God image can itself cause serious emotional problems and symptoms (e.g., irrational guilt and fear, masochistic self-denial, and profound feelings of unworthiness) and should always be assessed when religious addiction or abuse is suspected.

CONFRONTING ADDICTIVE AND ABUSIVE RELIGIOUS FORMS

Religious practice and ideology, at some time or other, invariably become addictive and occasionally abusive. The ego, its defenses and grandiosity, sooner or later uses religion to hide from pain, control others, or inflate the false self. This includes any and every religious belief and practice ever known, from Catholicism to 12 Step programs to Zen meditation. Psychology's understanding of dysfunctional human relationships offers a potentially corrective balance, a down-to-earth skepticism that can uncover and confront such defensive spirituality.

SUPPORTING OUR SPIRITUAL NATURE

It would appear from cross-cultural studies that all peoples have a religious orientation to the cosmos. Anthropologists, mythologists, and depth psychologists alike understand that our fundamental spiritual beliefs, often encoded symbolically in a culture's religion, mythology, and art, are really attempts to comprehend the sacred mystery of existence. To ignore such a deep, basic and universal human need in psychotherapy is to ignore an incredibly important source of human longing, creativity, understanding and life-transforming meaning. We have an inherently religious nature and the need to nourish this nature is universal.

ACTIVATING THE SPIRITUAL PROCESS

Gentle inquiry into the area of spiritual and religious concerns may itself stir the process of spiritual growth and development. Stimulating or encouraging our clients to explore their relationship with the sacred can awaken a larger spiritual process that then interacts and overlaps with the therapeutic process. This shares the process of healing not only with the client but also with the divine, and revalues the realm of grace, hope and gratitude. One's relationship with God is itself growth producing and transformative, and can be nurtured and awakened with sensitively expressed therapeutic interest.

ENTERING THE SACRED PRESENCE

Clarity and healing also occur when we learn to enter the sacred Presence, an experiential reality that lives in and around us filled with consciousness, guidance, forgiveness, and love. We can know and be guided by this mystical dimension, and such contact can change feelings, attitudes, and problems in ways that psychotherapeutic methods cannot. Here, the client's relationship with the divine becomes tangible and immediate. The Presence is a healing resource that therapist and client alike can learn to access and trust, often lifting therapy to higher levels of spiritual meaning and realization.

Time spent exploring the subjective reality of here-and-now-spiritual experience can also represent a valuable change of pace. It moves from the problem-solving, task-oriented work mode of traditional therapy into a kind of open, reflective, sacred space in which the client and therapist can pause and focus not on the how's but on the why's of life. It is a temporary shift in emphasis that sees problems and life itself as revelation rather than as something to be fixed. A very different consciousness, such reverential receptivity can literally invite the sacred into the consulting room. In the frenzy of everyday life, this change of pace is itself transformative, allowing us to see that life is its own purpose.

RECOVERING THE MYSTERY OF THE OTHER

In this age of sophisticated psychiatric nomenclature and diagnostic taxonomy, we often forget the real and wonderfully unpredictable mystery inherent in each client. To the truly open mind, there are always miracles and surprises when we see the other as a divine work-in-progress rather than merely a typical example of a particular diagnosis. Respect for this mystery honors our clients' uniqueness, their one-of-a-kind, never-to-be-repeated expression of life, and refuses to simply reduce or objectify them into a disease or psychiatric category. Furthermore, it encourages clients to honor and value their individuality without belittling or invidious comparisons. This kind of attitude makes life sacred and purposeful again, even when full of hardship.

FINDING RELIGIOUS ANSWERS IN TIMES OF PROFOUND TRAUMA

In times of major trauma, with its profound disorientation and soul-searching, the deep psyche often yields spiritual images and meanings that can give a larger frame of reference for the crisis at hand. This archetypal layer hints at ultimate purposes and spiritual realities that can make suffering more meaningful and bearable.

When a mother cries out, "Why did my child die?" we have to realize she is asking a *religious* question. We usually know *why* her child died (e.g., the cause of death was illness, murder, suicide, or car accident), but that is not the answer she is seeking. Such a desperate and anguished cry is literally a form of prayer. In her great pain, she is crying out to God for answers, relief, and meaning. If this mother could take this cry of her soul, praying further and listening within, exploring her dreams and intuitions, and reading whatever spiritually oriented literature speaks to her, in time understandings may emerge to her by grace alone that do in fact yield meaning, purpose, and even dignity to this great suffering.

Therapists need to have familiarity with the ultimate structures of meaning that inform both religion and the deep psyche in order to sensitively support the client's spiritual search and intuitions. If all experience is understood as necessary for spiritual growth, then even tragedy or mental illness can eventually be assimilated as an important and potentially healing part of this process.

MEETING THE NEEDS OF RELIGIOUS CLIENTS

Many religious clients are afraid to consult with secular therapists, fearing their beliefs will be challenged, discounted, or undermined. As a result, they seek counseling with practitioners of their faith or in church supported counseling centers. When these resources are not readily available, or when religious therapists use dogma to the detriment of treatment, then the needs of these clients are not served. A therapist who can understand and support a client's religious beliefs without compromising the integrity of treatment will minimize such fear and serve a whole population of clients who have for years avoided getting help.

AFFIRMING AND UNDERSTANDING LEGITIMATE MYSTICAL EXPERIENCES

Intense, immediate and real mystical experiences actually happen to people. Not only do these experiences occur, they are not altogether uncommon, though patients often conceal them from us out of fear, shame or confusion. Lukoff et al. (1985) point to survey research suggesting that 30% to 40% of the population have had mystical experiences and Gallop's 1982 survey indicates that over eight million people in this country have had a Near Death Experience. These experiences are not forms of mental illness though people do need to discuss their emotional meaning and impact. In fact, a mystical experience itself may be followed by the profound transformation of an individual's entire value system and understanding of his place in the universe, offering to psychotherapy an invaluable resource for personal and spiritual growth.

Mystical, Near-Death, and other non-ordinary experiences need to be distinguished from psychopathology and cared for on their own terms. In fact, additional categories in the American Psychiatric Association's Diagnostic and Statistical Manual have been recommended (Lukoff et. all, 1992) with non-pathological categories included in the latest revision (DSM-IV). Every therapist needs to be aware of such "non-ordinary" events and know how to differentiate them from common psychopathology, how to help, when to refer, and to whom.

DISCOVERING THE SPIRITUAL BASIS OF
PRESENTING PSYCHOLOGICAL DISORDERS

Years ago, Jung made a remarkable assertion. He said that neuroses were essentially a defense against spiritual or religious problems. Somewhere at their core, emotional problems reflect a search for ultimate meaning amidst existential confusion and fear. In this context, a neurosis may reflect an aborted spiritual insight or truth, or a refusal to experience the awesome nature of existence itself. Overwhelmed by the fear of non-existence, we recoil into neuroses to distract, displace, and discharge anxiety. At some point, if we are to grow, we have to face the underlying spiritual dimensions of existence and our own questions: Will I survive? Can I trust the universe? Is there any meaning at all? Where is God?

RECOGNIZING THE STAGES OF SPIRITUAL REALIZATION AND THEIR OPERATION IN THE PSYCHOTHERAPEUTIC PROCESS

If we understand our life experience from the cradle to the grave as a journey of spiritual transformation, which is essentially what Campbell concluded in his comprehensive study of the world's mythologies, then our personal problems and therapy have within them the seed potential for deep and remarkable growth. Campbell also likened the therapist to the ancient shaman, guide of the soul, who must be personally knowledgeable about the stages and purposes of the universal hero's journey (Campbell, 1949). He argued that the schizophrenic, LSD "tripper", the shaman, and the mystic all go through the same stages and crises of this basic journey (Campbell, 1972).

It has similarly been argued that the process of long term depth-oriented psychotherapy also follows these archetypal stages (Sullivan, 1989). The question arises, then, do we as therapists know how to recognize these inborn patterns of transformation and how our client's current problems reflect their archetypal structure? If we can, then therapy becomes more than simply reducing depression; it can be about initiating and supporting our clients underlying journey of personal and spiritual transformation, often the very reason they have come to us in the first place.

UNDERSTANDING THE HIGHEST REALMS OF HUMAN POTENTIAL

The higher realms of human functioning, and the ultimate spiritual goals of human development, have been described by all the great religious traditions and teachers. When we move from psychotherapy as treatment for emotional problems (the medical model) to therapy as a means of personal growth and enhancement, these teachings provide a profound road map of these higher dimensions of human functioning. In understanding this literature, we not only appreciate the "goal" of human evolution, we affirm to ourselves and our clients the essential and timeless nature of love, gratitude, forgiveness, mercy, humility, kindness, generosity, wonder, and the infinite preciousness of life. We learn how to live in the world as a sacred place, as sacred beings, with sacred purpose.

LEARNING THE VALUE OF SPIRITUAL LANGUAGE IN THE PSYCHOTHERAPEUTIC JOURNEY

The language and metaphors we use in psychotherapy have a deep influence on the way our clients envision their lives. When therapy moves from a clinical-medical language of disorders, pathologies, chemistry, and interventions, a model that teaches clients they are sick or brain-altered, to one that embraces poetic, symbolic, and teleological metaphors such as spirituality, soul, journey, and the sacred, then the process of therapy not only empowers our clients but stirs new meanings, motives, and forms for the healing process. We are so much more than our chemistry and our pathology, and the soul has a hunger for a language that can awaken its broader vision of our lives and our potential.

Supporting the Value of Religious Community

Spirituality often takes place, or takes the individual into, a religious community, and as psychological research has confirmed over and over, a healthy, open and democratic religious community has numerous positive and socially beneficial aspects that support a client's mental health and complement their work in therapy. A healthy religious community encourages spiritual growth, teaches timeless spiritual values, provides support and comfort at times of crisis, and offers corrective feedback when an individual's beliefs begin to lose their reality grounding or perspective.

Respecting the Reality of Spiritual Laws

Spiritual principles and laws really do operate in our lives. They can be seen through the eyes of faith, found in prayer, or discovered in one's religious frame of reference, and need only be applied to one's personal life to discover their importance. We also need to learn more about the spiritual laws that underlie healing and psychotherapy, and incorporate them more consciously in our work.

Potential Liabilities of Integrating Psychotherapy and Spirituality

"In the Name of God"

Everything imaginable has been done in the name of God. Religion has inspired acts that are beautiful, self-less, and sublime, as well as acts of terrible cruelty, carnage, and destruction. The unconscious power of this numinous force deep in the psyche is easily and readily appropriated by the ego, and its perversion to personal use inevitably leads to harm. Given this history, it should not be surprising that problems will also crop up when we seek to integrate psychotherapy and spirituality. Therapists need to be alert to the kinds of the confusion, temptations, and pitfalls that occur "in the name of God" and examine how naiveté, gullibility, and grandiosity create fertile ground for their development.

Coercive Use of Religious Practices or Dogma by Religious Therapists

When psychotherapy is conducted under the umbrella of a particular religion or sect, certain practices or dogma can be used in ways not always compatible with a clients' best interests. A fundamentalist Christian counselor, for example, may discourage a women from leaving an abusive marriage with Biblical or religious prohibitions against divorce, condemn an individual's nontraditional sexual orientation, or spend excessive time in prayer to the exclusion of clinically appropriate interventions. In these examples, the interests of the church overshadow the needs of the client and interfere with psychologically indicated therapeutic goals and interventions.

CONFLICTS OF INTEREST IN DUAL RELATIONSHIPS

A dual relationship is one in which therapist and client have another relationship outside the therapeutic one (e.g., business, social, community, romantic, or sexual). Dual relationships are now considered professionally unethical because of the potential conflict of interest existing between the therapist's personal agenda and the client's emotional needs, and because the psychological power of the therapist can foster conscious or unconscious manipulation of the client for personal gain. A therapist may also lose perspective when the emotional relationship interferes with clinical objectivity and decision-making. When a therapist operates in a religious community, interacting socially with his clients outside of therapy, the risks associated with dual relationships may increasingly contaminate the therapeutic work.

THE USE OF SPIRITUAL BELIEFS OR PRACTICES TO MASK UNRECOGNIZED EMOTIONAL PROBLEMS

Spiritual and religious beliefs and practices mask emotional problems in numerous ways. For example, the deep emotional wounds of childhood are not simply eradicated by spiritual practices. Unfaced, they will be replicated: The meditation that was so wonderful in time becomes a defense against intimacy or anger, repeating the client's original family distance and non-communication; the highly praised spiritual teacher evolves into the critical, abusive, or exploiting parent the client thought he had successfully escaped; or spiritual reading and practices wind up substituting for the experiences of life itself.

This process, called repetition-compulsion, is vastly more pervasive than people realize, and at one time or another affects all religious practices. Unless the seeker has psychologically identified and worked through such childhood injuries, they are guaranteed to repeat in spiritual and religious formats, particularly unhealthy ones. Excessive passivity, avoidance of interpersonal relationships or responsibility, extreme austerity, asceticism or self-abuse, literal or righteous beliefs, religious superiority, moralistic prescriptions for behavior, addictive practices and ideas, spiritual vanity and materialism, excessive conformity, all of these are symptoms of underlying emotional problems rather than signs of spiritual progress. Reflecting pathological attempts to control oneself or others in defense of unrecognized emotional wounds, they need to be confronted for real spiritual progress to occur.

CONFUSION CAUSED BY SPIRITUAL MISCONCEPTIONS

There are innumerable misconceptions and self-deceptions on the spiritual path. They may involve fascination with spiritual highs, secrets, signs, or psychic powers, the desire to escape ordinary reality, or the belief that enlightenment will cure all other problems. Contrary to such beliefs, spiritual experience does not mean one's personal or personality problems are solved. I have seen numerous people who had profound mystical or Near Death Experiences yet still have equally profound emotional problems in everyday life. You may have a higher understanding of life but you return to who you are and what you are working on. No one retires in enlightenment.

Failure to Distinguish Between
Psychoses and Partial Mystical States

Religious beliefs are not infrequently part of more severe psychopathology, especially psychoses characterized by delusions of grandeur (e.g., Jesus identification), religiosity (e.g., obsessive religious ideation), magical thinking (e.g., special powers), and auditory hallucinations (e.g., the voice of God or Satan). It is easy to be entranced by the power and apparent reality of the psychotic process, particularly for someone with a weakened ego or profound feelings of inferiority. A friend or therapist can also be seduced into believing that such religious talk represents a spiritually transforming experience or divine intercession. When this happens, religious conversation simply confuses and distracts the patient whose core psychopathology must be managed to recover. Even when mystical consciousness or content is emerging, the major diagnostic question is whether the client's ego functions i.e., reality testing, ego boundaries. are intact enough to integrate it

Competency and Boundary Conflicts Among Professionals

Confusion around the specific competencies and boundaries of the various helping professionals can also lead to serious problems and misguidance. Psychotherapists, clergy, pastoral counselors, spiritual directors, and spiritual teachers all have specific functions, realms of competence, and required training experiences. Despite areas of overlap, one kind of professional cannot automatically assume the functions of another. Eagerness and personal beliefs do not substitute for training and experience, and clients can seriously misdirected when we fail to recognize these boundaries.

For example, psychotherapists can not properly function as pastoral counselors, ministers, or spiritual directors within a specific religious tradition unless they have been fully trained and initiated into the philosophy, wisdom literature, and practices of that tradition. An interest in eastern religion or experience with meditation does not automatically qualify a therapist to instruct a client in these skills and philosophy. Nor can gurus or spiritual directors help a seriously disturbed seeker with spiritual techniques alone. Many therapists harbor animosity toward organized religion and have never understood or worked through their basic religious ambivalence. Such ambivalence may prevent them from encouraging clients to explore church affiliation or seek guidance from the clergy. In the same vein, many religious practitioners have never confronted their personal feelings or judgments toward psychiatric patients, tending instead to harbor unrealistic expectations, sympathies, or judgments that do not serve the patient's healing.

A related issue involves culture and language. When descriptions of mystical experiences from different religions are compared with careful philosophical and linguistic analysis, it is discovered that they are not necessarily equivalent (Katz, 1978). The Christian God is not exactly equivalent to the Buddhist's "nothingness." The way the Sufi mystic and the Native American experience the divine is heavily determined by the social, cultural, and physical context of the people involved. Even within branches of the major religions, there may be tremendous doctrinal variation and conflict. Competency, therefore, requires a mastery of language and culture that does not come with reading a book or attending a class.

THE DARK SIDE OF SPIRITUAL TEACHERS AND GURUS

Clients and parishioners alike tend to idealize their therapists, clergy, spiritual directors, and spiritual teachers. In doing so, they are vulnerable to the personal problems of these authority figures. When we as professionals have not addressed our own shadow issues (e.g., sexuality, money, power, narcissism), then the integration of psychotherapy and spirituality can be muddy at best and injurious at worst. Complicating matters, anyone is capable of inflation and self-deception - indeed, everyone becomes inflated with themselves from time to time and few of us have fully examined this side of ourselves. Worse, our professional training and peer review also tends to miss or ignore this shadow side until it becomes undeniable.

Growing from the fertile soil of self-deception are endless examples of eastern and western spiritual teachers or clerics who have had to confront their own alcoholism, sexual promiscuity, and financial exploitation of students or parishioners. Psychotherapists, too, can become grandiose about their beliefs and power, and there is something about spiritual beliefs and experiences that can elicit a particularly pernicious kind of grandiosity. These problems can emerge anywhere, and training in religion or psychology do not guarantee against their operation. It is primarily our psychological work on ourselves and our openness to the corrective feedback of peers and community that protects us from such insidious self-deception.

CONCLUSIONS

Integrating spirituality and psychotherapy is a complex challenge. Encouraging our clients to explore this path is an invitation to both the richness and the confusion of the religious search. Spirituality does not necessarily cure anything nor will it automatically solve our clients' problems or substitute for the hard work, training, skill, consultation, and continuing education required of the therapist. But the integration of psychotherapy and spirituality can make remarkable and often surprising contributions to the journey of healing, raising it from a purely psychological process to an opportunity for grace, revelation, and transformation, if we stay balanced.

PART TWO

BUILDING A MODEL FOR
A SPIRITUAL PSYCHOTHERAPY

Part II presents a simple yet versatile model of spiritual psychology and psychotherapy. The discussion begins a survey of the religious, spiritual, and mystical themes and experiences that can arise in psychotherapy and then examines the vastly larger array of religious, philosophical, spiritual, theological, mystical, indigenous, popular, and practical ideas and experiences such a model must be large enough to accommodate. A psychospiritual theory of personality, psychopathology, and psychotherapy follows, starting with a basic vocabulary and building progressively toward an unified understanding of psychospiritual development, its disorders, and their treatment.

CHAPTER FOUR

SURVEY OF THE RANGE AND FREQUENCY OF RELIGIOUS ISSUES AND EXPERIENCES COMMONLY ENCOUNTERED IN PSYCHOTHERAPEUTIC PRACTICE.

Contents: Survey of Religious, Spiritual, and Mystical Experiences and Issues Presented in Psychotherapy
Typical Survey Results
Check-List of Subtle Topics

A brief checklist of possible religious, spiritual, and mystical topics, themes, or experiences that can and do arise in psychotherapy is presented below. There is no particular order to the items nor are they meant to be narrowly defined or mutually exclusive. If you are a therapist, check off any that have occurred in your practice over the past two years. If you are not a therapist, respond as a client or would be therapist. If you don't understand an item, simply skip it. Answer quickly and spontaneously. When you have finished, add the number you've marked.

SURVEY OF RELIGIOUS, SPIRITUAL, AND MYSTICAL EXPERIENCES AND ISSUES PRESENTED IN PSYCHOTHERAPY

PART 1. CHECK-LIST OF OBVIOUS TOPICS

____"spiritual" crises however you define them
____religious conversions
____guilt produced by religious beliefs or experiences
____Channeling or communications with spirits
____"Near-Death" experiences
____religious hallucinations & identifications
____"out-of-body" experiences
____12 step spirituality
____psychotherapy as spiritual practice
____discussions about God, religion or religious beliefs
____experiences of direct contact with God

____religious dreams
____fascination with religious symbols
____child abuse rationalized with religious doctrine
____participation in revivals
____belief in miracles
____interest in non-Judeo-Christian religions or religious practices (e.g., Eastern, Native
      American, ancient or indigenous religions)
____Religiosity, scrupulosity, or overly rigid religious beliefs
____conflict between religious beliefs and therapeutic recommendations
____soul possession, loss, or retrieval
____religious healing
____past or present cult membership
____ritual abuse
____witchcraft, Satanism, occult beliefs or practices
____Kundalini signs or symptoms
____strange or culturally unfamiliar religious practices
____synchronicity as a spiritual process
____religious visions (e.g., on death bed, under anesthesia, during   meditation)
____interest in astrology, clairvoyance, Tarot, ESP etc. in psychotherapy
____use of LSD, peyote, or other drugs for religious experience
____meditation as a spiritual practice
____involvement with a non-mental health "healer," shaman, etc.
____non-ordinary states of consciousness
____felt conflict between therapist's and client's religious beliefs
____therapist uncertainty about whether to inquire about, discuss, or encourage religious
      beliefs in therapy
____therapist uncertainty about the reality or validity of a client's beliefs or   experiences
____therapist uncertainty about whether clients desire or need to talk about   religion
____therapist uncertainty about who is properly competent to discuss a religious topic (e.g.,
      clergy, mental health professional, spiritual director, shaman, healer)
____therapist uncertainty about revealing his/her own religious or spiritual   beliefs
____difficulty differentiating between genuine religious experience and
      psychopathology
____other(describe:_____)
____**TOTAL NUMBER MARKED**

PART 2. FREQUENCY

Again responding as a therapist, how frequently do you encounter topics from this list in your
normal practice?:
_____monthly?   _____weekly   _____daily

TYPICAL SURVEY RESULTS

In an informal survey of 180 mental health professionals during a recent professional
presentation, the average number of religious, spiritual, and mystical topics occurring in these busy
professionals' practices was approximately 15. Regarding frequency, approximately 50% of the
audience indicated that such items came up in their practices on at least a monthly basis, 25% said
they occurred weekly, and 10% discussed them daily with their clients. Very few people in the

audience were surprised by the number or range of topics that could come up and the majority noticed a personal correlation between the score they received and their interest in spirituality.

These informal results, repeated in subsequent presentations, clearly indicate that exploration of religious, spiritual and mystical issues in psychotherapy is not merely an academic exercise. Clients need to talk about them. It is likely, too, that the results would have been higher had this survey been given anonymously to the clients themselves, for many suppress such religious experiences and concerns fearing their therapist's disinterest or disapproval. In other words, these results reflect how often clients bring up such material, not how often they actually think about them.

One additional point needs clarifying. It is not that religious issues must or should come up all the time in psychotherapy, because obviously therapy is primarily devoted to the healing of emotional and behavioral problems. But at some point in therapy, and certainly in any extended or "long term" treatment, religious, spiritual, or mystical issues will come up (assuming that a therapist is genuinely open to hearing them), and when they do, they are probably very important to the client and to the work of therapy.

PART 2. CHECK-LIST OF *SUBTLE* TOPICS

There is a second list of religious, spiritual, and mystical items that are equally important in the therapeutic process, but because of their subtle nature, usually go unexamined. These are themes and experiences associated with spiritual and mystical awareness or, more commonly in our present secular and materialistic world, the absence of such awareness.

Direct mystical experience of the divine has occurred to people across all times, places, and reality orientations, and continues to occur today. It is one of the most beautiful and life affirming contacts with the holy available to mankind. Numerous examples of this experience are given in my previous book and it is summarized in the next Chapter. For our present purposes, the following brief description will suffice:

> In the mystic experience, the world is discovered to be infinitely beautiful, perfect, and precious. One feels surrounded by a sacred presence which seems to pervade and live in all things, animate and inanimate, creating a feeling of loving unity. The everyday boundaries of the self seem to be expanded or transcended, and one experiences a sense of universal harmony and serenity. Time is forgotten and the every aspect of life is profoundly fascinating, perceptually vivid, and effortless. This experience, which may last minutes, hours, and sometimes even days, evokes awe, reverence, unbounded joy, as well as feelings of love, safety, and trust in the cosmos. Whether small or large, it is felt to be a literal and unforgettable revelation of the sacred nature of being. Hopelessness, loneliness, and fear of death are, for this moment, totally eradicated.

Whether or not one has had this experience in its fullness, lessor mystical experiences and intuitions are not uncommon and share the same ultimate qualities albeit less intensely. Maslow called these moments of immediate, here-and-now, awareness of sacred existence "Peak Experiences" and found that they occur to nearly everyone at some time or other. Ask yourself or your clients about these kinds of moments, no matter how brief, and seek to increase your awareness of them, for they occur more frequently than most people realize. To focus your searches check those elements of the mystical experience that have occurred for you from the following list and reflect on the experience.

____heightened and vivid perception
____awareness of exquisite beauty in
the world
____experience of the world as
absolutely perfect and complete
____awareness of a loving and sacred
presence
____feeling of unity
____awe and reverence
____unbounded joy
____a feeling of profound serenity

____effortless movement or activity
____unconditional love for the world
____feelings of complete safety

____absolute trust in the universe
____expanded or transcended self
____a timeless consciousness
____fascinated absorption with activity or things
around you
____freedom from loneliness, isolation,
and fear of death

Human beings hunger for this core mystical experience. It can come in small ways - in the wilderness, holding a newborn child, in prayer or meditation, in love-making, or in large ways - as moments of ecstasy, satori, or enlightenment central to all profound religious experience. They can also come during intense athletic competition, sometimes called the "zone," and Csikszentmihalyi has labeled a closely related state of consciousness "Flow" because it feels like everything is moving smoothly and without effort, like a river. Too often, however, we look for these transcendent or unity states in substitute experiences, particularly in addictive processes (alcohol, drugs, relationships, power, money, etc.). When these experiential elements of mystical communion are chronically absent from a life, when there is no unconditional experience of beauty, joy, happiness, love, and safety, then a kind of spiritual depression develops. Though it may go unnamed and unrecognized by the individual, such emptiness is real and painful. Like any experience, you cannot really know what is missing until you experience it.

Perhaps the best analogy to the mystical experience is love. When a person has never felt loved in their life, either as a child or as an adult, then they literally have no idea what is missing. The resulting tension and depression may even become such a familiar and steady state as to seem normal. When love finally gets through, when the individual finally relaxes into the fullness of this remarkable feeling, only then do they gratefully appreciate its reality and profound value. The absence of sacred feeling, perception, and experience leaves the same kind of invisible and undetected scar.

Therapists usually recognize clinical depression and its origins in abusive, neglectful, or unloving childhood relationships. They actively pursue the depression in therapy, guiding the client into the unbearable experience of grief, numbness, and rage that underlies it and must be worked through to restore their inherent capacity for feeling and love. The same therapeutic principle holds true for the feeling, perception, and experience of the divine. Assessing for its subtle manifestations shows us how cut off our client may be to this intuitive and spiritual awareness.

One of the tasks of a spiritually oriented psychotherapy is to help the client open to this always present, sacred, here-and-now, wondrous dimension of existence. It is, by itself, a healing and transformative experience of divine being and grace that awakens the inborn capacity for joy, love, hope, and meaning.

CHAPTER FIVE

THE "VARIETIES OF RELIGIOUS EXPERIENCE"

*It is clear that, from this vast deadness of space, man is an
infinitely unlikely product. From basic matter comes an
organization of elements that is conscious, writes symphonies,
and creates satellite TV and cellular communication. We think,
feel, know, and love; and now we are participating in evolution
itself. This achievement is beyond all reason and probability.
We are a miracle. But what for?*

Contents: The Religious Psyche
                     Religious Questions
                     The Nature of Religious Formation
                     Facets of a Diamond: "Varieties of Religious Experience"
                     Religion and Psychotherapy: The Common Quest
                     Overview: A Common Story, Perennial Differences

This Chapter and its accompanying appendix review a variety of religious models and metaphors. The assumption behind this review is that our common and universal religious quest finds multifaceted expression, informing a broad and diverse continuum from first hand mystical communion to formal theological doctrine, from ancient religious traditions to new and emerging ones, and from aboriginal peoples to highly industrial civilizations. Each form has something unique to teach and across traditions are many common and recurring themes.

The purposes of this review are fourfold: 1. to examine how religion grows and develops, 2. to discover the kinds of ultimate truths or values contained in each religious form, 3. to grasp the universal religious and spiritual problems people bring into psychotherapy, and 4. to provide a foundation for our psychospiritual model of psychotherapy. But there is one more fundamental purpose to this review: It is a way of returning to the divine ground of the religious psyche in order to awaken our own intrinsic mystical capacity to sense, experience, and trust the sacred dimension of existence.

As a primer for psychotherapists, this Chapter cannot be a course on comparative religions. Its focus, however, recognizes that religion serves the same search as psychotherapy, asking questions about meaning and suffering, fate and purpose, healing and love, life and death. As the contents indicate, we begin our exploration with mankind's eternal questions, examine how religions are born as answers, and then investigate a sampling of specific answers from the world's great religious traditions. Commonalties and differences among religions are discussed followed by some observations about the religious experience as metaphor and its relevance to psychotherapy. Therapists should be familiar with the kinds of answers discovered on the religious search for its accumulated literature is filled with beautiful and illuminating insights, deep compassion, and reassuring wisdom.

THE RELIGIOUS PSYCHE

The religious search is ubiquitous. In every historical era and geographic location, the human psyche seems to intuit that there is a divine reality or principle within or behind the material one, and that we must try to know its purposes. We believe further that the pain and confusion of life, and indeed all that befalls us, are somehow related to this divine order. When we are in trouble, atheist and believer alike, instinctively cry out one of God's many names.

At the core of the human personality, where psychology and spirituality meet in primordial oneness, lies the religious psyche. It is a wellspring forever yielding life sustaining and life transforming meaning to the multifarious experience of human existence. Spiritual seekers find a living sacred reality in this core - as a fire, a stillness, a voice, a presence, a revelation, a black and empty void, an immensity, a prayer or hymn, or a stream of symbols and images. Religion is born and repeatedly affirmed from this numinous center which is, itself, divine.

In every religion, there remains a living spark of its founder's original fiery revelation and a view of the spiritual nature and purpose of the world. We study the "Varieties of Religious Experience," to borrow William James' famous title, hoping to know more about this revelatory process and its meaning for our existence, and to understand what it is that our clients are instinctually pursuing in the spiritual dimension of their psychotherapeutic journey, for that same pulsating spark of divine consciousness whispers to the heart and soul of each person seated before us in the consulting room.

RELIGIOUS QUESTIONS

Whether all religions can be reduced to the same fundamental message is a matter of some controversy. It is possible, on the other hand, to find much common ground in the questions we ask, the ones that awaken our religious impulse and intuition, and in time evoke a sacred reply. From this point of view, the religious search represents mankind's collective and ongoing yearning to answer the following timeless and recurring questions:

* Why was this world formed and why are we here?
* Is there any spiritual purpose to life on earth?
* What is our true nature and rightful place in the sacred order of things?
* What can we do in this lifetime to advance ourselves spiritually?
* What is the spiritual nature of misfortune, illness, sin, and evil? Why do they occur and how do we respons to them?
  What is the religious life and how do we remember and serve the divine in the everyday scheme of things?
* What is the purpose of religious ritual, ceremony, worship and celebration? How do we use them to meet the divine?
* Does the transcendent speak directly to mankind?
* How do we make contact with the sacred and how do we know when we have?
  Who is the religious or enlightened person or teacher? How are they recognized and what is their true role?
• What is death and how do we prepare for it? What happens after death and is it dependent on our lives or state of consciousness?

THE NATURE OF RELIGIOUS FORMATION

The term religion is used in both general and specific ways. In the former, it serves as an umbrella concept that covers everything mankind does in its search of sacred experience and understanding, connoting a process varying from simple, concrete, and deeply personal, to vast and complex systems of thought, language, art, and architecture that can imbue an entire culture with its metaphors. More specifically, the word may refer to a particular institutional structure and system of religious or metaphysical beliefs and practices.

A religion is born when someone tries to describe a personal, first-hand experience of sacred revelation and explain its message or significance to their community. If the individual is successful, a group forms seeking to understand, organize, and communicate this revelation. The story of this awakening and its message become the religion's centerpiece. Over time, the teachings are recorded as scripture and the original mystical experience is re-enacted in ritual and ceremony. The revelation may become a culture's central myth, defining for all those within the culture the spiritual nature of reality and one's place in it.

Religion, then, is the result of mystical experience, not its cause. New mystical experiences may occur or be pursued within an established religious system, and when they do, they are usually embodied in the existing symbols and metaphors: Christians may seek Christ consciousness, Buddhists find Nirvana, Native Americans encounter the spirits of animals, places, and ancestors, and Hindus experience Brahma, Vishnu, or Shiva in their various manifestations.

Religion as an institution serves the invaluable purpose of symbolically encoding (in oral or scriptural form) the profound content, lessons, and themes granted to its founder or founders. Its teachings, rituals, and disciplines constitute a map of sacred experience meant to assist the seeker toward the same enlightenment or sacred understanding of life. Studying its teachings, followers may subsequently contribute to the development of a theology and set of spiritual practices. Each religion gradually evolves into an institutional community of believers who share the basic body of beliefs and come together to worship through the prescribed ceremonies and practices.

Most people in the world grow up within a religious myth symbolically repeated all around them - in religious events and festivals, literature and art, media and cinema. It is so present that they take its tenants for granted. Jung argued that it is very difficult to leave one's own religious myth for another, and it is likely that, after all the searching pursued by western individuals, the majority will return in later years to the particular religious sea in which they born, perhaps with modification. The term myth in no way implies a lack of truth, as it is sometimes popularly used. A culture's mythology actually encodes its fundamental beliefs, view of reality, and the meaning it gives to life. To fully know an individual, we must know the mythology of his culture and religion.

Anybody who has taken the time to study the world's many religions is inevitably impressed with the following observations. The size, complexity, and richness of sacred literature in each of the major religions is astounding. One could spend a lifetime (and many do) grasping the depth, breadth, history, controversies, and subtleties of any one of the world's great religions, and still not know it all. Furthermore, the remarkable diversity of beliefs, sects, practices, personalities, and gifted individuals, often makes it difficult to determine what propositions truly represent the core of any particular religion's system of faith. The study of religion also reveals that each is a living, dynamic, and evolving process, growing and changing by assimilating new voices and new cultural trends. Over time, a religion may become a richly textured fabric of ritual and belief, change into something altogether different, or disappear entirely as those who hold it vanish into history's relatively short memory.

Formal religion, therefore, develops as the codified history and institutionalization of divine revelation. It flows from mankind's struggle to comprehend the profound and unfathomable mystery of the cosmos and its sometimes unbearable conditions and paradoxes. Although these mysteries can be sensed, intuited, and occasionally partially revealed in mystical experience, they can never be fully known. As a result, the search to apprehend the sacred will always continue, spawning new religious experiences, movements, and meaning. Institutional religion itself eventually moves too far from its original revelation, allowing egos to get involved in quarrels over increasing narrow interpretations of theology and liturgy. As differences multiply and personalities dominate, disenchantment with the ecclesiastical rigidity renews the desire for first hand revelation, and soon new religious ground is broken.

Not surprisingly, the same pattern of religious formation takes place at the individual level. Private revelation, from mystical experience to deeply felt spiritual realization, yields a new and highly personal teaching about the sacred nature of the world. When it is fresh and intimate, the experience is alive and meaningful. In time, however, every experience grows stale, becoming an idea rather than a direct knowing. Examining or debating personal beliefs with others, one soon realize their emptiness and rigidity, and the search for genuine and immediate religious experience begins anew. The cycle of revelation also repeats with every generation even within a healthy religion, for new believers must experience codified revelation in a personally valid and meaningful way.

Finally, as a religion solidifies as an institutional and community organization, more pedestrian psychological and emotional processes insinuate themselves into religious life. For many, religion is far more of a social than a spiritual affair, providing friendship, meeting dependency and security needs, and collectively ordering life in predictable pattern of religious holidays based on the original story of revelation. For many, then, it becomes a psychological process holding them in community and providing reassuring meaning across this amazing and otherwise seeming inexplicable experience we call life. As we will see later, the psychological well being of a religious community is only as healthy as its individuals and social organization.

FACETS OF A DIAMOND: "THE VARIETIES OF RELIGIOUS EXPERIENCE"

After exploring numerous religious forms, it has become clear to me that each is, metaphorically speaking, the single facet of a perfect diamond: the mystical nature of the universe. To underscore the remarkable diversity of religious experience, a simplified survey of traditions and movements is presented in the following Chart (discussed in detail in Appendix A).

Each religious tradition or movement is both a metaphor and a deep well of insight, wisdom, and meaning. Like the space shuttle observing the great land masses of earth, this sampling looks at contours, forms, textures or colors, leaving the myriad man-made boundaries and distinctions for others to map out (i.e., individual sects, divisions, and schools that develop within and between religions over the centuries). But meaning is also subjective and personal, and ultimately there are as many religions are there are people, for each person's experience is an individualized statement of faith, a unique repository of image, metaphor, meaning, longing, communion, and ideology. There are endless ways to mix these ingredients and as many spiritual paths are there people. Therapists need to be familiar with such wide-ranging religious thought and experience to be truly sensitive companions on the spiritual road. Though obviously abbreviated for the purposes of review, consider what relevance each religious paradigm might have in your personal life.

SAMPLING THE DIAMOND'S FACETS

The Judeo-Christian-Islamic Line
  Judaism: Monotheism and the divine meaning of history
  Christianity: The incarnation of God
  Islam: The ordering of society by divine law

Eastern Religions
  Hinduism: Dissolving self into Self
  Buddhism: The science of extinguishing the self
  Taoism: Flowing with the harmony of being
  Confucianism: The perfection of the social self

Western Philosophy and Psychology
  Our forgotten speculation on God and soul

Indigenous Religion
  Original contact with the immanent divine world

Mystical Experience
  Near-Death Experiences: Meeting the transcendent God
  Mysticism: Meeting the immanent God

Recent Religious Developments
  New Age: Resurgence of ancient archetypal themes
  12 Step Spirituality: A religion of powerlessness and surrender
  Recent Scientific Speculation: Mysticism revisited
  Science and Religion: The myth of opposition

OVERVIEW: A COMMON STORY, PERENNIAL DIFFERENCES

While the answers to the questions posed at the beginning of this Chapter may appear to vary widely, there is both a common, underlying story driving the religious search, and perennial differences among religious viewpoints secondary to the inherent limitations of human knowing.

A COMMON STORY

The essential spiritual dilemma of human existence is being separate from the sacred. Man's numerous religious stories, held in scripture and oral tradition, reveal a common theme. They tell of a time before time, or a consciousness before duality, when this separation was not the case, when no walls, no distance, and no egocentric mind kept humankind from its creator. But as mind, self, vanity, and greed developed, this joyous union or connection was lost. Not only are we now separate from God, we no longer experience the world as a sacred place.

Having lost our sacred consciousness, the story goes, human beings have also lost, forgotten, or no longer followvalues based on it. Prescriptions for sacred living have been revealed to countless prophets or aspirants (Moses' 10 Commandments, Jesus' Sermon on the Mount, Buddha's Four Noble Truths and Eight fold Noble Path, the Way of the Tao, Confucius' sayings) but few people follow them sincerely. These prescriptions have been replaced by the noise, excitement, enchantment, ego gratification, and materialistic worldviews of our complex civilization. Our purpose in life, the story suggests, has corrupted from spiritual unity to an egocentric individuality motivated by competition, greed, and self-aggrandizement.

Through all times, including the present, humankind has experienced glimpses of divine reality, revelations of an awesome and undeniable spiritual dimension. The power and beauty of these experiences shatter, at least temporarily, the illusion of separation and meaninglessness. Near-Death and mystical experiences are examples of such breathtaking, breakthrough phenomena that part the veil of ego and Maya. The source of all religious and ultimate values, such religious experiences convincingly demonstrate and announce the essential spiritual nature of the world, momentarily unifying the sacred and the profane, and teaching that life is itself a process of divine revelation.

Longing to experience sacred reality once again, people have also always sought ways to recover or reconnect with his original transcendental consciousness. Religious theology and spiritual practices are actually symbolic maps, albeit subtle and esoteric, teaching followers how to understand and experience the enlightenment described by the founder. Similarly, we seek out people perceived as wiser or closer to the divine than we, who can show us what they know or intervene on our behalf in the spiritual realm responsible for our life and its problems. Teachers, gurus, shamans, priests - they come in all forms but have the same functions: to teach us the universal story, guide and initiate us back on the spiritual path, and help us overcome the beliefs and personality structures that maintain our illusion of separation. When these barriers are dismantled, the story goes, one opens into the sacred that animates and underlies all experience.

In addition to this common story are many interesting similarities among the diamond's facets. Eastern and New Age religious beliefs both assert that you are what you think and that you are responsible for the suffering you have created. Indigenous spirituality and the mystical experience are also very similar. Both view the world itself as an inherently sacred place, with all events, human and natural, replete with spiritual meaning and consciousness. The importance and survival of the soul after death is yet another common theme among almost all religions, along with the thesis that life is meant to be a teaching .

PERENNIAL DIFFERENCES

There are also important and perennial differences between religions. The first appears to separate western and eastern religions as a whole, with the former focusing on the purification or strengthening of the self in order to know, serve, or contact God, and the latter emphasizing the transcendence or eradication of self in order to merge with the Absolute. In fact, Hinduism and Buddhism teach that the self and the personality are fictions, and that enlightenment involves overcoming these misconceptions. Interestingly, the mystical branches of all religions, eastern and western, have less trouble with this conflict, sensing that the separation, distinction, and even opposition between self and divine cease to exist the closer one comes to pure mystical experience.

Another area of perennial differences between religions involves our conception of the divine. Is God an intelligible consciousness that one can know personally, a vast and impersonal force, an emptiness beyond all comprehension, or our own real nature? Is there a single, monolithic God or a pantheon of higher beings or spiritual entities? Does the spiritual path move down from the head into our hearts, as some think in the west, or originate from the revelatory power of the inward, meditative practice and then move up and out, like the rising Kundalini? Is God immanent in the world or does the Creator transcend it. These conflicting viewpoints of the Absolute - full or empty, one or many, down-and-in or up-and-out, here or there - also represent different facets of the spiritual experience. Like the blind men and the elephant, each knows part of the divine but none know the whole.

The particular person, practice, culture, and human circumstance within which a mystical event happens also creates differences among religious forms and beliefs, clearly affecting its message, metaphor, and interpretation. For example, the sophisticated understanding eastern religions have developed about the phenomenology of mind arises from their emphasis on meditation, in which the mind itself is the primary object of never ending observation. Similarly, while it has been shown that the what transpires in the mystical and Near Death experiences is largely universal, the language, expectations, and culture of the individual clearly influence its content, description, and subsequent explanation. The anthropological study of religion also demonstrates that a culture's mythology and religion are profoundly influenced by its geography, food source, and stage of technological development.

RELIGION AND PSYCHOTHERAPY: THE COMMON QUEST

Understanding our client's religion, and the religious traditions of the world, is more than being sensitive to cultural and spiritual diversity. It allows us to understand the universal search for transformation that also structures and motivates psychotherapy.

The commonalties between religion and psychotherapy are not insignificant. Both begin with suffering which the supplicant brings to culturally identified experts (therapists, priests, shamans) in search of help. Practitioners in both traditions work from blueprints of healing and transformation founded on specialized training and experience. Hope, trust, and faith play central roles in the healing process, opening the individual to skilled as well as transpersonal intercession. And both are vulnerable to incompetence and malevolence. These commonalties are not accidental, for they reveal the single unifying archetypal and spiritual structure of help and transformation, and its recurring risks for the naive or ill-prepared.

Moreover, each religion can give us images and metaphors for the work we do. More than simply good ideas, they are symbolic keys to the tear-rusted locks of the psyche that mirror and indeed comprise the archetypal structure of psychological healing and transformation. When a client finds the insight or image underlying their life's struggle, the key turns, the lock opens, and consciousness expands. Then psychology and religion merge into a single transpersonal moment of realization. Issue by issue, insight by insight, one transforming metaphor at a time, therapist and client move along the path of psychospiritual growth and enlightenment.

Given the importance of this religious search to the individual, it behooves therapists to identify and understand their own religious model and expand its language to grasp the worldwide "Varieties of Religious Experience." Our goals should be to open ourselves to this multifaceted religious experience, nourish our understanding with wonder, respect, and study, and become sensitive to the religious symbols, metaphors, and longings hidden in our clients words and problems.

SUMMING UP

If we all experience parts of the whole, the most appropriate attitude to conflicts between them is inclusivity, personal experimentation, dialogue, and growth. The human mind is simply not large enough to comprehend the infinite entirety of the divine. Differences appear to exist because the psyche is like a prism through which the light of ultimate reality splinters into diverse religious experience. As long the whole is refracted into parts, conflict will ensue. Debating or attempting to reconcile differences between religious beliefs is far less meaningful than understanding that they reflect humankind's limited but evolving ability to know the sacred whole and its operation for the world.

We conclude that all religious insights are true in one way or another, and all converge toward one ultimate reality. The spiritual realm is as vast as the cosmos and cannot be easily reduced to a single system of thought or practice. While the divine shines through all cultures, times, and places, our comprehension of it is always limited by the interpretive concepts available. Each of us must find which metaphor of the truth resonates with our personal experience, for there are as many points of view about the spiritual path as there are religions and religious "experts."

Rather than argue about religious dogma, let us honor the intuition and longing that brings us to the divine in the first place, and let us all be beginners learning afresh each day how to open our eyes to the ever present sacred. The central religious problems of existence still challenge us, whether in the outback, the high-rise, the hospital, the courtroom, the civil war, the famine, the manufacturing plant, the temple, or the therapist's office. Balancing skepticism and faith, we walk the long journey of realization. Along its many twists and turns, we must heed this ancient advice: examine all experience, never turn your thinking entirely over to someone else, yet at the same time seek and trust the divine ground of being responsible for this entire remarkable and unfathomable mystery of life.

CHAPTER SIX

DEFINITIONS AND DISTINCTIONS: THE LANGUAGE OF PSYCHOLOGY, RELIGION, AND SPIRITUALITY

"Man is a stream whose source is hidden. Our being is descended into us from we know not whence."

Ralph Waldo Emerson

Contents: Psychological Concepts
             Religious and Spiritual Concepts
             Process Concepts

The foundation of any integrated theory of spiritual psychology must begin with a basic vocabulary, in this case, a selection of essential concepts from each of the contributing realms. A shared language is necessary to avoid confusion and semantic conflict, and to ensure that we are describing the continuum of psychological and religious experience in a consistent fashion. A common language is also necessary to construct a higher order theoretical system capable of embracing and ordering the sometimes disparate worlds of psychology, religion, spirituality, and mysticism.

Chapter Six presents selected psychological, religious, and spiritual concepts essential to grasping the nature of psychospiritual development, the personal wounding that inevitably occurs along the way, and the universal journey we all undertake, knowingly or unknowingly, toward healing and transcendence. The significance and interaction of these ideas will become evident in later chapters; here the goal is simply to elucidate a conceptual foundation. Technical vocabulary has been kept to a minimum and made as "user-friendly" as possible. For readers wishing further grounding in basic personality theory, additional terms are contained in Appendix B. These concepts can be skimmed quickly by those already familiar with their definitions. Religious and spiritual terms outnumber psychological ones in the text below because of psychology's relative unfamiliarity with them (the reverse ratio appears in the appendix for spiritual readers less familiar with psychological terms).

PSYCHOLOGICAL CONCEPTS

ego
self: true self
     false self
non-ordinary states of consciousness
transpersonal psychology

EGO

Ego is Latin for the pronoun "I." It refers to the one who is aware: the conscious thinking subject. Freud used it in this way in his original psychoanalytic writing.

The ego is the part o the personality felt to be in charge, the "me" that directs the voluntary functions of the mind and body and manages the less voluntary emotional and physiologic processes (e.g., feelings, attachments, emotional conflicts, bodily states). The ego is also the carrier of consciousness, the psychic structure capable of holding, experiencing, and relating to the contents of consciousness (i.e., body, mind, thought, feelings, self, other, world). In psychology, ego is generally conceived as having a positive and constructive meaning and function. A strong ego is important to deal with the inner and outer problems of life. In spirituality and religion, however, ego frequently connotes the belief in an existence independent and separate from God, often with the implication of an arrogant, self-centered, or inflated attitude. As such, it is viewed as an obstacle to be overcome on the spiritual path.

SELF

Self refers to the subjective ongoing experience (and subsequent inner cognitive construction) of "who I am." It is relatively stable and consistent over time, though it evolves with normal development and can change with new experiences, capacities, or information. There are two very different forms of the self:

FALSE SELF

The false self consists of inaccurate attributes or beliefs about "who I am." In childhood, it is often imposed through parental judgments or perceptions (e.g., "You are a lazy person" or "You are so responsible") and further modified by internal, personal conclusions (e.g., "I am lazy and worthless" or "It is my job to be responsible for others"). Ultimately it is organized to accommodate the people upon whom one's physical or psychological security depends (i.e., parents, relatives, siblings, teachers, and other authority figures). The false self can also be defensively inflated for purposes of superiority, power, or artificial self-esteem. Later it solidifies into a formal persona, an outer mask of identity that may have little relation to inner reality.

In truth, the false self is a wrong and damaging construction of "who I am." Children try to be what they perceive their parents' want or value, positive and negative, giving up their own genuine inner experience to do so. The resulting self is false because it does not truly reflect who they really are inside. It is damaging to the extent that it obstructs the growth and expression of natural, inborn self. The ego gradually learns to manipulate this false presentation, devaluing or exaggerating its qualities for purposes of dependency, compensatory self-esteem, or psychological defense against unconscious fear, shame, or emotional pain. In this regard, it is the most complex and entrenched defense in the personality.

TRUE SELF

This is "who I really am": my inborn, original, authentic, and most naturally forming self. The true self a living reality, one's real and essential being, the unique intellectual and emotional temperament discovered in the subjective experience of life. Like the singular coloring of a flower or wild animal, the true self is the nature one was meant to fulfill, with its own wondrous energies, talents, character, aspirations, and joy. It is, in effect, the psychological expression of one's soul or God given form. There is no more choice about this nature than about one's heredity. It is a gift meant to be opened by experience. Our challenge, and life's opus, is to welcome and cultivate this inner being as one's own.

The true self should be distinguished from the self-concept, an idea studied by psychologists and educators for decades. A conceptual representation of the self, The self concept can vary from a relatively accurate portrayal of the true self to a grossly inaccurate depiction as false self. We will also see how the relationship between true self and soul, and their profound betrayal in the development of the false self, are critical ingredients of psychospiritual wounding and dysfunction.

NON-ORDINARY STATES OF CONSCIOUSNESS

Bridging the gap between psychology and spirituality are Non-Ordinary States of Conscious (NOSC).This idea refers to experiences that radically alter or transcend our "normal" everyday mental state and identity (Grof & Grof, 1990). Non-ordinary phenomena, which include near-death, out-of body, and mystical experiences (see Chapter 14 for definitions and descriptions) shatter our conventional assumptions about reality, identity, mortality, and the embodied self. They are experiential phenomena beyond or outside the personal that bringing us into the transpersonal realms of the religious experience.

NOSC are not simply forms of psychological pathology. They occur to normal people, though often under extraordinary physical circumstances (e.g., near drowning, near death, high fevers, operations, starvation, dehydration, prolonged lack of sleep) or during extreme stress (e.g., terrifying accidents, catastrophic losses). They can also occur during psychotic episodes, resulting in overlapping mystical and psychiatric syndromes. Exposure to an NOSC often gives rise to what the Grofs refer to as "spiritual emergencies," states of crisis or fear of "insanity" surrounding an extraordinary experience for which one has no acceptable explanation.

As Grof points out, our scientific understanding of psychological functioning is based entirely on ordinary states of consciousness which have been studied for 100 years. In our twentieth century medical model, therefore, NOSC tend to be explained as forms of organic pathology, that is, physical or mental illness. Grasping the realm of NOSC requires a major paradigm shift that western psychology and medicine are just now beginning to articulate.

TRANSPERSONAL PSYCHOLOGY

This is the branch of psychology interested in just such non-ordinary experiences. Embracing humankind's intuition of and impulse toward an ultimate state of consciousness transcending separate individualized existence, transpersonal psychology addresses the dynamics and processes of psychospiritual development, its barriers, and the nature of the enlightened state (Boorstein, 1996; Scotton et. al., 1996). The term was first used by Jung to describe the collective unconscious and is currently used to refer to a vast range of subjects historically left out of western literature on psycholotherapy (e.g., shamanism, psychedelics, eastern religions, spiritual growth, out-of-body experiences, non-ordinary consciousness, and spiritual growth). Transpersonal psychotherapy strives to integrate an understanding of these psychospiritual processes into its theory and practice.

RELIGIOUS AND SPIRITUAL CONCEPTS

religion   spirit
spirituality   divine self
mysticism   God or Divine Being
soul   enlightenment

Less subject to the level of definition and objective verification historically required by science, religious and spiritual variables are not customarily used by psychologists and practicing psychotherapists. Some phenomena, of course, may be operationally defined and scientifically studied (e.g., religious institutions and behavior); others are almost entirely subjective (e.g., religious conversion experiences). Subjectivity, however, is not necessarily antithetical to science. Though pure experience (phenomenology) cannot literally be observed, it can in fact be described and studied, and often reveals a uniformity and predictability meeting scientific standards (e.g. the consistencies found across Near-Death reports). In addition, hundreds of years of definition and description of mystical and other non-ordinary experiences have been recorded in religious writings, with obvious and meaningful commonalties apparent across traditions.

Though minor definitional variations and doctrinal disputes may exist, these general terms have reference and significance across cultures and religious forms, suggesting an universal ground of experience justifying their inclusion in a scientific and spiritual psychology. Intuitively grasped by any sensitive individual, an understanding of these basic terms will come quickly and contribute immeasurably to the forthcoming psychospiritual model of personality. As above, the reader will find additional foundational concepts in Appendix B.

RELIGION

As discussed in Chapter 5, religion may be defined as an organized body of beliefs and practices developed from one or more non-ordinary mystical experiences. Its core may be revealed to a single founder, and then elaborated by others contributing progressively to a body of formal beliefs and wisdom. The canons of any religious system typically have to do with ultimate reality, divine law, the purpose of life, the human condition, morality and responsibility, and the nature and forms of sacred practices (ritual, worship, and celebration). A religion is also a dynamic and living process, and with time and experience, continues to evolve for its followers. Interestingly, the etymology of the word religion finds French roots speaking of an obligation or oath between man and the gods, and Latin roots referring to the religious or monastic life.

SPIRITUALITY

In general, spirituality refers to one's ongoing relationship with the transcendent realm or being responsible for existence and life's ultimate meaning. It is usually private, interior, and very personal, and may be expressed or found in prayer, contemplation, meditation, ritual, nature, inspirational literature, music, or service – however we experience our relation to the sacred in its most significant, tangible, and satisfying ways. Spirituality often includes a belief system framing how one personally and uniquely interprets his or her religion, its theology and practices, and whatever mystical intuitions or experiences have contributed to an understanding of the sacred.

Spiritual experience may or may not take place in a formal religious setting; in fact, one can be spiritual without any professed religion. Indeed, the concept of spirituality serves as a rich and versatile symbol of the relationship to the sacred that each person needs to articulate in a unique and personal way. For many, the concept of spirituality also includes a related notion of spiritual development, that is, the idea that our lives involve a process of growth in our capacity to know and experience sacred reality and purpose. This idea is often symbolized by metaphors such as journey, pilgrimage, or seeking.

MYSTICISM

Religious experience can be said to fall on a continuum from formal institutional dogma and behavioral prescriptions at one end to pure, subjective, and individual sacred experience at the other. Mysticism, the subjective pole of this continuum, denotes moments of rapture or ecstasy in which the transcendent is experienced in direct and unmediated communion. Always difficult to describe, there is nonetheless a profound certainty that one has actually, literally, and intimately been in contact with sacred reality or its consciousness. Described through all ages, it is the ultimate religious experience.

In theological thought, mysticism usually designates the highest state of spiritual knowledge obtained directly from the source regarding the sacred mysteries of the universe. Mystical experience can be "immanent," in which everyday reality is radically transformed, infused, or identified with the sacred, or "transcendent," lifting the individual beyond everyday reality into divine realms of being (e.g., heaven, paradise, universal mind, Nirvana, etc.). Mysticism can also be said to involve a gradient of experience, ranging from small everyday moments of awakening (the sense of awe and wonder we feel looking at the night sky) to the full blown ecstatic experience, discussed in more detail below.

SOUL

Soul is a rich, complex, and powerful symbol that needs to be considered carefully before settling on a working definition.

As an informal experiment aimed at discovering popular meanings (and current archetypal derivatives) of this word, I asked 24 consecutive people (clients, friends, and family, ranging in age from 11 to 60) to define soul. Their responses are contained in Appendix C. The reader is encouraged to write his or her own definition before reading the survey results.

Like any archetypal idea, virtually all cultures, from aboriginal to industrialized, have some concept of soul. Any survey of anthropology, psychology, religion, and literature will generally reveal the same recurring eight meanings: Soul is 1. the sacred within, sometimes viewed as our own divine nature, 2. an inner opening or connection to the divine , 3. the sacred spark, energy, or presence responsible for the individual's life, consciousness, and state of health, 4. one's personal consciousness that can be temporarily separated from the body and survives bodily death, 5. the "I" awareness or identity capable of accumulating spiritual experience across lifetimes, 6. that part of an individual that intuitively recognizes spiritual truth and moral law, 7. a psychological metaphor for the true self, and 8. a symbol for the imaginative part of the personality that spontaneously provides mythic images of life's meaning and events. This list of definitions is neither definitive nor exhaustive, but does capture the richness and multiplicity of this ancient symbol.

Soul's range of meanings is also a characteristic of its nature, referring as it does to something imprecise, dynamic, and ethereal, which cannot (and should not) be reduced to a single, simple, or finite idea. Indeed, this imprecision is a way that its essence remains vibrant, relevant, mysterious, and alive as a word. Used as a symbol, its meanings unfold as we continuously apply it to new experiences. Rather than settling on a single textbook definition, the final meaning is intentionally left ambiguous, so that *it* speak to *us*. And, like psyche, its mythic namesake, soul cannot be owned, bent, or mastered to serve the will of the ego or the ambitions of academic man. In the end, any use of the word soul should respect all its meanings as well as the tensions between them.

The relationship between soul and true self is central to the psychospiritual model of personality presented later. Soul and true self are like twins or mirror images: the former existing in the divine plane and the latter becoming its embodiment in the inner psychological world. As Emerson wrote, "Man is a stream whose source is hidden. Our being is descended into us from we know not whence." (Emerson, 1992). Soul then refers to this inner experience of our inflowing spiritual nature and identity. An awareness of the true self brings one into contact with soul, and the inner spiritual portal bridging the two worlds.

Mystics of all ages have proclaimed that the individual soul can merge with divine consciousness, sometimes profoundly, more often subtly, and it is here that the individual mind opens to the fathomless being of God. Here, too, is where transpersonal psychology meets mystical religion as two roads converging to the same point in the distance.

SPIRIT

A similar cross-cultural uniformity exists with the idea of spirit. Whether known as the "Great Spirit," Holy Ghost," the "Force," the "Presence," the "breath" of God, or the Taoist *Ch'i,* spirit permeates and sustains the whole enterprise of mind, self, body, and life. As mystics repeatedly describe, the cosmos is itself a sea of living awareness rather than an empty lifeless space. Everywhere present is a single supernal consciousness that knows, lives, and forms everything. It may be known through an interior experience of union or sensed as a Presence in the world. In fact, the mystic consciousness sees the whole world as radiant and resplendent with this Presence, and a vast and expansive understanding of life flows effortlessly from it. With experience, we can also learn to feel spirit acting within and between us, and turn to it for sustenance, support, and guidance. It is this divine consciousness, energy, being, and revelation that seeps or erupts during the enlightenment or mystical experience.

The term spirit may also refer to its individualized incarnation (e.g., "my spirit") or secondarily refer to other, nonphysical beings. In fact, many ancient and indigenous religions are filled with spirits of animals, ancestors, and natural or supernatural forces, some of which may be good and others evil. In this regard, spirit would refer to a non-material entity residing in the spiritual plane but not equivalent to the spirit of God or Divine Being.

DIVINE SELF

The divine self is discovered by the rare individual whose progressive experience of the inner spirit culminates in the birth or awakening of the Divine Being within: a "God-man" as a Hindu yogi might say or the incarnation of Christ Consciousness for the Christian mystic. This divine consciousness may gradually or suddenly take precedence in the personality, creating a divine self devoid of pride or self-interest. The personal self may or may not be entirely replaced, depending on one's spiritual progress, but the ego increasingly recognizes and incorporates the urgings of this "greater Self" within. Some of these exceptional individuals become religious activists who challenge injustice and hypocrisy in the world, surrendering their personal lives and concerns for the work of this higher consciousness. Others lead quiet lives of simple loving service.

GOD OR DIVINE BEING

As implied above, spirit is one ever-present manifestation of the all pervading, infinite, eternal, and unexplainable mystery of the Divine Being. God (or any other equivalent term such as Allah or Great Spirit) refers to the living and intelligent consciousness within, behind, and beyond reality known to all religions, enlightened beings, and everyday mystics. We use this term as a reference to this primordial cause, which is fundamentally beyond human knowing, comprehension, or definition. This Ultimate Reality can only be known in its refracted pieces, never revealing the entire divine mystery, which infinitely exceeds human intelligence. Every definition of God, therefore, is wrong, for the infinite mystery cannot be reduced to finite human categories any more than a single attribute can capture a whole human being. It is this unfathomable reality that we refer to as God or the sacred.

ENLIGHTENMENT

Enlightenment is a direct mystical experience of the divine. It may come unexpectedly to the ignorant and the spiritually advanced alike. In this moment of rapture, revelation, and unity, the individual unequivocally knows that the cosmos is alive, conscious, loving, and joyous, and that he is one with this eternal Presence. Ego and mind melt away, separation is seen to be an illusion, and the individual is awed at the infinite beauty, perfection, and all rightness of the entire spectacle of life. Though transitory, one knows for a timeless moment that reality is sacred. Contrary to common opinion, enlightenment is not a continuous state nor does it necessarily change the experiencer's everyday life or problems. Words for this experience from various traditions include satori, samadhi, moksha, fana, wu, self-realization, illumination, conversion, and revelation.

PROCESS CONCEPTS

Throughout the religious and spiritual literature, it is understood that sometime or other each person is either called into an active, challenging relationship with the transpersonal dimension or discovers an inner impulse to pursue divine experience and realization. Then begins a process of change, journey to God that can co-exist and interact with personal psychological growth and create a powerful orientation toward higher states of consciousness, meaning, and transformation. Drawn through stages of awakening, our descriptive language invariably becomes mythological, religious, prophetic and poetic, filled with the universal symbols of the sacred search.

CALL TO RELATIONSHIP

From the religious perspective, life problems often represent a call to relationship with the divine, varying from a gentle whisper to a dramatic and insistent demand. In this ancient view, God is understood to be a power outside the ego that chooses us, pulling us into authentic, naked relationship to itself. In the beginning, we gravitate to an image of God and a spiritual path that feel good and are reassuring to the ego. Confronted by events that shatter this comfort and security, however, we are given the opportunity to meet God more directly. This understanding places crises, emotional problems, and psychiatric symptoms in the larger perspective of our relationship with God, an ultimately loving confrontation that inevitably defeats the petty ambitions of the false self. This call to relationship often begins the journey to God.

Journey into God

Throughout the mystical traditions weaves the story of humankind's search to know God directly. It is characterized by endless theories, theologies, and practices. In the end, however, it becomes an intensely personal quest that cycles through joy, ascent, self-deception, collapse, darkness, and return, that eventually robs the searcher of everything: identity, possessions, attachments, and even religious beliefs - until there is nothing left but a naked relationship to God. It is the most difficult journey of all. Many begin with unrealistic ideas of perennial joy and bliss; most give up when the dark night of personal defeat and personality dissolution become too difficult; and a few continue knowing that nothing else can matter as much.

In this highly individual pilgrimage, the seeker, disappointed by life or longing for union with the Beloved, embarks on a search to know and meet the sacred one. Some take the journey out of love while others follow the desire for ultimate knowledge, service, or transformation. Along the way, the seeker encounters all the unrecognized emotional baggage that comes with being human - fear, greed, attachment, temptation, mortality, even evil. Eventually one realizes that all worldly attachments have been symbolic substitutes for divine love and must be surrendered to meet the Creator directly.

As the soul, that part of God's nature that is uniquely our own, is met by its source, it swoons in longing, love, and surrender. Then ego), self, and soul are dissolved into the engulfing brightness of being. This merging, and the associated loss of separation and individuality, can only be described metaphorically (e.g., a drop of rain dissolving into the sea, two candle flames uniting) yet points to a subjective experience of profound and universal religious significance. -One of the purposes of spiritual practices (e.g., meditation and contemplation) is to journey directly into this union with the sacred ground of Being. This complex, labyrinthine, and often painful psychospiritual process is managed and facilitated by ego, which is only surrendered when the union is complete.

Stages of Spiritual Growth

The idea of a spiritual search, journey, or pilgrimage of unfolding metaphysical experience is a universal one in religion and mythology, for it is a basic metaphor carried in the archetypal psyche. Its purpose would seem to be one of increasing enlightenment and mystical participation in the spiritual nature and purpose of the universe.

The sacred journey is characterized by its stages, of spiritual growth (described more fully in Chapter 7). Before the journey begins, one is satisfied enough with the adventures and achievements found in the "ordinary" material world. Sooner or later, however, our goals and assumptions are shaken or undermined by disaster, doubt, aging, or any of life's innumerable difficulties. We turn then to religion and spirituality, searching for meaning and remediation. Hope, exhilaration, disappointment, confusion, hell, and ecstasy are all encountered in our travels, until one or more experiences of realization or higher consciousness focus the search toward the experience of holiness. One discovers that the divine is not someplace else, but here and now, in an alteration of mind, a change in perception, a capacity to see, an opening of heart, and ultimately a transcendence of the self and the search. In endless archetypal ways, in literature, mythology, film, and fad, in every time and generation, this journey is replayed.

There are countless models of spiritual development. Each religion and each religious writer has one, whether explicit or implicit, examining the dynamics, stages, and the specific tools or understandings discovered along the way (the author's model is presented in the next chapter). To one degree or another, every person takes this journey, asks ultimate questions, and evolves a spiritual understanding of the universe and one's place in it. It is not surprising, therefore, that clients bring these issues, consciously or unconsciously, directly or indirectly, into the consulting room.

CONCLUSIONS

The vocabulary presented in this Chapter provides a basic conceptual foundation for understanding the psychospiritual dimensions of life. It will soon be woven into a conceptually rich integration of psychology and spirituality to guide our work as therapists. The basic terms outlined here and in the accompanying appendix are also important because they refer to real processes. As we will later see, mystical experiences, NOSC, stages of spiritual growth, cults, religious abuse and addiction, arise from these processes and powerfully affect our clients' lives. As therapists, we need to be acquainted with such diverse experiences. If we are ignorant or in denial, the unconscious message given our clients is "Don't ask because we don't know." And, if our only model for understanding psychospiritual experience is a pathologizing one, then we will subtly cause our clients to feel ashamed, crazy, or devalued in their religious search. When we omit spiritual ideas from psychology, we omit spirituality itself, repeating the split that has plagued psychological healing since the middle ages.

CHAPTER SEVEN

A PSYCHOSPIRITUAL THEORY OF PERSONALITY AND ITS DEVELOPMENT

Common to psychology and religion, and to any comprehensive system of thought for that matter, is the need for a model of how things work in the domain in question. Psychology calls this model theory, religion calls it theology. To integrate psychotherapy and spirituality, therefore, we need to develop a model of the psychospiritual workings of the personality.

Familiar and well developed ideas about human nature exist in both psychology (e.g., ego, self, personality, unconscious) and religion (e.g., soul, spirit, God, enlightenment). These ideas are supported in each area by extensive traditions of thought, experience, and history. Rather than proposing a whole new group of concepts, a psychospiritual theory of personality would ideally integrate the most important existing ideas from each field into a logical, creative, and systematic higher order synthesis: a psychospiritual model of personality. The purpose would be to explore the relationship and interaction among established psychological and spiritual variables, yielding new insights, meanings, and applications in each domain as well as specific contributions to psychotherapy in particular.

To be maximally useful, a creative synthesis of psychology and spirituality would ideally:

* utilize existing clinical and spiritual concepts rather than invent new ones;
* embrace the power and profundity of religious thought with well-grounded psychological concepts and methods;
* account for the interactive and interdependent nature of psychological and spiritual growth across the life span;
* describe the psychospiritual nature of human wounding, healing, and transformation;
* provide an orientation to our own subjective experience of being human (i.e., a phenomenology of personality);
* have direct, immediate, and meaningful application to the theory and practice of psychotherapy;
* provide a theoretical context for spiritual experience in the therapy process;
* balance faith and subjectivity with careful thinking, personal self-reflection, and sound clinical practice;

*   bridge the arbitrary historical fragmentation of the religious psyche (i.e, psychology, religion, spirituality, mysticism, philosophy, and metaphysics).

KEY ELEMENTS OF THE PSYCHOSPIRITUAL PERSONALITY

	Ego	False Self	True Self	Soul	Divine Self
What is the Origin?	Basic part of personality	Fabricated by the individual to fit parents' views, results in inflated view of ego	Inborn, natural, God-given self; who we were psychologically meant to be; the psychological reflection of the soul	God, Eternity; it is the divine counterpart of the true self	God within; the inner experience of Spirit or Divine Being
How is it known?	Discovered as "I"	Experienced as "should-oriented" self	Discovered as a spontaneous inner reality, a living thing	Discovered in contact with true self	With time & grace, it replaces the self as the center of the personality, where it is directly sensed.
What is its nature?	The director of the personality and its functions	A self-controlling idea; the "I" is wrongly identified with whatever pretense ego creates (superior, needy, inferior)	Emotional and feeling center of personality	The spiritual self that carries some small aspect of the divine in individualized form	God in whatever form known to the individual, e.g. Christ, Krishna, Great Spirit, etc
Typical Status?	Ranges from weak to strong; often distracted or lulled into complacency	Rigid; fixed in childhood as a defense against parts of true self	Wounded and vulnerable, underdeveloped, and needing attention	An idea, not a reality to most, inexperienced	Unknown by vast majority of people
Developmental Dynamics?	Capacity grows with stimulation, experience, & education	Fixed and rigid crystallization of false self	Requires love, attention, and support to grow	Contact with souls' divine origin opens to one's spiritual nature & purpose	Opening to the energies of soul/spirit fills person with sacred being
Purpose?	Protect and support True Self, adjust to reality, and help us on the spiritual path	Defense against emotional pain; compensate for inferiority feelings	Carries our God-given nature into the world & opens to soul	To express one's unique God nature and grow as a spiritual being	To express God's nature in the world

Consistent with these goals, a psychospiritual model of personality is now presented integrating key ideas from psychology and spirituality. Subsequent Chapters extend this model to the spiritual nature of psychological disorders, the process and stages of healing and transformation, and the archetypal constellation of these ideas in the religious psyche.

FITTING THE PIECES TOGETHER: A PSYCHOSPIRITUAL THEORY OF PERSONALITY

The psychological and spiritual concepts defined in the previous Chapter combine to form a dynamic and self-correcting system of personality organized toward progressive spiritual evolution. Grasping the interrelationships between these concepts will allow us to understand personality functioning as a psychospiritual process. The following chart reviews the essential interacting concepts. The reader is encouraged to spend a few minutes reviewing and reflecting on these terms in order to make them fresh, tangible, and personally meaningfully. As an exercise to explore these reference points further, the reader might imagine speaking from the vantage point of each separate personality part. What do you see, want, and say if you are speaking as the ego, false self, true self, soul, or divine self?

Mind and personality constitute overlapping and interacting systems of psychological organization in which these various parts function. The mind provides the mental operations for the ego to differentiate reality, self and other. The personality, including its executive, the ego, organizes and balances the forces of instinct, emotion, thought, soul, divine self, and God. The ego's relationship to the key personality elements (i.e., its capacity to perceive and balance them) determines the individual's mental state, psychological symptoms, and degree of enlightened consciousness (footnote: Appendix B contains definitions of mind, personality, mental state, and psychological symptoms).

The following illustration further clarifies these relationships, depicting the overlapping realms of the sacred and the psychological. In this model, ego's role in the spiritual journey is to seek God. To do so, it must understand and move progressively through false self, true self, and soul, eventually opening to divine self and God. God moves into the personality the opposite direction through the divine self, its individualized expression in soul, and into the sphere of true self which seeks to undo the tyranny of false self to influence ego. This convergence continues until the ego is capable of being merged with and lived by God. Ego and God become partners in this process of incarnation or transmutation so that soul opens to God's consciousness in the personality and ego gives form to God in the world.

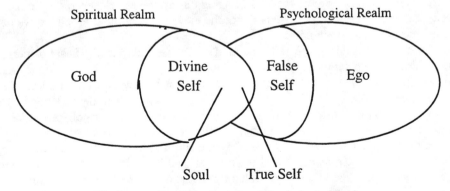

The Intersection of the Sacred and Psychological Realms

As the above illustration suggests, a key intersection of psychology and spirituality is the meeting of soul and true self. Soul exists in the spiritual realm and self in the psychological. This intersection is where soul creates, activates, and flows into self. The overlap of the spiritual and psychological spheres also implies that true self is subtly infused with divine energies and that the soul can be known psychologically through the true self. The dotted line represents a permeable membrane through which spiritual intuitions, dreams, and other subtle contacts with the divine stream into the psychological sphere when they can be known by the ego. Ego only meets God, however, when the false self is dismantled. The size of the false self barrier varies according to its grandiosity and centrality in the personality. The ego's persistence toward God and its understanding of these psychospiritual dynamics determines the individual's degree of spiritual progress.

Reflecting on one's own psychological functioning with the help of this model, it can readily be seen that what we customarily think of as "I" may actually refer to various different and distinct parts of the personality. It may be the "I" of the ego, the false self, the true self, the soul, or even to the divine self or Divine Being depending on the degree of one's psychospiritual evolution and penetration.

It is also evident from this theoretical outline that being a human being is a dynamic, conscious, and developing experience formed, lived, and awakened through multiple interacting parts. We are more than physiology, animal instincts, computer like brain structures, or neurochemical activity, for at the center of personality is soul and its opening to eternity. Putting the soul back in the center of personality profoundly reframes our nature, psychology, and purpose. Personality becomes available to the spirit within, and our lives are given back their implicit spiritual goal: absorbing the inflowing divine into human life, and through its operation, growing an increasing capacity for love and enlightenment.

In the traditional model, personality functioning is viewed as a homeostasis of conflicting forces that must be managed by the ego (e.g., conflicts between the conscious and the unconscious, emotions and conscience, needs and reality, unsocialized impulses and civilized standards of behavior), which of course is true, but it is much more than that. Putting soul back in the center of personality gives ego an even greater task and obligation. Now it must not only struggle to recover and nourish the true self, it must also understand the spiritual continuum of true self, soul, divine self, and Divine Being. It is this continuum that gives birth to a spiritual psychology and model of personality.

As the previous figure suggests, the true self, while clearly a psychological experience, is also an aspect or expression of the divine. It is God's gift to us in this world, an interior reality we are responsible to nourish, cultivate, and express. Residing in the realm of God and eternity, the soul is more than the true self; it carries the larger dimension of our divine being, experience, and history that can flow into our center. One discovers that feeling the true self stirs the mystical and other worldly energies of soul, exciting the self and bringing our awareness closer to the divine self, a form of God's nature in our own. As we experience the movements of the true self, so we come to know God and our own interior divinity.

Placing the true self, soul, divine self, and God or Divine Being in the heart of personality gives new meaning to the nature and dynamics of emotion. The true self is our emotional self. It is most happy when valued as the feeling center of the personality, when given opportunities for expression, and when it opens to soul or Divine Being in some way. When the true self is ignored, betrayed, or violated, on the other hand, we feel sadness, anger, despair, or collapse. Like a child too long rejected, the true self grows melancholy, lonely and mute. In this way, emotional states are more than simply psychological processes, they are spiritual as well. We feel wounding and sorrow when the joy and the gifts carried by the true self and its divine counterpart, the soul, are devalued or rejected. It is a loss of unimaginable magnitude, metaphorically equivalent to the very loss of the soul.

It should be pointed out that the soul itself is not wounded, the true self is, for it is the true self that feels the great despair of losing contact with soul and God. This is one reason why depression is so important: it indicates that a deep wound has occurred to the self, crippling access to both its psychological and spiritual life sources. In the theory of personality presented here, it can be seen that when access to the true self and soul are blocked, the whole personality falters.

Motivation, too, arises from the energies of the true self and slowly dies when those energies are chronically betrayed or forbidden. When in touch with the soul, we can be inspired to tremendous heights of activity and creativity, working days and nights without rest. The great composers, writers, scientists, athletes, and performers know and feel this reality. It is through the soul that the divine acts, prompting the ego to give expression to the true self and its gifts, and inspiring the whole spiritual adventure of life. The ego must learn to ask in every situation, "But Where is God?" and "How is God moving me here?" When this kind of contact between ego, true self, and soul is lost, inspiration wilts like a flower abandoned in a dark closet, and along with this abandonment goes motivation and creativity.

Those who have learned to experience the soul first hand realize that the greatest happiness and joy on earth come not from achievements or possessions but from contact with this living divine center of psychological being. Even a momentary connection with one's soul or indwelling spirit can evoke an ecstasy far greater than most can bear. Anxiety, depression, confusion, alienation, and the whole spectrum of hellish mental states, on the other hand, form when we are chronically or profoundly separated from the soul through the betrayal of the true self. In this conceptualization, our emotional experience can be a powerful barometer of our spiritual health.

As mystics from all ages attest, and as we will understand later, when we open to the soul and its spiritual vision, energies, and values, a subtle chemistry of transformation takes place. Our lives are once again filled with wonder, beauty, and inherent validity, and a world of shimmering light and radiance is found to be the real and actual nature of reality. When we ignore or reject true self, soul, divine self, and God, or when we feel forbidden from entering that realm of holiness in the world, then we court existential futility, meaninglessness, and the despair of aging, loss, suffering, and death.

Coming full circle, we can see that in this system of personality, the ego is very important. It is responsible for: 1. dismantling the false self; 2. locating and supporting the true self; 3. opening to soul and its transformational inspirations and energies; 4. incarnating the nature of God or Divine Being into personality as divine self; and 5. examining each step and stage along the way alert to the myriad forms of self-deception found on the spiritual path (in psychotherapy, this is called reality testing, in religious traditions, it is termed discernment). The ego, rather than being overcome on the spiritual path, actually has a very big job to do.

In this model, spiritual progress is also intimately tied to psychological health. The progressive transformation of personality cannot transpire fruitfully unless the personality is relatively healthy and healed of serious psychological wounds or personality damage. Too much damage forces the ego to spend all its energies defending against pain and coping with impairment in place of expanding consciousness into the divine. A basic purpose of psychotherapy, therefore, is to heal personality wounds and limitations in order to cultivate the psychological and spiritual ground for the inflowing divine. The life problems that break us open also serve this great purpose, as much or more than all the spiritual practices we could undertake. Breaking down the inner barriers of the false self, they expose the abandoned self and its need to reconnect with soul. Psychotherapy of the whole person recognizes that these psychospiritual interactions contribute centrally to the processes of healing and human growth.

Finally, this model argues that a spiritually oriented psychotherapy needs to recognize one more thing: that the ultimate purpose of this whole experience, this whole adventure of consciousness and life, is to find and know God here, now, in the eternal present. The sacred journey moves from ego to God, joining individual consciousness through the portal of soul to the consciousness of the immanent Divine Being, not in some later time, but in every experience we are given.

JEAN: ONE WOMAN'S RECOVERY OF SELF, SOUL, AND LIFE

Jean was in therapy with me for many years.

She was the oldest of three children. Her mother, though never treated, would probably have been diagnosed as borderline or schizophrenic. Explosive, erratic, dangerous, and terribly unnurturing, she would scream at the children, lock them outside all day, and tell them she wished they had never been born. The crazed look in her mother's violent eyes told Jean that she was literally capable of murder. To make matters worse, whenever her mother exploded, her father rushed in to appease her by harshly punishing the children further. Several times Jean's mother ran away from home for months at a time, only to be cajoled into returning by her father.

With this insanely controlling mother, family life was hell and the greatest burden fell on Jean as the oldest child. Her role was to keep her younger siblings quiet so they would not disturb their mother, and Jean learned to be constantly vigilant. She slept half-awake, watched her mother constantly, and tried to be perfect. With no other viable choice, Jean gave up her childhood and her true self to help the family survive. Using her ego's abilities, she created a totally compliant false self; so compliant indeed that she did not even know there was another self.

After high school, Jean went to work in a bank. She met and married Craig and was soon pregnant. When the fetus was about two months along, Jean was involved in a very serious automobile accident. Thrown out of the car onto the pavement, she had a Near-Death Experience in which she floated above her lifeless body, through a fog toward a light, and then to a beautiful meadow where a footpath lead to a bridge. On the other side of the bridge were various deceased relatives welcoming her to the other side. Although she wanted to stay in this tranquil and beautiful place, concern for her unborn child pulled her back and she awoke in terrible pain.

Months of bed rest followed this accident. To make matters worse, her husband could not cope with the stress and left Jean at her parent's home for the yearlong recuperation. There she again came under her mother's violent and domineering personality. Worse yet, her mother quickly took advantage of her weakened state, telling Jean she would have to give up her unborn baby. When her son was born, Jean held him only minutes before he was taken. Although profoundly devastated by this loss, her compliant false self never complained.

Jean eventually returned to work and moved away from her hometown. After a number of years, she sustained a back injury at work. It did not improve. Entirely dependent on her job, terrified of retribution for lost time, and still living in her compliant false self, Jean denied her pain. Eventually she was forced onto extended disability, and the survival anxiety she felt produced further debilitating psychological symptoms (chronic pain, severe sleep disorder, and depression). Endless evaluations and treatments failed to help and her condition worsened progressively. This is when she was referred to me.

It took us many years to understand Jean's childhood and what her psychological symptoms meant. When her Workers Compensation case settled, she retreated into a quiet and protected life. In this solitude, and with the guidance of therapy, Jean gradually found the true self she had abandoned a lifetime ago. It was a sensitive, kind, and gentle self that needed a strong ego to protect it. Still her symptoms did not improve much. Then, several years later, a most interesting thing happened. Jean received a call from her lost son Bill. He was now grown and wanted to see her. Somehow she had always known he would call, but felt she should wait until he was ready.

Jean and Bill met, met again, and were soon talking daily. Their bond developed rapidly. It was as if they had never separated, yet had to catch up on a lifetime of details. Then Bill asked her a surprising question. He described a recurring dream of drifting through a fog toward a bright light, reaching a meadow, and seeing bridge with some vague human shapes on the other side. Did she know what that dream could mean? Jean knew immediately: Bill's soul had been with her in the Near-Death Experience before his birth.

Following her reconciliation with Bill, Jean began to sleep more normally for the first time in fifteen years. She began to feel that her true self now had a family that genuinely cared about it, and would never demand its sacrifice again. Gradually her depression diminished and in time her pain fell into the background, though her ego remains fragile and some symptoms are still necessary to protect the vulnerable self. But for the most part, Jean has recovered her life.

How do we understand this remarkable story? To Jean, these events had profound psychological and spiritual significance. The sacrifice of her true self to her mother in childhood was repeated in the sacrifice of her own child, once again for her mother. Speaking in the language of myth and fairy tale, Jean's mother had stolen her soul, twice! It was a devastating double loss that crippled her entire personality functioning. The sacrifice of her career and independence then crippled even her false self, leading to a paralyzing complex of symptoms that demanded she face and work out these original psychological injuries, or die.

The first task of therapy was to help Jean confront her compliant false self. Though it had saved her life as a child, it was killing her now. Understanding its function allowed Jean to dismantle it and learn more about her original self, which she began to love and nourish. Naturally, as she did so, her connection to soul began to open, revealing the profound spiritual issues buried in her past.

Jean's NDE had been a literal journey to God during the darkest period of her life. It gave her faith in the divine and trust that the universe that was fundamentally loving, spiritual, and good no matter how much pain and suffering seemed to exist on the surface. It had also involved her son. Jean had a soul-connection with Bill; an invisible spiritual bond that held them together across space and time. Jean had tacitly held onto and trusted her soul's larger knowledge of Bill. When each was ready, and needed it most, this connection was restored. Recovering her lost child not only symbolized the recovery of her lost self, it created a safe and loving relationship in which it could grow. Jean's story ends with her feeling grateful to God, closer to her divine self (which she calls her "higher self"), but still needing to develop more ego strength to express her true self and its soul nature in the world.

Two years before her son returned, Jean gave me the first of the soul definitions recorded in Appendix C. She said, "We are not who we think we are. The soul is that part of us the religions refer to as 'I AM.'" Jean knew from her Near-Death Experience that it involved an observing consciousness that transcended body, personal biography, and identify. She prophetically added, "It is the part of you that just knows. Whether you like it or not, whether you want to acknowledge what it tells you or ignore it, it just knows." Jean's soul knew more than she did. It knew about her son. It knew she had to hang on until she could recover her lost and wounded self. Despite her seemingly impossible circumstances, Jean had enough faith to heed her soul's counsel.

A PSYCHOSPIRITUAL DESCRIPTION OF HUMAN DEVELOPMENT THROUGH THE LIFE SPAN

At fifteen I set my heart on learning.
At thirty I established myself (in accordance with ritual).
At forty I no longer had perplexities.
At fifty I knew the Mandate of Heaven.
At sixty I was at ease with whatever I heard.
At seventy I could follow my hearts desire without
transgressing the boundaries of right.
Confucius

Any personality theory requires an account of personality formation and evolution during childhood and across the life span. The development of spiritual awareness has been charted by numerous writers (e.g., Coles, 1990; Fowler, 1981, 1996; Genia, 1995; Oser, 1991; Peck, 1993; Rizzuto, 1991; Spero, 1992), with models closely tied to their religious or theoretical orientation (e.g., psychoanalytic object relations theory). Drawing on this literature, the psychospiritual model described above, and the author's previous description of male development through the life span, this section describes the unfolding drama of personality from the cradle to the grave.

As suggested in *Death of a Hero, Birth of the Soul,* there is a universal story lived by each of us across the seasons of life. Flowing with a hidden teleology, each season has its own energies and purposes, and each evokes, changes, shapes, and awakens the various aspects of an individual's personality. It would seem that the stages of life are oriented toward progressive transformations of the human psyche in the contacts ego makes with true self, soul, divine self, and God. The ultimate purpose of this developmental process is to evolve our individual and collective consciousness toward the highest realms of spiritual expression envisioned by the great religions. Understanding this universal story provides a developmental framework for the psychospiritual dynamics of personality formation and metamorphosis across the life span: its origin, natural development, highest forms of attainment, and completion.

Integrating metaphors from poetry, fairy tale, religion, and psychology, the universal story goes something like this. In the early springtime of life, a child's soul is still open to the mystical garden of being here on earth. As Wordsworth wrote,

> "There was a time when meadow, grove, and stream,
> The earth, and every common sight,
> To me did seem
> Appareled in celestial light,
> The glory and the freshness of a dream."

> "... trailing clouds of glory do we come
> From God, who is our home:
> Heaven lies about us in our infancy!"

Ego and its functions form naturally to explore this still enchanting paradise. There is original wonder and a "magical" self that tacitly knows its divine nature and origins. This, of course, is the "Garden of Eden" story and the first experience of true self. In fact, so much is undifferentiated that true self, soul, and divine self are commingled and blurred. Sadly, however, this "garden consciousness" and original self are soon lost to the universal wounds and social requirements of childhood - wounds of the mother, the father, of siblings, peers, school, and gender. These wounds force the child to betray the original self, yield contact with the soul, create a false self to survive, and in time "forget" the hidden gifts one was born to bring into the world. Ego, young and insecure, must turn against true self and soul to survive. Describing this loss, Wordsworth observed,

> "It is not now as it hath been of yore;
> Turn wheresoe'er I may,
> By night or day,
> The things which I have seen I now can see no more."

> "Shades of the prison-house begin to close
> Upon the growing boy."

To bring this story closer to home, the reader might reflect on the following questions: Can you remember the wounds that drove your true self underground and made you afraid? Was it your parent's divorce, your father's temper, too many moves, your mother's depression, the bullies in the neighborhood, the time your dad lost his job, being held back a year in school, a grandparent's death? Let one memory in. These are the kinds of events that make us forget the experience of wonder and starlight, and startle us instead into a world view of fear, struggle, and survival anxiety.

As a result of these wounds, true self and soul are forced underground in the service of developing an effective, acceptable personality and social adjustment: the false self. The false self may be compliant, conceited, competitive, or victim. It may feel unworthy, superior, or empty. Driven by falseness and false standards, the individual repeatedly betrays and devalues the true self. Misconceptions are internalized about self and world that will take decades to correct if ever. Sometimes the personality itself is so wounded or damaged that it becomes permanently distorted.

Misconceptions also form about God, injuring the child's original relation to the divine and forcing the "Garden" consciousness further underground. The child's earliest portrayal of the divine is highly imaginative, personal, and idiosyncratic, as if it were still influenced by memory and continued reality of this original relationship. Young children are naturally religious and their drawings repeatedly reflect archetypal religious themes (e.g., the sun as the divine father). Before the age of seven, Bible stories are uncritically accepted along with Santa Claus and the Easter Bunny. They are also exceptionally gullible, with religious ideation developing as youthful imagination incorporates the information provided by adults.

Increasingly, however, a God image is superimposed on this knowing. Heavily permeated by the child's earliest experiences with their parents, it can range from a benevolent and all-loving protector to a stern, all powerful, and guilt-provoking disciplinarian. Religious stories and myths, as well as formal and parental instruction, give further form to the early God image. While these ideas can impact the child's feelings of basic trust, safety, and worth in the universe, often they reflect more of an internal fantasy process than a genuine relationship to the divine, and this fantasy gradually replaces any direct knowing. Though some children retain their original capacity for divine experience, religious socialization inevitably contradicts direct intuition. Institutional images and conceptualizations soon become so distracting, confusing, or inconsistent with personal experience that they end up having little influence on soul's real journey through the first half of life. It is not God the child relates to now, but amalgamated God images.

In the late spring and early summer of life, childhood is replaced by the archetypal forms of masculine and feminine energy. For men, these are the energies of quest and conquest, ego and power, effort and goal. The hero, an archetypal organization formed in the psychological realm, is born. Unconsciously determined to restore his original connection to true self, soul, and eternity, a man heroically pursues whatever symbolically reflects his original nature. He carves out much of his life at this time, striving to find the golden princess, give form to the gifts of his soul, and compete successfully for a place in the world of men. For women, this quest for original wholeness has traditionally blossomed with the feminine energies of love, union, relationship, family, and the divine mystery of procreation.

This developmental model does not imply that men cannot express the feminine or that women cannot express the masculine - they can and do. It is simply that the dominant energies packaged in one's gender usually take precedence to one degree or another during the first half of life, to be replaced by the nondominant or latent energies that characterize the other gender. In other words, men often express traditionally feminine traits and values after midlife, and women express traditionally masculine ones in their second half. Culture, of course, plays a profound role in modifying these patterns, and we can forcefully betray gender's natural unfolding. But we're getting ahead of the story.

From each of these adolescent archetypal visions, a "plan" or "life dream" is born that fills the summer of life. It is a dream unconsciously intended to fix the core wounds, restore the hidden self, and find our way back to the sacred. Only we do all this by sublimation, striving to act it out symbolically in the material world. With these powerful and intoxicating energies, men build empires, women seek relationships, worldly competencies are forged, and lives are built. In the most secret and unconscious chambers of our hearts, however, this journey is driven by the longing to restore what we originally lost: our soul, its expression in the emerging true self, the divine self at its core, the mystical garden of earth, and our connection to God.

In the long and seeming endless summer of life, men and women continue the upward journey. We advance our skills, search for mentors, marry and make a family or other attachments, settle into our religion, and look forward to a continual and gentle climb to the crest of the hill. Somewhere on the way up or at the top, however, something else happens.

We might say that midlife is the top of the hill. It is as far as you can go on the upward climb. At midlife the great, externally focused heroic energies run out. The empires are built, kids are raised, but the quest for soul invariably fails for it has been subtly betrayed or forgotten along the way. Heroic striving now feels empty, compulsive, and false. The false self has become too large now, it dominates too much of the psyche. In one of several ways basic to the midlife passage, the false self of the hero or heroine complexes must die so that the ego can face the underlying emptiness of grandiosity, heal the childhood wounds such grandiosity covers, and face the inescapable reality of death itself. This is the descent into grief and ashes, the despair of unconquerable realities, and the realization that the original dream cannot work. You can't fix the past with family or success. You can't heal the wounded self until you find it. You won't know your soul if you betray it. You can't be constantly lousy and find God.

Descending into the depths of this painful disillusionment allows the insightful individual to locate and nourish the original self, reach into the abandoned soul, and discover the intrinsic gifts it has carried for so long in the summer of life. Now is the time to live and share these treasures, and in doing so, we give birth to the true self and its life-renewing work. It is the pain of defeat and disappointment that leads us to the true but wounded self and its transformational core of soul. If one cannot surrender the centrality of ambition or family to this archetypal midlife passage of death and rebirth, life will remain compromised. As Jung summarized, "Whoever carries over into the afternoon the law of the morning must pay for it with damage to his soul."

The second half of life is a new wilderness. The fall season of our long journey can be a time of the true self's ripening and harvesting, and as such, it can offer the very work of our soul. At this time, the gifts hidden in the original self can find their fullest expression in the world. For men, these energies now move outward, bearing the true self and its growing capacity for love and generosity into the world of creative expression, noncompetitive friendships, and the larger community of mankind. For women, it may be a time of pursuing those goals and achievements of the true self long delayed by family making. This is also the time for our spiritual blossoming as we search for something larger to serve than success, materialism, or children.

The realm of mysticism naturally comes next. The mystic is simply the one who seeks to know the sacred in a direct and immediate way. In the heart of each individual, in each ancient soul, is a longing for the original contact. After all, we live in the sacred, it is our origin and nature, but we dulled or lost its original shimmering brilliance in our stress-filled lives. In essence, each of us is a mystic. Such is the teaching of all the great mystics. Direct mystical experience, as we have seen, is the source of all religion, with its profound influence on art, culture, and ultimate human values. So returning to the realm of spirit after the hero's death would be the most natural destination of all for this story.

As the truly mature individual ages and becomes more permeable to the mystical awareness now leaking through the soul's membrane, self can open to soul and into the divine as the actual center of consciousness. The divine self increasingly fills the personality's core and concurrently the world itself is recognized as filled and radiant with Divine Being, for this is the essential mystical vision. It is this living, wondrous, divine reality, inside and out, that provides what we need most: joy, love, purpose, meaning, and courage. Not simply a God image, this is the original spiritual context of life forgotten, or worse, devalued by "modern" civilization. With it, an individual comes home to the sacred that has always been there, the sacred originally "lost" in childhood. Whether we return to organized religion (for the sacred lives in the heart of every religion) or simply learn to live more in everyday mystical consciousness, our deepening spirituality heals the artificial split between spirit and matter, psyche and soul, this world and the "Kingdom."

Inherent in the sacred milieu is a cosmic order, a spiritual reality that we must learn again to recognize and serve. Our world depends on it. Moved increasingly by awareness of the divine Presence, one becomes a steward or caretaker for this sacred garden, focusing especially on those most in need in order to protect and grow their divine possibilities (e.g., children, suffering or disenfranchised people, animals, and earth). In whatever form it takes, the spiritually realized are naturally drawn to serve this order with spontaneous and loving generosity. But keep in mind, this whole journey requires our own conscious and enlightened participation. Those who refuse consciousness or betray the soul for the sake of security and false self inflation will not bear these spiritual fruits. They will abort their incarnation and the journey itself. Their ossified shell will have to await its breaking at the transition called death.

We can see, then, that the journey of life begins and ends in the wonder of existence. Mystical consciousness, known throughout the ages, gradually and subtly returns to the spiritually mature late in the second half of life, and brings with it a vision of reality offering an altogether new and soul-nourishing value system. It shows us that reality itself is sacred and that the "Kingdom of Heaven" is indeed spread all over the earth but men do not see it, as Jesus said in The Gospel According to Thomas. To the extent that we can age with such consciousness and wisdom, we will find ourselves returning to sacred ground, and discover the original spiritual nature we lost so long ago. The quest itself, we learn, was always a symbolically disguised journey to find our way home. It is an individual's perception that changes, not the world.

Then, for the spiritually advanced, even the true self, like a blossom, completes its cycle of expression and subtly recedes back into unity. What is left, for those capable of such experience, is simply the experience of no-self, that is, the nature and presence of God everywhere. A life in this final stage lives from that vast, all pervasive, and loving divine consciousness, incarnating it as the divine self, sometimes lifted and carried by it in swoons of love, and often teaching it by example to others. The individual self is now mostly gone. The world is not only found to be the mystical garden described in all the scriptures, it is eventually seen as a state of mind, a fiction, a play of divine energy and consciousness. We live now as an invitation to bring others to the same wonder of Being. What an individual does with this sacred awareness depends on the maturity of his ego, his depth of realization, and his particular capacity for integrating the experience of Cosmic Consciousness into his life. No one is perfect, no one does it all the way, but each instinctively and intuitively seeks this religious quest and its self-transforming potential.

STAGES ON THE WAY

Examining this story from the perspective of our psychospiritual theory of personality, we can see that the contents of consciousness (i.e., ego, false self, true self, soul, divine self, God) go through a series of pre-established developmental stages, stopping wherever development is arrested. These stages of realization comprise the sacred journey of life and greatly influence the individual's religious, spiritual, and mystical growth. As such, they represent developmental stages and can be described in the following sequence:

INCHOATE EXPERIENCE

At birth, there is only the opening of soul and the confusion of the undeveloped ego. This is the chaotic, archaic, and archetypal world of infantile experience. "Inner" and "outer" are undifferentiated and the mystical experience is everywhere present, surrounding and pervading numerous, ever changing primitive psychological states. Without the development of stable mental functions, we are incapable of organizing, understanding, or remembering this time.

Birth of the Ego

Gradually inchoate experience is differentiated by the ego. Using its neurologically maturing cognitive and motor functions, the ego strives to master inner and outer stimuli, including sensory experience, body movement, emotional reactions, and intellectual growth. This development involves the constantly interactive field of body, family, and environment. With time and seemingly endless practice, the experience of existence, reality, and physical incarnation eventually stabilize.

The True Self

Gradually the germ of true self is activated. Swaddled like an infant in the core of the embryonic psyche, the germinal self is present at birth. It is the true person and, like the seed of a redwood tree, it awaits the right conditions to break its shell and grow into a prearranged nature. Activated by bodily sensation, the loving mirroring attention of the child's caretaker, and the dynamics of the family psyche, by the age of five or six the individual begins to experience this self in its own desires, natural gifts, and the far reaching longings of its soul.

The Self as Genuine Experience

On and off, over and over, everyday, in big ways and little, the individual comes to know the true self as the emotional center that feels, values, and experiences life. This subjective self moves the ego naturally with its own unbounded energy into activity, play, joy, curiosity, and connection. Physical, sensual, sexual, creative, and emotional energies thrive and multiply as the ego makes direct experiential contact with the true self. In early childhood, without the inhibition of "self-consciousness," the true self is expressed with total spontaneity. Increasingly, this spontaneity comes into conflict with the needs, limits, and boundaries of parents and society.

True Self and Inner Conflict

As the child develops, adult perceptions and behavioral requirements are imposed, creating interpersonal conflict and the development of conscience with its standards and critical voice. Eventually defeated (to greater or lessor degree) in this conflict with adults, the true self and its connection to soul are forced inside, into the dark unconscious, over which are layered negative or incorrect self-perceptions and rules of acceptable behavior. The soul now seems out of reach, locked in the center of the psyche or, worse, seemingly possessed by the other. Behavioral prescriptions and prohibitions, along with whatever erroneous beliefs are internalized about the self, create an inner boundary blocking access to the soul. Then, because the pain of this loss and the risk of more serious rejection are too great to bear, we forget all this happened and live falsely, according to the rules of others who long ago gave up their true selves and their connection to soul.

THE FALSE, SOCIALIZED, RESTRICTED SELF

To the detriment of the true self emerges the false one. It is a required adaptation. Built on the foundations of all that the family and culture value and devalue, it becomes like a suit of clothes. Put on so often, so automatically, in time we no longer realizes it is unreal. Conscience, with its prescribed standards of morality and strict rules of conduct, now controls the personality. In fact, we very often view these standards as virtues and strive to fulfill them. We will see that many of the disorders of adult personality are directly related to the ego's destructive relationship to self and soul. This is not to say that the true self is dormant along the way, for it seeks repeatedly to be known and valued. The conflict between the true and false selves becomes particularly intense at midlife, often threatening the individual's personality organization and social adjustment.

RE-DISCOVERY AND RENEWAL OF TRUE SELF

Eventually, if one is fortunate, one learns to find the true self again and recognize it as the natural psychological center of being. We discover it in times of joy and inspiration, when its energies fill and move us, and when we fall in love. We can also know the true self by its absence, when the pain of its betrayal breaks the wall of repression, forcing us to feel and explore its deep woundedness. By midlife, however, we know the soul has been betrayed and begin a descent into grief and ashes to find it again. Feeling this wound with empathy and love, the true self is gradually healed and reanimated.

THE BLOSSOMING OF TRUE SELF AND TO SOUL

Anyone who looks within gradually discovers that the true self is a remarkable energy, a veritable fountain of always forming being, a flower blossoming in and from the radiant light shining through the soul. The true self emerges like the lily from the depths of soul - a gift of grace. With the realization that the true self is given by the Divine Being comes an immense joy and a desire to live that form even more. One is gradually unfettered from the judgments and prohibitions of conscience and conventionality, and with less and less false self to inflate identity, we are simply and ecstatically happy and free to love in any and all ways possible. Knowing that soul is larger than self allows it to flow into us, expanding the creative possibilities of its expression in the world, a process that can intensify after midlife. In this joy, life is renewed as a spectacular dance of relationships, an opportunity for boundless generosity and service, and an abundant expression of holiness. The soul, our spiritual self, wants so much from us, and the spiritually mature thrill to its ever renewing call to loving consciousness.

DISCOVERING THE DIVINE SELF

Also housed in the depths of the religious psyche is the "other": the sacred and living awareness of the divine. Learning how to experience true self and soul brings an awareness of this other consciousness. In this Presence, one discovers the possibility of becoming an expression of God's being in one's own particular form. This is the possibility of the divine self, an agency with an agenda entirely apart from self and soul. It is God's agenda. Ego's task is to discern and embody the operation of this consciousness without becoming false and inflated.

THE DIVINE MARRIAGE

Sacred literature around the world speaks of a time on the journey when the ego dies. In light of our theoretical model, it would be more accurate to say that it is the false self that finally disintegrates, replaced by an inner merging of ego and soul. Jungians call this the *coniunctio,* the inner divine marriage that often occurs most deeply during and after the midlife passage. Christians speak of the marriage to Christ. With this union, the ego, carrier of consciousness and director of cognitive functions, is now filled and transformed with the inflowing Divine Being, In spiritual terms, this is equivalent to the soul finding union with God, at least temporarily. But the ego does not die, for it is still a necessary organizing container for this new form.

NO SELF OR SELF-AS-DIVINE-GROUND

Finally comes the unity found in the experience of "no self." The true self is gradually replaced by the Divine Being, the Self of all existence. There is virtually no separation now, for there is no separate self to create the experience of duality. Absorbing the soul, the divine self has become the Divine Being. This kind of unity happens naturally though quite subtly as we age. The perceptual reality of subject-object and self-other becomes paper thin, increasingly outshined by the radiant field of Being and the all pervasive transcendental consciousness. Individual consciousness, freed from its identification with any particular worldly form, opens to a larger consciousness that is known to be everywhere and everything. In this stage, all beings are truly known and loved as one. Though the "individual" may continue to utilize the ego organization to deal with the world, he recognizes that everything is God. Love is all that exists now, and compassion, for the "individual" in this particular form naturally seeks the liberation of all those who remain tragically imprisoned by identity and attached to false images, goals, and beliefs.

FORMAL RELIGIOUS BELIEFS AND THE SOUL'S JOURNEY OF CONSCIOUSNESS:

As implied above, the child's religious beliefs are steadily modified through the life span. Maturing after the magical and impressionistic years of early childhood, adolescents, with their rapidly developing abstract abilities and related idealism, strive to understand their given religion and search for means of authentic expression. Young adults, driven by the need to find a successful place in the world, usually settle into the existing values of their family and culture. At midlife, however, faced with disappointment, disillusionment, and aging, many adults begin to search for personal and experiential religious answers. Authoritarian or institutional beliefs must be re-examined and tested. In some ways, the spiritual journey really begins at this time, and the second half of life is its wilderness. For those few who truly meet the psychological and spiritual challenges of midlife, a highly personal, intimate, and mystical experience of religion is achieved. Based on increasingly direct awareness of divine consciousness rather than belief, its continued unfolding has the potential to lead into the highest stages of spiritual realization

As the reader readily recognizes, these stages portray an idealized path of psychospiritual evolution. Its steps are symbolized by the great religious figures and their epics. Very few individuals, however, go much beyond the integration of the true self during their lifetime, though many at that stage intuit and pursue its possibilities.

AGING AND MYSTICAL REALIZATION

*There is, after all, something eternal that lies beyond the hand of fate
and of all human delusions. And such eternals lie closer to an older person
than a younger one oscillating between fear and hope.*
Albert Einstein

*The old must often try to be silent, if it is within their power, since silence
may be like space, the intensely alive something that contains all.*
Florida Scott-Maxwell

We are not the same person at 70 as we were in childhood, adolescence, or even our early twenties or thirties. The personality continues to change and evolve into something new, eventually arriving at a point where personality is translucent to the light and consciousness of eternity. We do not just drop the ego, as some have mistakenly believed eastern religions assert, it just becomes more and more porous and transparent to the living divine Presence.

If the first half of life is devoted to the development of the ego and its competencies, the second half is devoted to the opening of consciousness. The journey of life first takes us out into the world in symbolic search for the mystical garden and true self that we lost in early childhood, and then brings us home again to the present and immanent sacred as we age. We eventually realize that what we were searching for all along has always been here. We are that. The journey into this final realization, however, is through the difficult and divine fires of aging.

Interestingly, most people do not become more religious with aging. Rather than pursue new spiritual awakening as they move toward death, they continue with the beliefs that steadfastly guided them through life. As implied earlier, this continuity of belief does not mean their consciousness is not undergoing change, only that most older people dismiss these new experiences or interpret them within their existing religious framework. It is often the individual who has always been on a path of spiritual self-realization that discovers the kinds of experiences described here.

Although the highest stages of realization can theoretically occur at any time, and there have always been cases of divinely conscious children in the religious lore, self-realization is a process that most of us will know imperfectly, gradually, and most profoundly, through personal defeat. It is the failure of the false self and the defeat of the ego's control over life, that finally bring us to the divine. Such defeat occurs more and more frequently in the second half of life, when aging, loss, and physical decline weaken the false self's dominance of ego, exposing us first to the underlying state of the true self, and then to its relentlessly loving engulfment by the divine. In fact, it is often near the moment of death that the divine shines through most noticeably, as chaplains, nurses, and hospice workers readily attest.

With enough strength and guidance, the ego can voluntarily surrender the grandiosity and control of the false self, and understand that failure and defeat are the predestined journey back to God. Indeed, there is no escaping this journey. Understanding its nature and destination, however, allows us to participate more positively in the process of divine disintegration, and this is one of the most important tasks of aging. God is finally seen to be both the creator and the destroyer, and destruction is found to be as sweet and loving as it is painful. If we look closely, it is understood that our pain is directly proportionate to our resistance. When we stop fighting, we go home.

The more advanced stages of spiritual realization, therefore, tend to take place in the second half of life. Each great defeat or loss demands that we release our attachments and know that what remains is the sacred itself, manifesting and operating everywhere in our behalf. Retirement, deaths of loved ones, personal injuries, progressive physical limitations, loss of energy, irrelevance to the larger culture, these conditions strip identity and control, and yet as each piece is dissolved in the fires of aging, we find that there is still something left. That something is God. With each loss, the membrane between the psychological and sacred realms grows thinner, until divine consciousness pervades all of existence. If we can surrender consciously and gratefully to this great process, the journey will be sweeter and each will be a light illuminating the way for those coming behind.

CHAPTER EIGHT

THE SPIRITUAL MEANING OF PSYCHIATRIC DISORDERS: A REVISED TAXONOMY

Contents: Human Problems as Psychospiritual Issues
The Spiritual Significance of Common Psychiatric Disorders
The Ego-Soul Matrix
Spiritual Health

HUMAN PROBLEMS AS PSYCHOSPIRITUAL ISSUES

True to the spiritual premise of this book, we need to appreciate that human problems always entail multiple dimensions of meaning. For example, a diagnosis of cancer has physical, medical, economic, psychological, social, and spiritual significance. Each dimension has its place, principles, and values in the human drama, each is "more important" than the rest at certain times, and none can be excluded without doing damage to the richness and essential unity of life. So, too, circumstances such as divorce, job loss, accidents, loneliness, depression, or the failure of religious faith have multiple impact, for wherever a problem starts, it will eventually touch other levels, and when it is severe, no level can escape its reach.

How do we understand the spiritual dimension of human problems and their development into formal psychiatric disorders? The answer to this question, of course, depends directly on how we understand the spiritual purpose and meaning of life itself. Our examination of religion, spirituality, and personality suggest that life's ultimate purposes include:

* growing spiritually, that is, from false self to true self to divine self to God, and awakening the spiritual nature of personality, life, and the sacred journey;
* developing the ego's comprehension and sophistication regarding spiritual tasks, problems, and development;
* finding and deepening our relationship to God as a living sacred presence, and opening progressively to this consciousness within and in the world;
* finding our way back to the sacred here and now, that is, healing the separation of self and divine, spirit and matter, this world and the "Kingdom,"
* understanding and participating in the unfolding dynamics of enlightenment in the living divine universe,
* bringing the teachings of enlightenment into to the world of duality,
* learning to know and experience the sacred in joy, love, gratitude, and generosity,
* building spiritual community and relating to others in a truly spiritual way,
* knowing first hand that ultimately God provides the meaning and purpose of life.

With these purposes in mind, problems on all the dimensions take on new and added significance. From cancer to job loss, from crisis to depression, one needs to ask transpersonal questions like: What is the spiritual task or learning here? What psychospiritual personality conflict does it reveal? What is the spiritual purpose, path, or teaching contained in this experience? Where is God in it? How is this problem given to me to know God's will? What does it say about my relationship to the sacred? What does my soul long for? Where is enlightenment? How have I been ignoring the spiritual dimension? How am I being divinely molded and shaped by this situation? The reader will find a comprehensive discussion of such everyday psychospiritual human problems and questions in Appendix D. The accompanying Chart and examples can also be used in the process of Spiritual Assessment described in Chapter 14.

THE SPIRITUAL SIGNIFICANCE OF COMMON PSYCHIATRIC DISORDERS

Psychospiritual dynamics may create, intensify, or complicate diagnosable psychiatric problems. Using the integrated vocabulary and developmental theory presented earlier, it is possible to discuss the spiritual nature of emotional disorders and formulate a kind of spiritual taxonomy. The reader is encouraged to consult a textbook on Abnormal Psychology and read the Diagnostic and Statistical Manual of the American Psychiatric Association (DSM IV) to review the current medical model of psychopathology. When each disorder is re-examined through the lens of psychospiritual theory, a deeper significance can be found profoundly influencing how we understand and treat its symptoms.

From a spiritual point of view, the core wounds underlying the development of psychopathology involve ego's relationship to true self and soul. Myth, superstition, religion, poetry, and depth psychology universally agree that our mental and physical health decline when we lose connection with these vital centers of personality. Individual disorders arise from the hidden betrayal, devaluing, or misalignment of ego, true self, soul, divine self, and Divine Being. Relationship problems occur when we betray or devalue those same parts in the people around us.

The following list of disorders is meant to be representative rather than exhaustive, for a primer cannot consider every possible diagnosable condition. It is extensive enough, however, to demonstrate how a spiritual model may be overlaid on the conventional medical one. Keep in mind, also, that this conceptualization is not intended to replace or discount chemical and genetic etiologies of psychological disorders.

A SPIRITUAL TAXONOMY OF PSYCHIATRIC DISORDERS

Crises: "Acts of God"
Adjustment Disorders: "Accepting the Spiritual Challenge"
Depression: "The Betrayal, Abandonment, or Eclipse of the Soul"
Anxiety Disorders: "Flight from the Soul"
Panic Disorders: "The Fragmenting Self"
Post-traumatic Stress Disorder: "Soul Trauma"
Psychosomatic & Somatoform Disorders: "The Soul's Last Voice"
Chemical Addictions: "Spirit in the Bottle"
Sexual Disorders: "Body as Temple, Body as Sacrilege"
Mania: "The Hero's Dangerous Flight"
Psychosis: "When the Religious Psyche Leaks In"
Narcissism: "Victory of the False Self, Defeat of the Soul"

Antisocial Personality: "Evil and the Aggressive Personality"

CRISES: "ACTS OF GOD."

Jung once defined God as whatever came across his path to disrupt his ego or its plans, making known to him that there was a larger force or intentionality operating in the universe. Viewing crises as "acts of God," of course, is the religious attitude that has always dwelled in the psyche. When terrible things happen, we invariably ask God "why." Often, however, we fail to listen or give credence to the answers received, which may come through intuition, dreams, discussions with others, or further life events. To the faithful, prayerful inquiry and contemplation can reveal the hidden spiritual meanings needed to cope and move onward.

Sometimes, crises represent a growth process that forcibly challenges the ego, false self, relationships, or our entire life container to either change or break to allow a new form to be born. Though we often resist such challenges, life involves constant cycles of stability and change, the completion of one stage and transition to the next, for the development of soul. Like a tree seedling pushing through cracking cement, growth disrupts and transforms out dated forms, for the old eventually becomes stagnant and limiting. Clinging to permanent security, blocks the expression of self, soul, and the inner sacred in our life and world. A disruption of security, on the other hand, can dramatically open a sensitive consciousness to the operation of the Divine Being. When we recognize the presence of higher purposes in our existence, we understand that everything is intrinsically spiritual; then even catastrophic events can become profoundly meaningful or transforming opportunities.

ADJUSTMENT DISORDERS: "ACCEPTING THE SPIRITUAL CHALLENGE."

Adjustment Disorders are a first level of reactive or emergency emotional distress. They arise in response to situational crises that shatter or disrupt our customary security and ego control (e.g., death of a loved one, loss of a job, financial setback, divorce). We may react with anxiety, depression, confusion, physiologic distress, inhibited motivation, or anger. This distress represents and requires the emotional work of coming to terms with change. A new equilibrium, and often a new life structure, are achieved when the work is done.

A deeper, soul-oriented growth occurs when we understand the spiritual significance of life change and the limitations of our spiritual vision that made it so difficult to accept. Sometimes what looks like an accident is the true self undermining the false self in order to resume its stunted growth. Sometimes a crisis is God challenging us to wake up to the spiritual purpose of life. Indeed, it is often the unwanted event that truly expands consciousness to the greater tasks and teachings of the sacred journey. When personality rigidities or vulnerabilities prevent the ego from knowing true self and soul, more serious emotional disorders often result.

DEPRESSION: "THE BETRAYAL, ABANDONMENT, OR ECLIPSE OF THE SOUL."

Depression can arise from many sources - loss, loneliness, and failure. But inside each apparent cause, there is another more important spiritual one. Depression arises when we betray, abandon, or withdraw love from the true self, its gift, and its connection to soul, or when the needs of self and soul are eclipsed by the ego's failure to cope with life stresses or the demands of others. The true self falls into sorrow and hopelessness when it is ignored or forgotten too long; it mourns more deeply still when severed from soul or when its gifts have been devalued or discarded. Love grows the true self. In its absence, the self suffers deeply, and this suffering is known as depression.

Depression also arises when the true self is rejected or condemned by stern and unloving messages from others or one's own conscience, often in response to failure. The deepest pain of all occurs when we turn against our self in blame and self-loathing. It is the pain of self-hatred that evolves into the most severe and pernicious depression, defying both reassurance and reality feedback. Others may think we are not so bad, but it is our own love and forgiveness we need most, and that is exactly what is withheld in depression.

Loss of soul figures powerfully into the depressive state. In indigenous cultures, illness and depression are often understood to result directly from this loss. For pre-industrial peoples, healing literally involves going in search of soul. In disorders of religious faith, a more contemporary example, the individual's life and worldview are bereft of spiritual hope and meaning. These states arise in people whose religious impulse has been damaged by childhood misinformation or abuse. They are not permitted to know their soul, trust its mystical intuitions, and take the great spiritual journey to reunion with the sacred. Depression here is a great, hidden, unvoiced melancholy, as if the soul had already died, as if one were forbidden to believe in, to know, or to be loved by God. To live with this sorrow in the soul is a great darkness.

Depression may also be another word for the "Dark Night of the Soul," the metaphorical description by the Christian mystic St. John of the Cross for that phase of the spiritual journey when we are unable to connect with God at all. This impasse is almost unbearable, emptying life of joy, meaning and hope. At such times, it seems like God has forsaken or abandoned the believer. Coming after years of productive and gratifying spiritual connection, or during periods of overwhelming loss and seemingly unanswered prayer, the "Dark Night" feels like a stagnant or dead streambed whose stench is everywhere. Worst of all, in the midst of this confused and painful "death," one forgets that the "Dark Night" is actually a transformation. The passage of the "Dark Night" will be discussed further in Chapters 14 and 15.

When depression is understood in this larger psychospiritual context, its suffering can be given meaning and value. But deadened prematurely by medication or pressure to "get over it" by family or friends, the spiritual value of depression (i.e., locating an injured self, finding soul, and asking ultimate questions) may be lost. Sometimes, however, severe depression can prevent any meaningful psychospiritual inquiry, and at such times, medication can be itself be a "Godsend," a healing gift of humankind's scientific creativity.

ANXIETY DISORDERS: "FLIGHT FROM THE SOUL."

Anxiety and fear are closely related. Classically, the fear response has been associated with external reality dangers and anxiety with internal psychological dangers. Psychological dangers include loss of security or self-esteem, approval from others, or the defensive control of threatening unconscious impulses, ideas, or behavior. What all of these dangers have in common is the fear that an unconscious impulse or insight would be catastrophic to the preservation of the false self and the survival of the true self.

In anxiety disorders, the ego is often terrified of knowing the nature and condition of the true self, either because the wants of the self are frightening or because its injuries are too painful or horrible to face. As observed in the universal story, we commonly suppress much of ourselves to preserve basic dependency and security. The true self, then, becomes what Jung called the shadow, and we are unconsciously apprehensive that it will be exposed and devalued. Anxiety disorders arise when the true self and soul desire to act in ways that would risk our perceived security and self-esteem. Such deep psychological fear can take the form of phobias, panic disorders, or post-traumatic stress disorders depending on the particular circumstances and wounds. In each, there is a "flight from the soul," that is, an escape from knowing something unbearably upsetting.

PHOBIAS AND PANIC DISORDERS: "THE FRAGMENTING SELF."

While Panic Disorders can take many forms, what they typically have in common is anxiety so extreme that one fears that the false self will literally fragment, and with it, one's physical survival or sanity. To stay unconscious of its real cause, the individual's terror is defensively displaced onto something else (e.g., going outside, knives, spiders) that can be avoided, giving the illusion of control. The feared object or situation then dominates the individual's life, creating further defensive distraction from the real problem. When the defense does not work, the terror breaks through.

Like any other symptom, the spiritual purpose of such acute and disabling fear is to bring the individual's attention back to the root cause, the damaged or unacceptable self, so that a process of healing can begin. The ego's journey home, often with the guidance of a therapist, eventually brings it to a more accepting and loving contact with the injured or rejected true self. With time and grace, its connection to soul and the spiritual process is renewed. Here, too, medication may be of assistance for fear itself can become crippling.

POST-TRAUMATIC STRESS DISORDER: "SOUL TRAUMA."

When the true self and soul are exposed to something so horrific that it cannot be faced (e.g., terrible violence, the immanent threat of personal annihilation, or major catastrophes that undermine fundamental security), the traumatic emotional response is dissociated, that is, it is defensively placed outside of consciousness. The ego simply cannot face the true self's pain and horror. But the horror will not stay dissociated and leaks back into consciousness through flashbacks, nightmares, or fear of the event's repetition. In this way, the anguish carried in the true self asks to be assimilated piece by piece.

A uniquely spiritual aspect of the Post-traumatic Stress Disorder is the soul's sensitivity to morally outrageous events: murder, war, rape, violence, torture, and carnage. Deeply connected to spiritual laws and principles, the soul cannot accept such atrocities, which symbolically constitute "soul trauma." The true self, younger and less experienced than the soul, is shocked by the sight of them. Limited in the amount of horror it can face, however, the self can feel literally overwhelmed or torn apart, and must be healed before the soul's outrage and call for constructive action can be heeded. Healing for many people, therefore, eventually involves voicing the soul's opposition to morally unacceptable situations and demanding social justice.

PSYCHOSOMATIC AND SOMATOFORM DISORDERS: "THE SOUL'S LAST VOICE."

The body provides a physical experience of the true self, for all emotions are "embodied" there. Love, hate, jealousy, sorrow, bitterness, fear, even false self, are expressed in body language. We get "choked up," "scared shitless," "broken hearted," or "uptight," and then get referred to our ears-nose-throat doctor, proctologist, cardiologist, or psychologist. When feelings are buried, in other words, they are buried alive, and the physical costs of suppressing painful memories and emotions affect the body's functioning, producing psychosomatic and somatoform symptoms as well as immune system dysfunction.

Physical illness, encoded in the body's language of emotions, is the "soul's last voice." When spiritual laws and realities are ignored or denied, the resulting conflict or unhappiness creates problems in the psyche. When psychological problems are denied, they fall next into the body, where physical symptoms, illness, and even death may result. This cascading sequence occurs because the individual cannot or will not listen to his soul's knowing voice.

On the positive side, when an individual's physical symptoms finally get his attention and draw it back to the psychological and spiritual dimensions of the problem, the path of healing may begin. Sometimes it is too late for physical survival but not too late for psychological and spiritual growth. Terminal cancer, for example, allows many people time to confront the unfinished psychospiritual issues of their lives, and in the process, open to a potential for love and spirituality unknown before the illness.

CHEMICAL ADDICTIONS: "SPIRIT IN THE BOTTLE."

Colloquially, alcoholic beverages have for centuries been know as "spirits" symbolically owing to their original use as means of reaching the spirit world through chemically altered consciousness. Originally, intoxication was a ritual doorway into an altered state for sacred purposes (e.g., contact with healing spirits, soul flights, ecstatic communion). In the great religious traditions, the most profound joy is found in the mystical union. To the ignorant and uninitiated, "getting high" can be mistaken for altered and blissful states, and the first experience of inebriation is close enough to bliss for the spiritually desperate that it triggers an intense desire to recover it. The alcoholic is one who pursues chemical "ecstasy" as a substitute for the spiritual one. But finding it in the bottle does not work: the "good" feeling gets further away and physiologic dependency begins an insidious stranglehold of soul and life.

Some alcoholics are so damaged by historical wounds to self and its connection to soul that they seek the anesthetic comfort and peace provide by the chemical spirits. Others are so incapable of modulating the spiritual dimension that they indulge it through compulsive intoxication. The relationship between alcohol and spirituality is most apparent when the alcoholic "hits bottom" and experiences a degree of genuine mystical breakthrough secondary to profound physiologic, emotional, and spiritual depletion (Bill Wilson's experience is a classic example).

Drug addiction, too, may be a misdirected quest for religious ecstasy through substitute chemical highs that very quickly turn dark and self-destructive. The individual hungers for the natural joy and expanded consciousness of the mystics. Hooked instead on chemical "bliss," the individual pursues it repeatedly until physiologic dependence occurs. Heroin, "ecstasy," cocaine, LSD, marijuana, and countless other drugs have been used directly or indirectly in search of pure religious experience, only to chain the seeker to the addictive process. Then the mind-altering numbness of the addictive agent hides the underlying emptiness and the anguish of withdrawal, but must be continued to avoid the worsening state of both. Jung was the first modern psychotherapist to recognize this connection between addiction and spirituality, and emphasized the importance of surrendering the will to a "higher power" to break the downward addictive spiral.

SEXUAL DISORDERS: "BODY AS TEMPLE, BODY AS SACRILEGE."

Sexuality, too, can express our spiritual longing for ecstatic communion directly with the divine. The body is one of our most personal and immediate experiences of the divinity in creation. Sexual arousal has long been esoterically understood to be the visitation and embodied experience of divine energy. Indeed, specialized sexual exercises (tantric yoga) have been practiced in the east for centuries to reach this kind of enlightenment, and for some, orgasm is a doorway to cosmic ecstasy. Sexuality may also symbolize archetypal union of the masculine and feminine faces of God or the secret bliss felt in communion with the divine consciousness. Similarly, when it is not trivialized as a sales gimmick or pursued for instant gratification, the libido is a powerful channel for the life force, an energy of divine origin that momentarily consumes and unifies the individual selves experiencing it.

At the metaphysical level, sexual problems reflect an obstruction or distortion of this inherently spiritual experience, usually as a result performance fears, religious guilt, or the unconscious repetition of an early traumatization to intimacy. Healing sexual dysfunctions, however, requires healing the whole personality. Nurturing the true self, its physical experience and safety, and the ego's capacity for spontaneous experience must be accomplished before genital sexuality can be more than the exploitation of sensation for personal gratification. With time and discernment, orgasm can become more than physical pleasure, it becomes a divine one. Then we enter sexual experience as a sacrament rather than a sacrilege, and the divine mysteries flow once again in the temple of the body.

MANIA: "THE HERO'S DANGEROUS FLIGHT."

In manic states, there is excessive energy, hyperactivity, markedly increased sexuality, grandiose schemes, occasional religiosity, and an exaggerated assessment of personal ability. The individual believes he can accomplish impossible things instantly and without need of relaxation, sleep, patience, or normal human relationships. Out of control, this hero seeks to fly like Icarus above the rules of reality, until his imagined wings melt in the manic blaze and he crashes hard to earth.

Like depression, manic episodes occur in response to a loss or disappointment that is too great for the false self to hide, often because it stimulates or repeats an unseen childhood trauma. This deep wound begins to flood the core of the personality, an unconsciously terrifying event that propels the ego into heroic action. The manic individual feels that only extraordinary and magnificent achievement can save it from unbearable pain or destruction. The inner wound also acts like a undersea volcano, precipitously exposing and releasing too much of the soul's creative vision and divine energies at the center of personality. It is not surprising that some of the world's most creative geniuses suffered from this disorder. Unfortunately, the ego becomes overly excited by this unmodulated eruption, riding its waves of creative energy like a surfer, higher and higher, until he crashes against the rocks of physical, emotional, and mental exhaustion.

While a genetic basis to this disorder predisposes the individual to the "hero's dangerous flight," and while it can now be effectively managed with medication, the spiritual issues involved are no less powerful and important, especially in the realm of creativity. The manic soars with this glimpse or intuition of his soul's cosmic vision, producing a profound and nearly intoxicating inspiration. To use it, however, the individual needs to develop a healthier ego capable of dealing with psychic pain, healing the injured self, and integrating the soul 's vision in a more natural and regulated way. Only then can its life giving energy and inspiration contribute meaningfully to his spiritual unfolding and to his community.

PSYCHOSIS: "WHEN THE RELIGIOUS PSYCHE LEAKS IN."

Like manic eruptions, psychotic episodes can reflect the rush of cosmic energies and images from the deep core of personality but in an even more primal way. The kind of symbolic and archetypal mentation found in dreams, mythology, and religion leak through a failing ego, progressively undermining its reality functions, and creating a new, dramatic, and compelling psychotic reality. When psychotic reality submerges the ego, the individual is unable to use its symbols or images constructively. Instead, there is enormous confusion, misinterpretation, and mistaken identity, with the individual believing he is God or is directed by God's voice. While the psychotic may indeed be in touch with powerful religious themes, messages, or realizations (e.g., ultimate conceptions of good and evil, awareness of the indwelling divine, or universal religious truths), he has too little ego capacity to understand or integrate them.

Psychotic breakdowns sometimes happen when the true self has been totally replaced by a brittle false self too weak to cope with the life stresses confronting it. Schizophrenia, for example, can emerge when the internal, external, and physiologic demands of adolescence exceed a marginally functioning ego and false self. World destruction delusions symbolize this experience of impending personality disintegration. The mixed contribution of genetics, brain structure, neurochemistry, and social-developmental processes to this complex disorder do not discount the equally important psychospiritual contributions of false self, true self, soul, and divine self, and Divine Being. In fact, sometimes psychotic regression occurs in the service of personality reorganization, as if there were a need for the false self to collapse for the true self and soul to reorganize the personality in healthier ways. As with manic episodes, however, symptom management must generally precede psychotherapy, for an overwhelmed ego can achieve little emotionally or spiritually.

Occasionally the energies overwhelming the ego are predominately spiritual, that is, the individual is flooded with nearly pure sacred or numinous realizations or perceptions. In this case, the crisis may actually be a spiritual one. The immediate diagnostic question, however, remains whether the individual has the ego capacity to deal productively with this material, a matter we will be returning to in Chapter 14. With spiritual emergencies, the therapist's psychospiritual orientation can be very important, validating the client's religious experience yet at the same time guiding and protecting the individual so that mystical insights can be truly useful to his healing and spiritual growth.

Another example of spiritually generated psychosis is the shamanic crisis described by anthropologists. An individual destined to be a tribal "medicine man" often experiences what psychiatrists would diagnose as a schizophrenic episode - a major psychotic break with reality replete with hallucinations, bizarre mentation, and erratic behavior - except that it is understood by indigenous peoples as contact with the spirit world. Such contact is felt to be a sign of supernatural healing potential, for entry into the dimension of spirits is a highly prized ability. In India, too, young people who fall into profound and socially debilitating mystical states, sometimes for weeks at a time, are protected and viewed with great respect. Many, such as Ramana Maharshi, are later revered as enlightened saints.

As we will see later, religious material may also be no more than a defense against a meaningless existence, an exaggeration of the false self to compensate for secret feelings of inferiority, or an indication of deficient ego structure and function. The result can be a chronic and debilitating psychotic process that, despite its outward appearance, does not serve the individual's spiritual growth. Always the measure of a spiritual experience, is whether the individual truly grows in insight and maturity from its impact.

PERSONALITY DISORDERS.

Personality Disorders form when otherwise normal personality traits become excessive, inflexible, and maladaptive. They customarily develop in people who have been severely damaged by early and repeated psychological traumatization, often within the in the first one to three years of life, resulting in profound deviations of the normal developmental course. Each Personality Disorder can be analyzed from the psychospiritual perspective, but for the sake of brevity, only Narcissistic and Antisocial Personality Disorders will be discussed here.

NARCISSISM: "VICTORY OF THE FALSE SELF, DEFEAT OF THE SOUL."

When a child's true self has been catastrophically devalued, co-opted, or rejected by parental figures, he has no other survival choice but to give up his soul entirely and create the false self they require. Throughout childhood, the individual strives continually to develop this false self to match, merge with, or compensate for the parents' narcissistic superiority and achievement demands. The young narcissist may not even realize that the self has been lost.

For many, the narcissist is the hero of western culture who refuses to give up the competitive quest for superiority at any cost. Winning, wealth, and self-inflation are all that matter. Unwilling to let go of the false self, and fearing that there is nothing underneath it, the narcissistic ego seeks to dominate, control, and oppress the realm of self and soul. Unable to face his deeply buried inner pain and shame, the narcissist is also unable to access the religious strata of the psyche. His personality has become the barrier: How can he know or surrender to God when his ego insists on being God? Eventually, every narcissist is defeated by life. Marriage and family fail, work betrays him, illness and age rob him of his athletic prowess and good looks. Interestingly, this defeat is also the cure, but only if it can be valued as an opportunity to yield false striving and recover a soul lost decades earlier.

ANTISOCIAL (PSYCHOPATHIC) PERSONALITY: "EVIL AND THE AGGRESSIVE PERSONALITY."

Antisocial behavior occurs when there has been such violence to the developing self that it is injured beyond repair. Physical and emotional abuse, chaotic and unsafe conditions, intense shame, and profound parental disinterest force the ego to deaden its emotional center in order to survive. To overcome this unpleasant numbness, the Antisocial Personality seeks stimulation, excitement, and even violence to feel alive at all. And, without the experience of an inner, wounded self, the Antisocial character never develops empathy for the wounds of others, creating a capacity for cruelty beyond comprehension. In this profound developmental damage are the seeds of evil, for where there is no empathy, there is no conscience, tenderness, or love. Moreover, when the true self and soul have been successfully exterminated, nothing is sacred.

THE EGO-SOUL MATRIX

As implied by our psychospiritual model of personality and related spiritual taxonomy of psychiatric disorders, the integration of psychology and spirituality involves an interaction of variables from each realm. A particularly important relationship within the personality exists between ego and soul. The Ego-Soul Matrix (below) illustrates this interaction and its implications for healthy psychospiritual development, and we will be adding to this model repeatedly over the course of this book. Though it may seem a little complex at first, familiarity with this schemata will allow it to grow into an extremely useful conceptual and diagnostic tool.

In this theoretical matrix, the psychological term ego is denotes the conscious "I" of the individual (i.e., the conscious observer and doer) and the ego functions at his or her disposal (e.g., attention, perception, cognition, learning, memory, speech, behavior). The religious term soul (and the closely related word spirit) refers to the sacred dimension that the ego can learn to know and sense. Soul and spirit are aligned on the axis of spirituality and operate in tandem in the healthy personality.

The vertical axis ranges from a highly developed ego at the top pole (i.e., ego as a separate entity and identity is in charge, ego functions, including defenses, are efficient) to very low functioning one at the bottom pole (i.e., ego and its functions are disorganized, ineffective, or submerged in unconscious processes). The horizontal axis similarly ranges from a rich and full spirituality at the right (i.e., well developed contact with and awareness of soul and spirit) to the absence of spiritual connection at the left (no such contact or awareness).

It should further be pointed out that there are actually two sources of consciousness in this model: one associated with the ego and the other with soul and spirit. In both Freudian and Jungian psychoanalytic theories, ego is the carrier of consciousness (i.e., the "I" is usually identified as the one who is conscious). The ego can be conscious of the world, the body, and the inner life of feelings and thoughts. The ego can also become aware of the spiritual realm. As previously discussed, becoming conscious of soul means sensing one's own inflowing spiritual nature, and this nature has its own energy and desires which create the experience of the true self. Even more profoundly, becoming conscious of spirit opens into another source of consciousness altogether. It means sensing the Divine Being as a conscious presence within and without to whatever degree one is capable or graced.

The other key variables of the psychospiritual model of personality can be found across the quadrants, which are numbered for reference. Perhaps the easiest place to begin explaining this model is quadrant 2.

The Ego-Soul Matrix

Ego

False self		True self	
Unhealthy spirituality		Healthy spirituality	
Rigid or defended		Healthy personality	
personality functioning		functioning	
	3	2	

Soul
Spirit

	4	1	
Darkness, Shadow		God	
Unconscious		Divine Light	
Rejected, wounded self		Infinite Consciousness	

Quadrant 2: I was reflecting one day on the intuition that the true self and the soul were essentially equivalent or mirror ideas, except that one came from psychology and the other from religion. The true self, I realized, is the psychological manifestation of the soul, which is why we so often use these terms interchangeably. Then I realized that ego and soul must be in a healthy relationship for the true self to form and function positively. The ego, with its capacity for awareness and intelligent perception, is necessary to perceiving the energy of soul and its incarnation as true self. When ego is in a supportive, sensitive, and open relationship with true self, one's soul is known and honored inside the personality and, through behavior, given expression in the world. In addition, the true self of the other is valued and honored, hence interpersonal relationships are authentic and healthy.

The ego's capacity to know, feel, and differentiate the world creates reality out of undifferentiated being and true self out of soul. It is the interaction of ego and soul, therefore, that gives birth to the true self. Ego is equally necessary for the development of a healthy spiritual path, for without individually directed consciousness and discrimination, neither soul nor spirit can be sensed and known.

Quadrant 3: In quadrant 3, there is maximum ego and minimum soul. How do ego and soul get separated and what is the consequence? This quadrant refers the countless ways we betray, abandon, forget, diminish, or reject the true self, and hence our soul. We can trade soul for fame or fortune, give it up in a co-dependent relationship, become too "selfless" in work or life, or ignore the physical signs or symptoms of its abandonment in the body.

When ego abandons or betrays the true self in pursuit of material ambition or emotional security, it creates the false self. Religion and colloquial wisdom refer to this betrayal as "selling one's soul." In one form or another, fame, success, or survival are chosen over the expression of true self. Ego then loses touch with self, soul, spirit, and the genuine spiritual path. Often, the false self, no longer willing to serve or express God, instead seeks to be God. The ego, disconnected from soul, begins to run the personality like machine, compulsively pursuing the false self's ambitions.

Quadrant 4: Eventually the false self breaks down. Sometimes the ego simply cannot keep it going (e.g., years of workaholism), other times people or circumstances turn against us (who can be married or work for a narcissist forever?), or perhaps our arrogance simply leads to disastrous decisions. Whatever the case, when ego betrays or abandons soul, that is, when ego severs self from soul and exploits it for false purposes, tremendous pain is produced. The pain of this betrayal is buried in quadrant 4, beneath ego's defended consciousness and far from soul.

Where there is neither ego nor soul/spirit, therefore, one finds the dark, unconscious psyche filled with the repressed, rejected, wounded, and disowned parts of the true self, the pain of its abandonment, and the angry shadow material that results. Consciousness, individuality, and spirituality are excluded in this darkness. When ego breaks down, it falls into the hidden wounds of quadrant 4 .

Quadrant 1: Where there is essentially all soul/spirit and no ego, we find God - pure and uncontaminated by egoic concerns. As mystics know, experiences in this quadrant are outside the control of ego, given instead by grace. Here only God exists as infinite light and consciousness. The origin and primal cause of being, this quadrant is numbered 1.

The Ego-Soul Matrix also conceptualizes the relationships between personality, religion, spirituality, and mysticism in their various healthy and unhealthy variations (below).

The Ego-Soul Matrix in Religion, Spirituality, and Mysticism

Ego

Unhealthy Religion and Spirituality (Ego dominates without Soul & Spirit)	**Healthy Religion and Spirituality** (Ego supports Soul and Spirit)
False teachers; individual evil; religious abuse & addiction; false spirituality & self-deception; collective evil (mob behavior, oppressive religious norms).	Traditional spiritual path: ego functions are skillfully used to discern the soul and spirit, learn spiritual techniques, and understand the spiritual meaning of life; healthy personality development.
3	2

Soul
Spirit

4	1
Breakdown of religious and spiritual beliefs, practices, and organizations; exposure of religious hypocrisy and dishonesty; painful self-examination.	Moments of temporary enlightenment that occur spontaneously; natural healing through renewed contact with soul and spirit; rediscovery of God; renewal of spiritual path.
Collapse of Unhealthy Religion and Spirituality (No Ego, no Soul or Spirit)	**Mystical Breakthrough** (No Ego, all Soul and Spirit)

Healthy religion and spirituality require the interaction of ego with soul and spirit, for the ego is necessary to grow the skills of consciousness imperative on the spiritual path. When ego exists without genuine connection to soul and spirit, that is, when it is devoted to false self without the capacity to feel and know the sacred, then terrible things begin to happen in the name of religion. Narcissistic or psychopathic personalities may become religious leaders or teachers, and evil in the form of religious abuse and addiction thrives. Serious social dysfunction also forms as the false self becomes a collective experience spawning violence, undifferentiated mob behavior, the abuses of war, religious oppression, and neglect for the suffering or disenfranchised (e.g., the poor, the mentally ill, the disabled, the weak).

Sooner or later, unhealthy religion and spirituality break down, unraveled by its own emptiness, dishonesty, and the antipathy of others. Falseness and deceit are confronted, and unhealthy structures crumble, making room for new contact with spirit and soul. Rarely and unpredictably, the ego is briefly overwhelmed with spirit, producing moments of mystical enlightenment where there is no self, no ego, and no control, only pure union. These moments occur in a separate quadrant because they cannot be controlled by the ego or spiritual practices. It should be pointed out, however, that such spiritual healing does not require this full mystical experience. The Tao says, "Stillness and tranquillity set things in order in the universe." This means that when the ego stops trying to dominate life, when the false self gets out of the way, things naturally flow back into their proper, God-given order. Wherever this experience of unity is found, spiritual healing and restoration take place. This descent into grief and its connection to divine healing is effectively described by such Alcoholics Anonymous' phrases as "Hitting Bottom" and "Let go, let God." Or, in Christian parlance, the reconnection of ego, self, and soul allows one to be "born again," that is, returned to the world free of false self and filled with the energies and inspirations of soul and spirit.

wounds of personality and society. When ego's construction of false self breaks down or simply no longer works, one is called to descend into quadrant 3 in order to locate, experience, and re-integrate the rejected and wounded true self. Here the ego has no control. It cannot force its will. It can only surrender and open to the pain it has caused the true self.

The experience of pain and suffering in quadrant 4 is itself a healing process. Empathically feeling one's deep inner The psychopathology discussed in the preceding spiritual taxonomy arises primarily because the ego turns away from true self and soul (personal and other). Emotional and psychiatric symptoms develop from the pain and damage of this violation, from the inherent dysfunctionality of the false self, from the loss of a truly spiritual life, and from the refusal to bring consciousness and concern into the resulting pain works it through and begins to restore a loving relationship between ego and true self. With reconnection to the true self comes renewed contact with the soul and its opening to the sacred. The individual is pulled back into connection and alignment with the divine, allowing further healing and renewal to occur in quadrant 1, producing countless epiphanies (e.g., the infusion of new insights, creative energies, hope and joy about life's possibilities). In this cycle of self-betrayal and healing, we are touched by God whenever we break down and surrender egoic control. The true self is healed and the ego assumes its proper role of supporting true self, soul, and spirit.

CONCLUSIONS

The purpose of this psychospiritual perspective on human problems, with its associated spiritual taxonomy and the Ego-Soul Matrix, is to help therapists and clients alike reframe and revalue the emotional struggles of life as deeply meaningful psychospiritual processes, and to give them new tools for understanding and treating emotional problems. The spiritual dimension of life is everywhere, intersecting with physical and psychological phenomena at all levels. A theory of psychopathology and psychotherapy, and for that matter, of everyday life, that recognizes the importance of the soul, spirit, and the spiritual life offers therapists and clients new (and ancient!) avenues of healing and personal evolution.

From the psychospiritual perspective, problems are teachers with the divine inside each one of them. Personality dynamics may be said to exist for our edification and purification, giving us natural feedback about the spiritual laws and purposes operating in our lives. Emotional pain, psychiatric symptoms, and interpersonal conflict force us to confront the many ways we have personally violated and betrayed both our soul, the souls of those we love, and the divine. The more we know the world to be spiritual, the more all of its events, issues, and problems will be understood as necessary parts of the sacred journey.

Recognizing how we betray the sacred will also show us how to cease damaging it in the world. When we harm others, it is not usually because we are intentionally cruel but because we are limited in our ability to know the pain we are causing. As consciousness opens compassionately to our own wounding, the capacity to cause pain in others diminishes radically and their suffering can evoke the same tenderness and concern. Therapists and patients become simply people who seek to understand the processes of self, soul, and God in order to heal themselves and awaken to the true nature of the world. This is the work of a spiritually oriented psychotherapy.

SPIRITUAL HEALTH

If we are going to look at the psychospiritual nature of emotional disorders, we must also examine the nature of spiritual health. What is spiritual health? In the model presented above, spiritual health would embrace a nourishing and centering connection between ego and one's own psychospiritual nature, that of others, and God as immanent presence through community and the natural world. The specific components of spiritual health consist of the following:

*A meaningful belief in the spiritual reality of the world.
*A God image or idea that is positive, loving, forgiving, comforting, and transformative.
*A tangible feeling of connection to the divine presence.
*The capacity for ecstatic release and happiness in the experience of God.
*A loving, positive relationship between ego and true self, soul, divine self, and God.
*A willingness to consider the possibility of an indwelling divine self and potential for divine consciousness.
*A positive and loving experience of the body, including sexuality, as a literal manifestation of divine creation.
*Relationships with family, friends, and community that recognize the spiritual unfolding of others as the highest value (even when we may still be compromised by personal needs and attachments from fully supporting this value).
*A positive and life-affirming spiritual philosophy that explains why we are here, the goal and purposes of life and the world, the nature and principles of divine law, our rightful place in the scheme of things, and the spiritual significance of birth, development, vocation, marriage, children, relationships, illness, suffering, death, and the nature of sin and evil.
*Connection to a community of worshippers with shared values, shared works, and loving relationships.
*Skepticism, objectivity, and balance to keep one foot in the real world and to recognize the real and ever-present dangers on the spiritual path (e.g., religious abuse, addiction, self-deception, dependence).

Having addressed the spiritual nature of emotional problems, psychiatric disorders, and healthy functioning, it is time now to address the spiritual experience of psychotherapy.

CHAPTER NINE

A PSYCHOSPIRITUAL MODEL OF PSYCHOTHERAPY

HEALING: GENERAL PRINCIPLES

Across time and tradition, from ancient shamanic remedies to the latest medical advances, healing is about restoring balance. Regardless of the historical era and its philosophy of illness, healing techniques generally involve physical, psychological, community, and spiritual processes. In this discussion, the physical sphere is deferred to the established principles of both traditional and non-traditional medicine (i.e., western, eastern, herbal, and manipulative).

Restoring the balance at the psychological level means healing individual emotional wounds, improving coping skills, promoting balance among the various needs and functions of the psyche, and nurturing the natural experience of joy and love, the psyche's greatest healing gifts. As we have seen, the most serious psychological cause of emotional problems involves wounds to the true self. When this self is not valued, when its essential needs for love, safety, security, and creative expression are insufficiently met, or when the lawfulness unfolding of its own nature is denied, then wounding or damage takes place in the psyche. The individual concludes, "I cannot be who I really am" and the magic germ of self is relegated to the darkness of the unconscious where its growth is stunted or distorted until reclaimed.

Psychological wounding is not the same as damage. Wounding produces emotional pain, for we hurt deeply when the fundamental needs of the self are rejected. Damage, however, occurs when the wounding is so profound or pervasive that the normal structures of personality cannot to develop or form in distorted ways. Both wounding and damage limit the individual's capacity to meet and balance the psyche's needs in relationships, sexuality, work, play, exercise, creativity, and spirituality.

Healing also requires restoring an individual's relationship to community, for illness and psychological suffering have social roots as well. Lack of meaningful community identity, value, and role leave people feeling lonely, unimportant, or estranged. Everyone needs to belong to the human family. When we believe that there is no love or place for us, the true self slips insidiously into depression, despair, and alienation. A community that includes all members, values and supports every voice and gift, makes opportunities for truth telling and self-examination, and knows the essential principles of service and social justice - this is a community that can heal itself when wounds occur. When these fundamental skills are absent, then wounds to the community fester in symptoms of poverty, violence, uselessness, loneliness, illness, ethnic tension, and disparate social castes.

Restoring health in the spiritual sphere occurs at individual and community levels. The individual finds a relationship with the sacred along the continuum of religion, spirituality, and mysticism described earlier. The community finds relationship to the sacred through religious ritual and celebration. Collective activities hold the community together in a common experience that connects everyday and sacred realities. In religious ceremony and ritual, temporal and eternal, personal and universal, meet (at least temporarily) in a healing unity that transcends individual or secular approaches. Religion can also confront the community's social conscience, urging it to face and heal individual and community wounds.

Traditionally, psychotherapy has operated primarily at the psychological level, restoring emotional balance within and between individuals and their families. It has not addressed either community or spiritual wounds beyond encouraging alienated people to seek a relationship to community or making spiritually relevant suggestions or referrals (e.g., join a church, see your clergy). There are times, as we have seen, when psychotherapy can and should open itself to the spiritual sphere. To do so, however, we need to consider the range of healing forms and methods practiced across traditions and continents.

HEALING FORMS

The forms of psychological and spiritual healing are legion and range from exquisitely simple to remarkably complex. Their breadth, variety, richness, and power in healing human pain and suffering are illustrated in the twenty types noted below. The success of each type depends on the provider's consciousness, intentionality, and skill. Although some may seem alien or unfamiliar to therapists, each can be an effective component of a spiritual psychotherapy, and each can be misused and abused.

HEALING FORMS

Psychological Healing	Spiritual Healing
touch	shamanism
caring	sacred places, forces, & objects
hope	spiritual touch
placebo	prayer
relaxation	faith healing
meditation	meditation & contemplation
hypnosis	ritual
counseling	spiritual teachers
psychotherapy	psychic counseling
	pastoral counseling
	spiritual direction

Of the twenty types of healing, four are particularly pertinent to the goals of psychospiritual integration in the west: counseling, psychotherapy, pastoral counseling, and spiritual direction. A discussion of the remaining types and their potential contribution to a spiritually oriented psychotherapy can be found in Appendix E.

COUNSELING

To the sequence of increasing complex forms of psychological healing noted above, counseling and psychotherapy contribute the additional elements of scientific knowledge and guidance. Counseling seeks to improve the psychological functioning of an individual, marriage, or family through teaching, caring, guidance, and communication. Tending to be problem-centered, time-limited, supportive, and often directive, the goal of counseling is to help the individual relieve situational distress and improve adaptive functioning.

PSYCHOTHERAPY

Psychotherapy generally involves a more depth-oriented and concerted focus on the wounds and damage affecting the individual psyche. It seeks to uncover and heal the original emotional injuries and ameliorate their harmful impact in the personality. In contrast to counseling, psychotherapy tends to be personality-centered, longer term, and focuses on the client's experience of the therapy relationship as a healing and corrective process. Moving from symptoms to their causes in deep personality wounding or damage, psychotherapy is more intensive and intrapsychic than counseling, aiming at the roots of suffering rather than their expression in everyday problems. The training of counselors and therapists differs too, with greater education and personal psychotherapy generally expected from long term psychotherapists.

There are many schools and forms of counseling and psychotherapy, including behavioral, cognitive, and psychoanalytic, and many offshoots to each. Medically oriented psychiatric treatment provides additional modalities, including medication and hospitalization.

PASTORAL COUNSELING

With the arrival of institutional religion came specific forms of spiritual guidance based upon them. Pastoral counseling is one example. Typically conceived as a ministerial function, pastoral counselors are ministers (or selected lay people endorsed by a religious faith group) who acquire additional training in psychology and psychotherapy. Drawing from the wisdom, resources, and authority of the particular religious tradition and the tools of psychological counseling, they seek to provide integrated spiritual and mental health service to help people in difficult times. Often the aim is to reconcile an individual's personal suffering or questions with the tenants of ultimate meaning embodied in the faith, addressing specifically religious issues such as meaninglessness and suffering, disobedience and sin, faith and doubt, illness and death, and pride and humility. Merging sacramental and therapeutic acts, pastoral counseling may also employ confession, absolution, spiritual guidance, and even faith healing.

SPIRITUAL DIRECTION

Usually associated with a specific religious tradition, spiritual direction is a specialized form of spiritual guidance. The Spiritual Director, who may or may not be a formally trained cleric, and his directee typically meet once every four to six weeks, far less frequently than is customary in psychological approaches. Their sessions focus on the directee's experiential relationship to God in the present moment, and on discerning how God is acting and moving in his interior and exterior life. Together they seek to become open to the presence of God in the directee's prayer experiences, relationships, work, problems, and life decisions. In essence, both parties seek to understand the unfolding mystery of the God's actions and desires in the life of the directee.

Spiritual Direction is not intended to be practical problem-solving, psychological counseling, psychotherapy, moral or theological advice, penance or confession, or friendship. Rather, spiritual direction is meant to be a prayerful, reverential, and personalized exploration of the directee's first hand religious experience in which God acts as the ultimate Spiritual Director.

PSYCHOTHERAPY, SPIRITUALITY, AND MEDICINE: CONTRASTS AND INTEGRATION

No healing specialty can do it all. Rather than place psychology, spirituality, and medicine in competition, it is far more appropriate to compare and contrast their capabilities, and then to explore how they might be most skillfully integrated.

Psychological healing approaches have historically ignored the individual's need for a spiritual life. Reducing healing to a scientific and technical process, traditional psychotherapy under-utilizes the powerful ingredients of faith, prayer, and grace, as well as the whole gamut of spiritual healing forms and methods. Spiritual approaches, on the other hand, often overlook the hidden or potential psychopathology of both client and healer, and fail to assess the empirical efficacy of the healing practice. Medical approaches tend to incorporate psychological and spiritual principles without knowing it (Appendix), so they are used haphazardly and below their full potential.

Simply mixing psychological, spiritual, and medical techniques, however, is not necessarily the answer. A supermarket approach to healing, which borrows eclectically from many traditions without deep and extensive training in any, runs the risk of superficiality, incoherence, misapplication, and internal contradiction. The decision to integrate spirituality and psychotherapy, for example, is not an all-or-nothing choice; it actually represents a continuum of choices ranging from pure non-spiritual psychotherapy to pure spirituality. This continuum is displayed below:

It can readily be seen from the Integration Continuum that a therapist has a range of choices in matters of religion and spirituality, from denying them altogether, discussing them as client concerns, actively inquiring into the client's spiritual's life and subjective spirituality, or actually inviting the sacred into the hour itself. It is anticipated that interested therapists will explore this continuum gradually, moving from left to right as experience, knowledge, comfort, and confidence grow.

THE INTEGRATION CONTINUUM

Spiritually Resistant Psychotherapy	Spiritually Receptive Psychotherapy	Spiritually Active Psychotherapy	Spiritually Experiential Psychotherapy	Pure Spirituality in Psychotherapy
No interest in client's spirituality, referral to clergy; refusal to discuss spirituality	Openness to discuss client's religious and spiritual concerns and experience at client's initiative in the context of psychotherapy	Interested inquiry by therapist into client's religious history and spiritual views (e.g., doing spiritual assess-ment).	Exploration of client's subjective spirituality,(e.g., prayer experience, closeness to God)	Being in the Spiritual Dimension with the client; exploring God's presence and impact in the therapy hour.

A PSYCHOSPIRITUAL MODEL OF THERAPY

Among all my patients in the second half of life - that
is to say over thirty-five - there has not been one whose
problem in the last resort was not that of finding a
religious outlook on life. It is safe to say that every one of
them fell ill because he had lost that which the living
religions of every age have given their followers, and
none of them has been really healed who did not regain
his religious outlook.

Carl Jung

Drawing on our previous discussion of the psychospiritual nature of personality, its evolution over the life span, and the development of emotional problems and disorders, a psychospiritual model of psychotherapy can now be formulated. Its task is to heal emotional wounds, access and nourish the client's true self, initiate the spiritual journey, and provide tools of discernment and guidance along the way. In this model, therapy would address the following stages and tasks:

PSYCHOLOGICAL PHASES

STABILIZATION

An individual, overwhelmed by emotional pain or dysfunction, cannot do the deep work of spiritual psychotherapy. The therapist's first task, therefore, is the stabilization and alleviation of acute distress. Active counseling, reduction of life stresses, and occasional medication will usually restore the client's ego defenses and coping resources sufficiently to move into psychotherapy proper.

BEGINNING PSYCHOTHERAPY

Most clients come into therapy with little if any vision of the deep work that must be done to heal old wounds and restore the true self. Instruction (with informed consent) about the nature and goals of psychotherapy, therefore, is necessary to provide this vision, though such teaching is best done gradually as the issues unfold in therapy. To do this work, therapists need to be trained in the principles and course of long term therapy.

DISMANTLING THE FALSE SELF

As we have seen, symptoms arise from the our wrong relationship to true self, soul, and the sacred due to our attachment and dependence on the false self. The first task of therapy, therefore, is to dismantle the false self by confronting its defenses (e.g., grandiosity, self-sufficiency, perfectionism) and gently reaching the pain of the betrayed and wounded true self. These injuries of the past must be faced and resolved for therapy to proceed. Rather than seeking only to alleviate the presenting symptom, a client needs to understand its origin and purpose, and then make contact with the true self to the real journey of psychological and spiritual growth.

RESTORATION OF THE TRUE SELF

Nourished by understanding and love, the true self will begin to grow again, unfolding in whatever way is true to its nature and inner lawfulness. The gifts and aptitudes of temperament are also found in the true self; indeed, the true self is the gift. The therapist's role is to help the ego nourish and support the true self rather than suppress or discount it. From the experience of self, a new life is gradually born.

The psychological phases of depth-oriented psychotherapy take much longer than implied in this over-simplified conceptualization. They may occur over several years. But so does the development and cultivation of any great creative talent, and we do not bemoan such sacrifice when the product is worthy. The product of this journey is the infinitely precious art work that is one's life. Then, as therapy proceeds, it moves increasingly into the spiritual phases of this journey.

HEALING EARLY WOUNDS TO SPIRITUAL LONGING

Religious fear, shame, guilt, or misconception are universally present in American culture, crushing or devaluing our inherent spiritual longing. Pride, greed, and materialism distract us further. These obstacles to divine experience, discussed in greater depth in Chapter 14, need to be recognized and progressively eliminated. Identifying them is critical, for many clients not only have little contact with their spiritual longing, they have no idea that it is missing. Obscured by psychological wounding, a client's spiritual longing must be accessed with patience and sensitivity, until it has the strength to function on its own. For those who are ready and interested, healing the wounds to spiritual longing initiates the sacred journey with its intrinsic phases, tasks, and lessons. It should be pointed out that fewer and fewer people reach the advanced stages of psychospiritual transformation but many can appreciate the way and its relevance to their lives. As the chemistry of transformation proceeds, the therapist's role gradually shifts from psychotherapy to spiritual guidance, direction, and initiation.

SPIRITUAL PHASES

OPENING TO SOUL AND SPIRIT

As discussed in Chapter seven, the true self is intimately associated with the soul, for it is the soul's expression in psychological form. Learning to feel and trust the true self brings us into soul, so much so that the line dividing them may eventually become porous or non-existent. The true self is then filled with the energy, excitement, creativity, wonder, and joy of soul. Simply feeling the true self releases these energies which at times seem boundless. The ego, with the therapist's guidance, must learn to express these energies of spiritual incarnation: in the world. In opening to soul, we also learn to act increasingly from its natural center of love and kindness, and discover therein interests, activities, and talents never before expected, leading, in time, to the work of our soul.

The energies of soul naturally bring contact with the divine self, for they resonate with the same essence. This indwelling manifestation of sacred presence and consciousness awaits our loving attention. Here is the inner God in whatever form the individual discovers. It may be experienced as the higher self, intuitive wisdom, a Presence within, or an inner force, personality, or consciousness that is not one's own. We can also develop an awareness of the outer manifestation of spirit with its gentle, accepting, healing, immanent and omnipresent consciousness. Involvement in formal and informal spiritual activities (e.g., contemplation, prayer, ritual, meditation, religious liturgy and service) further develop our skillful awareness of the Divine Being.

DISCERNMENT

The dangers on the spiritual path are everywhere and must be clearly identified (e.g., grandiosity, addiction, abuse, distraction, self-deception). Under the therapist's tutelage, the individual learns to support the soul's growth and its relationship to spirit through discernment skills, discriminating genuine experience of the divine from fantasy, wishful thinking, or misunderstanding. The therapist's task at this point is to blend psychotherapy and spiritual direction in supporting the client's continuous experiential opening to soul, divine self, and Divine Being. Learning to access and trust this process becomes an increasingly important Challenge and theme of the therapeutic endeavor.

A LIVING SPIRITUALITY IN THE TRANSFORMATION OF CONSCIOUSNESS

The impulse to explore one's spirituality and the spiritual meaning of life increases over time, resulting in series of mystical realizations and a progressive transformation of consciousness. For example, understanding that the true self is the soul's psychological nature, that a divine self moves within, that consciousness and the world are pervaded by the divine Presence, and that separate, individual consciousness is an illusion masking one's actual identity with the divine, these realizations awaken a mystical process known to sages throughout time, gradually but literally transforming one's experience of existence. The therapist's role here is to help the client discriminate, understand, and support these developments. One can readily imagine, on the other hand, how the spiritually ignorant therapist might easily pathologize and suppress them.

DEATH OF THE SELF

A time comes when the personal self disappears. Like a blossom, the true self is a beautiful but temporary formation, a gift, but when its nature has been fulfilled, its structure naturally dissolves. The release of the self eventually releases attachment to the self-concept, freeing the individual to more directly experience mystical awareness without concern for reputation or security. Gradually soul and divine self merge to become the source, flow, and nature of one's actions. The ego's task at this stage is to surrender its control of consciousness to this indwelling unfolding of God, welcoming and embodying the subsequent transformation of purpose and personality. Becoming increasingly what God is (i.e., consciousness, love, freedom, and joy), we also long to awaken this same consciousness in others. In time personal individuality no longer matters, for it was a passing reflection of the whole. Now one is the whole. Again, a therapist unfamiliar with the natural and progressive death of self will fail to support the rare client that comes this far.

THE FLOW OF GOD

With consciousness radically transformed, the enterprise of life moves with a different cadence, or perhaps more accurately, without a cadence: as silence within chaos, as timelessness within time, as love within all experience. With no individual self, there is nothing to be, lose, or defend, and one is radically open to the revelation of sacred Consciousness and Being everywhere. The world is seen afresh as the continuous creation of the living, breathing, divine cosmos. Life is now an act of communion, reverence, wonder, and celebration, literally moved and filled by the flow of God.

THE VAGARIES OF SPIRITUAL GROWTH

Though this series of healing and transformative stages may sound easy, it is anything but. We go forward, make gains, and then, terrified by the changes asked of us, beat a hasty retreat to the familiar confines of the false self. Spirituality is wonderful as long as home, job, spouse, family, income, self-esteem, and body are secure. When this base is threatened, spiritual growth may be quickly abandoned in heroic efforts to restore security. Yet when security is restored, we realize that something more important was lost. Little by little, in this back and forth process, we yield our attachments to things, people, and security and begin instead to trust the buoyancy of the divine sea to hold and see us through. But keep in mind that nobody does this perfectly and everyone spends much of their lives in resistance. Nonetheless, surrender, dissolution, reunion await us all and whenever we release ourselves, the journey moves forward. This becomes the teaching and experience of spiritual psychotherapy.

By now, the healthy skeptic should be asking, "Does therapy or anyone, for that matter, really experience these stages?" "Do I actually have an inner divine self and can I really know the Presence directly?" "Why would anyone want to go through the death of self?" "How do we know any of this for sure?" Such questions are relevant and deserve concrete and practical answers.

Most depth therapists will recognize the general validity of the psychological stages described in this model and intuitively appreciate that they do not necessarily occur as a simple linear sequence "in real life." A model is an abstraction, not a prescription This is even more true for the spiritual stages which are significantly more subtle and fluid. Moreover, the subjective discrimination of spiritual energies and states, involves changes in consciousness that are easily missed, minimized, or dismissed by people who are busy, distracted, or skeptical.

Nor does this gradual opening of consciousness mean that all problems from earlier psychological stages are fully and completely resolved. On the contrary, conflicts associated with our earliest wounding, though much reduced in the psychological sphere, end up being replayed in our final our relationship with God. We must work them through again this ultimate arena. Here we struggle with the same themes of security, safety, and love in ultimate terms, for here we must face the final transformation of body, mind, and spirit

How do we know any of this for sure? In the spiritual journey, each must answer this question individually - carefully exploring the very phenomenology of existence to know for sure.

CONCLUSIONS

Spiritually oriented psychotherapy takes us into our deepest wounding but then adds the powerful ingredients of soul, divine self, Divine Being, spiritual practice, and mystical experience to the healing mix. The idealized series of stages described above can take a lifetime, many lifetimes, an eternity, and must be understood, cultivated, guided, and awaited. A psychotherapy that truly seeks to grow and liberate people from suffering must know the whole path, and a therapist interested in pursuing a spiritual psychotherapy must take the journey himself - as far as possible.

A spiritually oriented psychotherapy, therefore, utilizes insights and tools from humankind's timeless religious journey, but in an inclusive and psychologically sophisticated manner. It addresses both the client's evolving personal beliefs and the archetypal structures that inform them found in the perennial religious traditions. But healing includes more than client and therapist alone, for it specifically invites the sacred into the consulting room and into the work of therapy. Finally, spiritual psychotherapy encourages the client to find his own personally meaningful spiritual awareness and life journey. Not surprisingly, this is a model that will appeal to those whose interests and temperament naturally draw them to the sacred.

To summarize and further conceptualize the integration of psychological and spiritual methodologies, we return to the Ego-Soul Matrix.

THE EGO-SOUL MATRIX IN PSYCHOSPIRITUAL HEALING

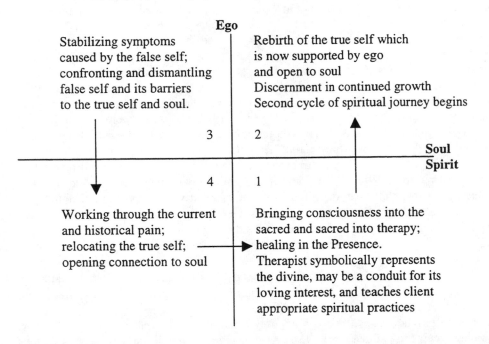

Ego

Stabilizing symptoms caused by the false self; confronting and dismantling false self and its barriers to the true self and soul.	Rebirth of the true self which is now supported by ego and open to soul Discernment in continued growth Second cycle of spiritual journey begins
3	2

Soul
Spirit

4	1
Working through the current and historical pain; relocating the true self; opening connection to soul	Bringing consciousness into the sacred and sacred into therapy; healing in the Presence. Therapist symbolically represents the divine, may be a conduit for its loving interest, and teaches client appropriate spiritual practices

Psychotherapy typically begins in quadrants 3 or 4. Emotional symptoms and dysfunctionality caused by the false self organization or its breakdown bring the client into therapy to locate and work through the pain of the abandoned true self. Therapy seeks to dismantle the false self (quadrant 3) and reclaim and heal the true self (quadrant 4). As self opens to soul, one is drawn into the sacred (quadrant 1) where healing contact with the divine occurs or can be facilitated. At times, the therapist embodies the divine through his caring, unconditional love, acceptance, forgiveness, and blessing. At other times, the therapist acts as spiritual guide, director, or teacher assisting the ego's opening of personal consciousness to the divine. Eventually touched, nourished, and healed by the divine in one way or another, the client naturally moves back into the world (quadrant 2), expressing his true self and soul this time with the support of an educated and compassionate ego. As we will see later, this journey continues through a second spiritual cycle which involves giving up the true self.

Quadrant 1, then, is the healing spiritual domain missing since psychology's split with religion. The archetypal structure illustrated by the Ego-Soul Matrix locates and legitimizes the place of spirituality in the healing journey. The therapist directs the psychological work of quadrants 3 and 4 and then guides the client into the spiritual dimension of quadrant 1 where God moves the work. Formally and explicitly restoring the sacred to the healing process gives the therapist the courage and vision to develop his role and skills in this realm, and to integrate them into his existing psychotherapy practice (e.g., as guide, spiritual director, teacher).

THE SACRED NATURE OF PSYCHOTHERAPY

In its origins and core, psychotherapy has always been a sacred process. A spiritually oriented model of psychotherapy simply seeks to return to this foundation.

Even the etymology of our professional language reveals the hidden spiritual meanings behind the practice of psychotherapy. The word psyche is Greek for soul, and "ology" incorporating the Greek word logos, means thought. Blending these word roots, Hillman translates psychology as "reason or speech or intelligible account of soul" (Hillman, 1985). Therapy comes from the Greek therapeia, which means support and caring, but in the religious context of early Greece, it may also have meant "service to the gods," or "doing the work of the gods" (Houston, 1987). When we combine these roots of our modern term psychotherapy, we see that it originally meant "to serve soul" (Hillman, 1975).

Psychotherapy, then, goes beyond fixing, treating, or healing emotional problems; in its ancient etymology, it is about facilitating the divine principle, the "work of the gods," to serve the individual's soul. The Jungians often refer to psychotherapy as "soul-making," a reference borrowed from the poet John Keats who described the secret purpose of the world as "the vale of soul-making." (Hillman, 1985). This original connection between psychological healing and spirituality is thus secretly and wonderfully maintained in the professional words we use everyday.

The sacred nature of psychotherapy is further evident in the religious assumptions thoroughly embedded in its original form. While the essence of psychotherapy derives from the simple act of one person sharing sorrow, guilt, fear, or suffering with another, it was always more than that, for our ancestors were also very religious. The ancients viewed the entire cosmos, animate and inanimate, as full of spirits and spiritual laws. Personal suffering shared in this context is saturated with spiritual meaning. Suffering arises from violating the sacred order, and healing involves atonement for such wrongdoing and disrespect. From this original experience emerged the basic rituals of confession, atonement, and absolution. Imbued from the start with such fundamental spiritual meaning, this basic and beautiful act of sharing pain with another is naturally and inherently religious. In the archetypal ground, it is holy.

Indeed, modern psychotherapy, though seemingly cleansed of such prescientific spirituality, actually continues to embody, albeit covertly, the original ritual-symbolic process of its religious ancestry, for it cannot truly be separated from its archetypally sacred nature without losing its meaning and effectiveness. The basic task of psychotherapy is still to create a sacred space for the client to reveal his suffering. The therapist, as witness to this confession, unknowingly serves as the representative of the holy to whom the client has come in search of healing. Like a member of an unseen clerical order, the therapist prescribes the necessary acts of atonement (e.g., confession, catharsis, forgiveness) that restore the sufferer's relationship with the underlying divine order (in modern parlance, the unconscious or emotions). Consistent with this congruence of religion and psychotherapy, the client must be sincere in his self-examination, wish for healing, and reparations to be released from his suffering. It is also understood that all suffering cannot be relieved, for some is necessary for our personal and spiritual growth.

The psychotherapy client tells his story in order to understand its personal and universal significance. At the personal level, he hopes that telling his story will somehow reveal the nature, source and cure of his distress. As his pain is discharged through the therapeutic acts of confession, catharsis, and forgiveness, the individual story reveals a larger, universal and spiritual one, for every seemingly pedestrian biography is actually filled with mythic significance. This archetypal epic, various labeled the Hero's Journey (Campbell, 1949) or the "Story of Everyman" (Robinson, 1995), teaches that profound spiritual meaning lies behind the stages and struggles of the life journey. This deep, inborn sequence of experiential stages uses the client's life circumstances and his story as a theater for the unfolding of his soul. Omnipresent in this story is the Divine Being and the sacred order of life.

The universal story also secretly encodes a symbolic description of a healing journey home. We learn that our pain drove us from the original sacred oneness, and that we created a personal story of suffering or victimization to cope with it. Our desire to fix this pain further distracts us from the imminent divine present, and we travel years trying to fix ourselves instead of becoming conscious. We need to tell that story in psychotherapy in order to heal the pain it carries. With no more historical pain to build a personal story on, we re-discover sacred reality and the original mystic consciousness of our ancestors. Most psychotherapy clients miss this step into the spiritual-archetypal dimension, for their therapists have also missed it. It is for the therapist to lift the veil of ignorance, illuminate the sacred story, and, with eyes of faith, show the healing self the sacred nature of the world.

The therapist's goal is to attend to the client's soul in its journey of transformation. The therapist is, in Campbell's words, the doctor of the soul (Campbell, 1949) who helps the client discover how he betrayed his divine origins. In this process, the client recovers his original self and its relationship to his own soul, opens to his own divine nature, and discovers a mystical connection to the ultimate that radically changes his perception of the world and his place it. In this larger context, psychotherapy is truly a profound and sacred undertaking.

One of the most important parts of this healing process is the therapist, whose person and functions are critical to the cure. The spiritual psychotherapist must be an individual whose training and philosophy embrace not only the traditional diagnostic and treatment skills of his trade, but also the universal concepts and practices of the religious arts. As a person, he must have taken his own sacred journey, first because he must know the territory, for a guide can only take a client as far as his own first hand experience, second because his own journey is in fact an initiation into the spiritual realm, and third because he must be deepened and leavened as a person to do this kind of work. A therapist closed to his own divine evolution will be equally closed to that of his client. The therapeutic initiation he offers also serves the spiritual unfolding in his own life, for there is no resting or sitting still for long in this work.

Like the shaman, the therapist must also be willing to take on the client's pain. He must be able to feel it, bear it, and relive the same kinds of experiences from his own life. Known clinically as projective identification, the therapist accepts and holds within himself the traumatic emotions that the client is not yet strong enough to feel. Like a tuning fork, the therapist vibrates with this dissociated pain as his own experience. At times confusing and uncomfortable, this process is unavoidable and skillful therapists learn to use it. Like the shaman, the therapist lets this material into his own soul and holds it until the client is capable of feeling it directly. Finally, the therapist must be willing to be real and to be touched by the client as a real person. It was the human relationship that produced psychological wounding in the first place, and it is only the human relationship that can bring healing. The "I-Thou" encounter is itself a deeply sacred meeting (Buber, 1966).

Psychotherapy is ultimately meant to restore our relationship to the divine world and the soul in a conscious, immediate, experientially undeniable, and life-enhancing way. It is not enough to relieve distress, the therapist's task is also to awaken the unconditional, immeasurable, and sacred experience of life along with all its untapped potentials in each person. We are meant to be so much more, for there is something divine in each person that seeks expression and the whole process of living is itself a divinely directed experience of transfiguration. The therapist's spiritually centered presence becomes an all-embracing love and silent ongoing prayer for this work. It recognizes the urgency of the soul's yearning to grow, dance, learn, love, and know what it is made of and from where it came. Asking for divine guidance, the therapist also trusts that the client's material will reveal the needs and directions of his soul, for the soul knows far more than the therapist where the healing will be found.

At the highest level, psychotherapy teaches us about healing the world. The most threatening problems in the world today are man made: violence, poverty, hatred, starvation, unemployment, violence, population, and war. Learning to live beyond the false self's greed and to love without condition from the soul are two of the sacred tasks of life and psychotherapy. This is the medicine the world perennially needs to heal its illusion of separateness and the warfare that results from it. The always existent, indestructible Presence - which so many religions teach is man's essential nature beneath the disturbances of mind and emotion - is itself enough. Competition ends when this existence is known. Then God is found to be the energy, the motive, the origin, and the experience of life, and everything we do becomes a sacred act. The ultimate purpose of psychotherapy is to heal our capacity to see and know this reality. This kind of healing heals our world.

As split parts of a common shamanic ancestor, therapist and priest mirror each other in serving the same divine order. Our tools are merely different words for an identical process of growth and transformation. The sacred nature of psychotherapy reveals that we are psychologists and priests both. Finally, consistent with this conceptualization, it can be argued that psychotherapy embodies within its secular forms the powerful dynamics of the ancient Vision Quest, a ritual journey of profound transformation practiced by indigenous peoples. The similarities between psychotherapy and Vision Quest are described in Appendix F.

The Metaphysics of Spiritual Psychotherapy: Facilitating the Divine Principle

Spiritually oriented psychotherapists usually have an implicit model of therapy that combines traditional treatment theories and methods with a more or less developed metaphysical or spiritual orientation. It is an orientation that arises from the therapist's own firsthand experiences with spiritual paths and practitioners, and, in this day and age, may draw selectively from diverse spiritual traditions. The therapist's orientation typically involves beliefs, values, and attitudes regarding the spiritual nature and purposes of life and reality, and encompasses many or most of the following themes and beliefs.

Spiritually oriented psychotherapists usually believe in a purposeful and loving universe. This faith assumption implies that our lives and our problems are neither accidental nor insignificant, but reflect the meaningful operation of invisible forces, laws, and agents working for the benefit of the universe and all sentient beings. It specifically implies the existence of an intelligence, higher than man's, that resides in (or as) the universe, and is responsible for it. This power created humankind, is concerned for its welfare, and somehow takes part in every life.

A related belief held by spiritually oriented psychotherapists is that life on earth is "intended" for man's spiritual growth and maturation. This implies that we are here to learn about fundamental spiritual laws and values concerning existence, love, responsibility, the consequences of behavior, and higher states of consciousness. The problems in our lives arise from and illustrate these fundamental principles. Part of this belief asserts that the universe works in non-linear as well as linear cause-and-effect ways. In non-linear causation, events that may seem unrelated with respect to material laws are profoundly connected by spiritual laws. This assumption, known as synchronicity, implies that things happen "for a reason," that they are causally associated with our thoughts, feelings, intentions, behavior, higher needs, and those of others. This kind of causality is meant to teach us something about ultimate spiritual truths.

It is further assumed that if one ignores spiritual laws, physical, psychological, and somatic consequences will follow. There is a unity of world, psyche, soma, and spirituality that affects the individual, his illness, and his healing, and we must learn to recognize, honor, and submit to this unity to be healthy and have a healthy world. In line with ancient shamanic beliefs, it is further assumed that suffering and illness follow from our misalignment with the spiritual realm, creating a " spiritual disorder" which must be identified and corrected. It is further understood that healing and transformation flow directly from contact with the transpersonal dimension.

The purpose of a spiritually oriented psychotherapy, therefore, is not just to relieve symptoms, but also to find their spiritual purpose and significance. In this framework, relief may at times be secondary to discovering the goal of the symptoms, particularly when a client's complaints are unrelenting. The therapist helps the client discern and understand the spiritual nature of his personal problems, and therapy moves from the psychological to the spiritual plane by asking questions that shift its focus. Can the client feel or notice the presence, grace, or calling of God in his difficulties? Can he ask the spiritual universe for help and direction, and learn to listen within and without for its response and guidance? Can he learn to live more fully and reverentially in the presence of the holy, surrendering his need for control or understanding? What fears get in the way?

One of the greatest tasks of the therapist is facilitating or activating the client's indwelling divine principle. He begins with the basic assumption that the divine is trying to express its nature and will in the client's life. At the spiritual level, the client's problems follow from conflict between false self and soul, that is, between the desires and motives of the conscious, socially conditioned self and the divine within. The client needs to notice, listen, trust, and respond in increasingly sensitive and meaningful ways to the subtle whisperings of his own soul. Part of this task requires identifying his resistance and distrust, that is, the many ways he discounts, betrays, devalues, or ignores his own spiritual experience.

The therapist must also trust the operation of the divine principle. While he can know a great deal about the psychological origin and causes of his client's emotional symptoms, he cannot assume he knows its ultimate purpose in the cosmic mind. Knowing that the spirit is working everywhere, in every minute, awakening his consciousness even as he reflects on it in the therapy hour, a therapist must learn to wait, trust, and watch. It is there. A profound shift in awareness gradually takes place for the spiritually oriented psychotherapist. Although traditional methods of diagnosis and treatment are available and utilized, the therapist also keeps his attention prayerfully, reverentially, and receptively open to the presence and will of God - in himself, in the client, and in the dynamics of the hour. Even more profoundly, he recognizes that somewhere deep in the therapeutic process, God, not the therapist, is in charge. The therapist's goal is to seek attunement with this divine Presence.

The value of reverential silence, of going within to pray and listen, is an element of this work far more familiar to clergy than psychotherapists. If we are to help our clients experience the divine consciousness and intelligence living in the center of their interior darkness, this inner awareness must become an integral part of therapy . Prayer, for example, is often misunderstood by our clients, who either discredit it as useless or over simplify it as simply petitioning for solutions to life problems. Prayer is, in fact, one of the most important ways we make direct contact with the sacred Presence. It is a learned skill, an art, a sanctuary, a source of strength, and an opening to God's action in our lives. Despite its ancient origins and natural existence as an inborn human faculty, prayer represents an untried medium for the vast majority therapists who believe it is outside their professional province.

Finally, spiritually oriented psychotherapists often assert that healing may involve methods beyond those of traditional psychological practitioners, including any and all of the spiritual healing modalities listed earlier. This is perhaps the most controversial and taboo area, with few therapists speaking directly or honestly about their use of such nontraditional activities. In their beliefs and methodologies, therefore, spiritual psychotherapy may go beyond conventional treatment. Though spiritual practices are never forced or required of the client, prayerful discernment regarding the client's readiness and need may lead the therapist to invite discussion of them and assess the results.

Myths from around the world explain that we are spiritually wounded, that once we had a connection to the divine realm that has been lost. We are separated from the divine and injured in our capacity to know the sacred now, here, directly. It is said that God did not leave man, man left God by asserting his own personality and its willfulness. Overcoming the barrier of a separate personality becomes the highest work of a spiritually oriented psychotherapy. This is the great step beyond traditional psychotherapy;- moving from an egoic, self-centered orientation to one based on the soul's unending journey into the divine. The whole enterprise of psychotherapy is about healing the pain in our stories so that the false self and false cultural beliefs about the nature of existence no longer control our seeing. In the ending of time and story, we return to our sacred origins and a new principle for living (Robinson, 1995).

The inner and outer events of life are the workings of this divine principle. The therapist can learn to see problems in this way and serve as a witness to the client's struggle, so that the client, too, can learn to see through the eyes of faith.

PART THREE

THE SOUL OF SPIRITUAL PSYCHOTHERAPY: EXPERIENCES IN THE CONSULTING ROOM

Dear God,
   Answer me this,
   did we have some pre-arranged agreement,
   grounded in confidence?
   Based on the idea that we would never forget each other?
   Were we so close that we dared the cosmos
   and laughed at the possibility of separation,
   even for a moment?

   Well I tell you this,
   if you exist at all,
   I cannot remember your face now.
   I search open dusty trails for your footsteps,
   and do not find them.
   I watch the wind as it moves through the trees,
   looking for you in the spaces.
   I listen for sounds just beyond my hearing,
   hoping to hear your voice again.
   Just to hear you take one breath would last me a lifetime.
   There is a place just beyond the breaking of my heart
   that calls to you.
   I cannot find you now.
   It is only the ache of my longing
   that tells me
   that you ever existed at all.

   Were we so sure,
   so in love,
   so whole,
   so complete,
   that we took the bet?

                                    Rob Allbee

Rob Allbee's poem poignantly expresses the reality and power of spiritual longing. A relentless hunger, it guides us like salmon or migrating birds to the source of our longing. Part III explores this subjective reality as I experience in my therapeutic work and as it has touched the lives of those I have known personally and professionally. The section concludes with suggestions for clients on the varieties, goals, and selection criteria for various spiritually oriented growth formats.

CHAPTER TEN

SPIRITUALITY IN THE CONSULTING ROOM - PERSONAL REFLECTIONS

Content: My experience of spirituality as a therapist
The spirituality of psychotherapy
Functioning as a spiritual psychotherapist
Personal assumptions about the spiritual dynamics of therapy
and healing
The ultimate philosophy underlying my work

It is early one spring morning. I sit in my spacious office which is the living room in an old home renovated for psychotherapists. It is a large, comfortable, inviting room, tastefully (but not extravagantly) decorated, with high ceilings, indirect lighting, a fireplace, and curved windows. A frog motif runs through the art and miniatures, subtly reflecting themes of transformation experienced in my own midlife dreams. Morning light streams through the corner window, dancing with the percolating coffeepot. I am the first one in the building.

In this reflective moment, I find myself musing on my experience of spirituality in psychotherapy. What *is* spiritual about this work? How do I function as a spiritual psychotherapist and what are my assumptions about the metaphysics that underlie this work? As I quietly contemplate these questions, responses coalesce naturally from within. Such questions and replies are the footprints of my own inner journey. This Chapter contains a sampling of personal intuitions, attitudes, and experiences on being a spiritual psychotherapist. May they inspire the reader to trust the same inner well of spiritual knowing.

MY EXPERIENCE OF SPIRITUALITY AS A THERAPIST

I love this work and the people who come into it. This basic and unconditionally loving attitude creates an unspoken atmosphere of welcome, support, and safety. It is a spiritual orientation of valuing each person who enters into this process and into my life as a therapist. Here, too, I can express the inborn kindness, caring, encouragement, and appreciation central to my spiritual nature (for those familiar with the Myers-Briggs Type Inventory, I am an INFP), which is naturally and compassionately tuned into the feeling nature of human experience. I am also grateful for having done my own personal psychotherapy over the years, which allowed me to find this warm and spiritual home in myself.

And if I go deeper into this theme, I know profoundly that the room itself is full of spirit, of sacred being, and that I can call on this greater intelligence throughout the therapy hour. I am not distracted by this "other", but gently feel its presence in the room - an invisible sea of divine being, of infinitely loving consciousness always in and around us. Contact with this Presence evokes feelings of joy, wonder, serenity, and love in me, and sometimes an ecstasy too big to stay with. I often wish I could share this experience with my clients to soften their fear-driven belief that life is essentially hardship, scarcity, loneliness, and danger. I know it would be misunderstood too early in therapy. Sometimes I share it later when people are ready.

The next realization I have is that I am more than a professional psychologist; in a most ancient way, I am a healer, shaman, initiator, and guide. These archetypes are inherently spiritual, and I feel their mystical energies. Well-worn clinical skills and experiences are not forgotten; but they are imbued with a kind of energy and perceptivity. A spiritually oriented psychotherapy brings therapist and client alike into the great religious journey of life. Though most have lost sight of this principle in their lives, it operates nonetheless and will operate better when consciously understood. As a "doctor of the soul," I love helping people discover their own spirituality, mystical awareness, and whatever religious model fits best, and find that the larger religious life is deeply nourishing to the soul work we do in life and psychotherapy.

This work is my spiritual practice as well. Here I hone my own consciousness, examine the fundamental spiritual principles and realities of people's lives, and learn how to help, love, and serve in the most meaningful ways I can. For me, it has become a calling.

THE SPIRITUALITY OF PSYCHOTHERAPY

What is spiritual about psychotherapy? The whole thing is! Psychotherapy is a sacred mystery in which two miraculous lives are shared with the divine in a way that serves healing, realization, meaning and joy. Honored as a profoundly spiritual endeavor, it is indeed a prayer that transcends the specific theory or techniques of the practitioner.

I believe the work of therapy is spiritual because we are spiritual beings and because the ultimate goals of life are spiritual. We come into this world to know, love, and serve the omnipresent loving consciousness that, moment-by-moment, creates, sustains, and indeed is the entire enterprise of life. Problems that defy the ego cause us to search for deeper spiritual meaning and direction. Psychotherapy is one of the places we can do this with particular sensitivity. As the universal mythology goes, we have forgotten our spiritual nature and part of our life's work is finding it again. When psychology is practiced in this way, it becomes a spiritual discipline.

Psychotherapy becomes more immediately spiritual when we consciously invite the sacred into it. Calling on the divine for guidance, revelation, and blessing during "in-the-trenches" psychological work brings therapy into the spiritual domain and the spiritual domain into therapy. Such prayerful petition is not necessarily an outer act; it need not even include specific words or ritual. It arises from the calling of the heart and the nature of the awakened soul. Whatever happens then is filled with the spirit and the challenge of discernment. We learn that there is, in addition to client and therapist, another in the room with infinitely greater power and perspective. We learn to trust and communicate with that divine reality in ever more personal and meaningful ways.

Deep in its essential nature, therapy is also the teaching of joy lost long ago in the wounds and injuries of childhood. In recovering this original joy, we literally discover our original nature and God's. Joy is one of our birth gifts, and in it we find the unconditional love, freedom, and generosity of God, for God's nature is awakened in joy. In a subtle, gradual, gentle way, psychotherapy acts as a midwife, birthing the joy of an infinitely loving being that heals wounds beyond the reach of any technique. Bringing this joy into the therapy relationship, we bring it into the world.

FUNCTIONING AS A SPIRITUAL PSYCHOTHERAPIST

Most people do not come into therapy to talk about religion, spirituality, mysticism, or metaphysics. These topics inevitably show up, however, in the human need to find the larger meaning of life, particularly our existential crises, personal wounds, and emotional suffering. Whatever breaches the soul opens it to the sacred. Most therapists simply don't identity the spiritual dimension of the presenting problem.

For me personally, integrating spirituality into psychotherapy takes several forms. The first is my own silent, prayer inviting holiness into the work. "God, guide my work today. Help me find what's really important to discuss in each hour. Help me be a good and sensitive therapist." Another form involves asking the client when ready, to explore the personal meaning and role of spirituality in his life and problems. "What is the spiritual nature of your struggle? Where is God in it? What is the spiritual challenge here?" I also ask about the client's spiritual, religious, or metaphysical beliefs to examine their nature and healthiness. Then, as the Integration Continuum illustrate, the client may be encouraged to explore the immediate, first hand, and personal experience of the divine presence. "Can you sense another consciousness in the room? What is it's nature? What do you feel in this Presence? What do you need to say to it? How does the Presence communicate to you? Can you ask it for what you need?"

It is not that I talk about spirituality all the time in therapy. It is especially not about converting, persuading, or convincing anyone of anything. Sometimes spirituality is simply a matter of my own interior openness to the Presence in prayer, sensitivity, and faith. Spiritual consciousness then intermixes, cooperates, and interacts with treatment. I may, for example, feel stuck, distracted, bored, or confused. Perhaps the material a client is presenting feels dead or intellectual, and I begin to ask God how I can bring this hour back to life. Then, while I am in this communion, the client unexpectedly opens to something really meaningful - a tear, a dream, a topic they have been hiding, a feeling about me. Though I can't prove it, I am certain that my dialogue with God is somehow related to this shift, and that my intention, prayer, and concern have affected the therapy process in a spiritual way.

I ask the client what he believes to make his religious orientation more conscious and available. The client's model truly doesn't matter in the beginning. It can be a very personal and idiosyncratic intuition, or a well articulated world religion. Beliefs provide the vessel and the oars to move into spiritual waters. For religious beliefs to be constructive, however one needs to believe in something that is mostly positive. Then, in time, the client begins to sense that the spiritual possibilities of life are miraculous and infinite, and that his original presenting problems mark the beginning of a new phase of spiritual growth rather than irredeemable misfortune.

In discussing the client's beliefs, my purpose is to stir interest, address any harmful misconceptions, and encourage additional points of view. Introducing religious and spiritual ideas from the world's many traditions, for example, may enable the client to reframe his problems in new or spiritually revitalized ways. For example, a client might be encouraged to wonder how his life includes spiritual tasks and processes in addition to the physical and biological ones, to speculate about the higher purposes of life, or to consider the transpersonal nature of consciousness. He might be also encouraged to confront the negative consequences of certain beliefs and practices (e.g., judgmental attitudes, harmful beliefs about guilt, or compulsive religious activities).

For many clients, the final step is to experience the sacred directly. Inviting Spirit into psychotherapy is like being in prayer together. The focus is on a conscious, quiet, peaceful, unhurried, and loving receptivity, allowing both therapist and client a safe and trusting space to contact holiness in the room. In this atmosphere, we explore the subtle and intuitive dimensions of sacred awareness, sensing the Presence that fills the room, offering itself to us and acting through us. Striving to stay consciously open to God and to the offerings of grace through whatever is thought, felt, perceived, or said, and without any pressure to fix, perform, or figure out, I am free to feel and be in God's presence without the burden of goals or tasks.

Surrendering to this greater reality, new ideas and possibilities specifically excluded from a more problem-fixing mentality can emerge. We are opening to something much larger than the ego and its viewpoint; we are consciously and literally opening to God and admitting, in this moment, our total and absolute dependence on his grace. Appreciating the wonder, beauty, and mystery of God's presence in us and in creation, we enter what is essentially a mystical consciousness that includes everything in its field of awareness: this moment, this room, and whatever problems or concerns we have been discussing. When we relax focused attention in this way, our field of consciousness widens: things become brighter, lighter, more distinct, more beautiful, more alive. In this mode of being, one's problems take on a very different kind of existence.

It could further be argued that mystical consciousness experienced in a quiet, prayerful, spiritually focused hour is an opening to eternity itself, with an agenda vastly different from that customarily associated with our everyday ego and its goals. It is an awareness of the presence of God, right now, in this moment, in this world, guiding us always. Such holy experience, outside of time, dissolves our typical encrusted roles and beliefs, melting them in the warmth of divine Presence. We are changed, softened, and awakened in this timeless and hallowed contact.

The mystical consciousness known in this kind of work further teaches that there is a power within and outside the psyche that can be known and trusted, even when everything seems to be going wrong. We learn to experience this power, to open to it, ask for its guidance, and even to regress temporarily into a child-like, wide-eyed innocence in its presence. This is a relationship of naked intimacy, increasing dependence, and, sooner or later, surrender in the service of transformation and renewal, until one's consciousness is literally permeated with the divine. My work as therapist is to support this subtle osmosis until the client can develop the courage and skill to embrace it.

The way I look at a client is also transformed when I move into a spiritual consciousness. Rather than clinically address symptom patterns, diagnoses, intrapsychic conflicts, and repressed emotion, each person is seen in an entirely new light, as a mystery not a disorder, with a divine potential flowering in the depths of his psyche. I listen to the need for eternity living in each soul, and to the individual's longing to know the holiness and mystery hidden everywhere in creation, including his own life and being. It is the soul's health that matters here. My attitude and consciousness change when I see the client as a spiritual being. In the place of a pathologically impaired individual sits a miracle who may teach me more than I teach him. It is the divine we are touching and seeing when we relate in this way.

Regular therapy is not replaced by this orientation, it is nourished and guided by it. We do not abdicate our skills and ethical commitments, we awaken them. The hard work of psychotherapy continues and takes up the great majority of out time, especially in the beginning. But when the client is ready, we offer them this kind of guidance. If they refuse, we honor that refusal, which is often an indication that there is more psychological pain to heal before spirituality can be found. Spirituality cannot and should not be forced. Like love, it is awakened by its own nature and the loving response of another. But this spiritual orientation offers a gift of hope at times when all roads seem to be impassable, and presumes that life changes in its own way when the divine is invited into it.

PERSONAL ASSUMPTIONS ABOUT THE
SPIRITUAL DYNAMICS OF THERAPY AND HEALING

Personal experience has convinced me that the cycle portrayed in the Ego-Soul Matrix occurs repeatedly in the process of therapy. The cultural pressure to achieve a successful or glamorous false self draws us out of touch with soul and spirit (quadrant 3). In fact, clients often come to therapy wanting their false selves fixed or improved. Disconnected from the true self and its grounding in soul, and unguided by the spirit, we all commit so many foolish, misguided, selfish, or harmful acts. The pain they cause, and the inner emptiness of prolonged separation from self, soul, and spirit must be addressed (quadrant 4). In the depths of our suffering, in the humility of our powerlessness and failure, in the total surrender of grief and defeat, we discover there is yet something else holding and sustaining us always - God. In this humble discovery, we are touched by the sacred (quadrant 1) and given new life, hope, and spiritual possibilities.

The sacred is the loving source, sustenance, and nature of life and the cosmos. Our lived relationship with this source is what we call spirituality and from it flows our healing. The therapist understands the journey, makes the diagnoses, dismantles the defenses, and supports the client in the underlying experience of pain - all this is the work of psychotherapy - but it is God that heals and restores life, God that inspires the process, God that forgives our damaging acts, and God that gives life its ultimate meaning, purpose, and hope. Moreover, when we learn to invite God into our work, we start noticing new experiences, possibilities, and Changes neither expected nor planned. Therapy becomes a collaborative experience between therapist, client, and God. A skillful facilitator I may be, but I am neither the healing nor its cause.

Another assumption I have focuses on the essential spiritual nature of the psyche. Divine consciousness, wisdom, and healing are deeply centered in the personality, and flow into us when we need them, when we ask, and when our problems demand God's perspective. But we have to listen, and listening requires skillfulness, spiritual faith, and a coherent belief system. Great pain, heart-felt longing, and profound questions move us into this deep interior, and there we wait for its revelation. Indeed, life is a continuous revelation, but what is it saying to me now? What do these problems mean? How is my life a work in progress in the hands of the Creator? What is God's prayer for me? When we reflect on such ultimate questions, a gentle and persistent knowing rises from the indwelling divine. It is also this consciousness that we enter when we Spirit is invited into the therapy hour.

The order and pace at which problems are worked through in therapy is also structured by the religious strata of the psyche, which regulates the unfolding process of enlightenment throughout the life cycle. Its regulatory function must be respected and understood, for each season and each issue has its purpose and teachings. Introducing ideas out of season will not only fail, but can be harmful and disturbing. Healing, moreover, may not always look like what we want. While the ego believes it knows best, religious traditions around the world recognize this to be one of humankind's great self-deceptions. In faith, we take what God offers and ask humbly, gratefully, and sincerely how it is a sacred teaching, an opportunity, a gift. Even problems are holy, and when we wrestle with them, we are transformed by that very holiness.

Finally, I believe that spirituality is transmitted and awakened in the therapy relationship through an invisible, usually unnoticed energetic process of consciousness. This is not some mysterious ESP or aura reading; practiced therapists know that part of their own inner experience in the therapy hour consists of split off emotions, sensations, and motivations that the client is unable yet to bear. This process is examined consciously by the skillful therapist to understand the client's unconscious experience. What therapists don't realize is that it can also be used in the reverse direction, that is, from therapist to client. Thought, intention, emotion, directed imagination, and prayer as forms of energy can create corresponding forms in the other. In this way, a therapist learns to elevate or awaken the client's awareness, creating a level of consciousness and opportunity in the hour that was not there before. This activity is not intended to manipulate the client toward any particular ends; it serves to awaken his own sacred center of consciousness.

THE ULTIMATE PHILOSOPHY UNDERLYING MY WORK

At the experiential level, integrating spirituality into psychotherapy begins with my own spirituality. As I learn to feel and live in a prayerful openness to God, and trust the loving intentions, guidance, and assistance that come from that source, therapy moves effortlessly and naturally into spiritual dimensions when the time is right.

My spiritual experience of psychotherapy is further enhanced by an awareness of the deep and mirrored symmetry uniting psychology and spirituality. At the highest level, there is no wall between the psychological and the spiritual - they are two sides of a single coin. Spiritual vocabulary is simply a way of referring to the ultimate form and purpose of the universe, and the divine laws and purposes that regulate it, in other words, to the consciousness, mind, and heart of God. Our psychological vocabulary describes the practical and emotional manifestations of spirit in our lives. Unhappiness, distress, and emotional symptoms are our way of knowing that divine laws have been violated, and that our psychological and spiritual work is to restore our relationship to the sacred.

But the symmetry of spirituality and psychology allow me to trust the client's movement into the sacred. It's all sacred. There is no required timing - we'll arrive as consciousness changes. It is a therapeutic mistake, therefore, to push into spiritual talk before the wounds of the self are sufficiently healed, especially with those people who have felt that religious words only strangled their heart and soul. Once emotional injuries are healed, it may take only a few simple questions to move the client into the Presence and initiate his lifelong spiritual journey.

For me personally, the adage "life is a revelation, not a problem to be solved" is central. Every aspect of life represents the omnipresent will of the Creator continuously working itself out in our big and little experiences. We need to ask directly, often, deeply, "Where is God?" and listen to our own knowing. Holiness is everywhere, asking us to see and join it. It is our nature, too. Our greatest challenge is embracing this life as a sacred journey and a Presence, over and over, deeper and deeper, until we become one with its consciousness, will, and love. We cannot know God's infinitely vast and ultimate purpose but we can know that God provides the ultimate meaning and purpose to our individual existence. We must learn and incorporate it.

A second fundamental belief of mine, which is found universally in mystical experience, is that everyone and everything belongs to the universe. Each is inimitable, perfect, beautiful, and infinitely precious. Our greatest failure as people is simply not to fully be what we are. Restricting ourselves with fear, censorship, and invidious compariaos, we are always coming up short. Too often we live others' lives, false lives, lives that are neither our own nor God's, and we forget the gift of divine consciousness that resides inside, that we came into the world bearing. Trying to escape fear, hurt, or loss, we hide in the ego's phony castles: money, popularity, narcissism, or power. Such security is a terrible trade for the incredible and sacred adventure of being.

In the end, one of the central questions addressed in psychotherapy is not one of how to survive intact, with ego enthroned and calling all the shots, but how to let oneself be melted by the intense, sacred, and transforming problems of life. Being good, going to church, saving for retirement, having power, being special, even praying - none of this will prevent this melting. The sacred universe does not honor this self-deception; it will rise up one day to take everything you have (especially all of quadrant 3). Behind the illusory security of supermarkets, sanitized homes, fast food, and the promise of perennial progress, the world remains untamable and beyond control. One may be visited with a death, an accident, a handicapped child, a work failure, a broken heart, a terrible mood. With no permanent escape or solution, the cycle of the Ego-Soul Matrix must be lived consciously and completely.

As Jung said years ago, the religious journey begins with the defeat of the ego as false self, for ego identity is, in the end, a barrier to the divine. Life demands that each of us respond to God's presence and action. We may be moved by desire and enchantment, shaken by fierce winds, and one day forced to surrender totally in the ultimate sacrifice. This is the universal story and the magnificent reality underlying life. This is what it takes to know God. A psychotherapy that recognizes these truths, is one that will support the deepest human transformation of all.

We are formed, permeated, and supported by the conscious divine universe, an enormous and compassionate Being intent on awakening our souls to the infinite wonder, joy, and creativity of existence. Expanding our limited consciousness and fulfilling the divine will within us is an awesome and highly individual project, which an enlightened psychotherapy is ideally suited to support. The great challenge of our time is integrating not just spirituality into psychotherapy, but divine consciousness into personality and life. For this call, psychotherapy can and should be one of many catalysts.

CHAPTER ELEVEN

CASE STUDIES IN PSYCHOTHERAPY AND SPIRITUALITY

One might imagine that spiritual experiences in psychotherapy would be dramatic, "far-out," or extraordinary, like reading auras, channeling past lives, faith healing, other worldly visions or visitations - and perhaps for some people these things happen. On the whole, however, experiences of spirituality in psychotherapy tend to be very ordinary, just as they are in everyday life, for ordinary life is holy. In my practice, spiritual experiences more commonly involve:

* Reflections on the spiritual dimensions of a problem (e.g., an illness, crisis, disappointment)
* Discussion of a dream with spiritual content
* Confronting negative beliefs from a history of religious abuse (e.g., sin, unworthiness, guilt)
* Facing and dismantling addictive religious behavior and its psychological origins
* Finding and reclaiming the true self and its connection to soul
* Struggling to make sense of one's relationship to God
* Entering into Presence in a conscious and deliberate way
* Opening to the mystical nature of the world
* Learning to use ritual to embrace the spirituality of a major life passage
* Spending time in meditative silence or prayer
* Appreciating the significance of profound spiritual events (e.g., Near-Death or mystical experience)
* Understanding the religious archetypes of life
* Discerning whether a religious feeling or intention is egocentric or sacred in origin

The accounts that follow are from everyday folks. Not saints. Not horrendous sinners. Not extraordinary, larger-than-life people. But people I know and clients I have seen. They are stories about life, marriage, struggle, happiness, defeat, and the search for soul, spirit, and mystical consciousness.

"DEATH OF A HERO, BIRTH OF THE SOUL"
JOURNEY THROUGH QUADRANTS 2, 3, AND 4

Jack had worked hard his whole life. He learned this work ethic from his father, who would get up at 4:00 a.m. to do a milk route before going to his regular job as a carpenter. Jack had also learned to be self-reliant. If you wanted something, you went out and earned it yourself. Lawn jobs, paper routes, working with his father. Dad had a temper, too. Especially about work: you didn't want to cross him and you didn't complain. That's just how it was.

Through high school, Jack earned enough to buy his own clothes, extras, and an old clunker to drive. Without the financial means or family support to go to college, he went to work. He found that his outgoing personality, perfectionism, and strong work ethic made him a natural salesman, and he moved rapidly through several companies always winning higher salaries and better perks. Jack finally went to work for a large pharmaceutical outfit, and was promoted steadily until he became manager of the west coast sales division. He directed marketing campaigns, led motivational sales seminars, learned to hire and fire people, and his walls were covered with awards. Jack also found time to go to night school and eventually finished college and an MBA. This was his life: long hours, no complaints, always moving up. He knew the hero mode well. If you had enough ambition, there was nothing that couldn't be done. There was not much time for his wife and family. Still, Jack rationalized, he was supporting them well. He'd make time later when he could slow down and relax.

Somewhere around the age of fifty, things seemed to change. The company was downsizing. Too many middle managers with high salaries. In fact, the salary of a fifty year old manager could now buy two twenty-five year old college graduates. It was affecting profit margins. Rumors circulated that the main office planned to clean some of them out. Get younger guys who were lean, hungry, and less expensive. Sales quotas were also increased and everybody was working harder than ever before. Then the company was sold to a huge conglomerate. Cutting would begin soon at all levels. There would be heads on the line. Nobody was safe. New and even higher sales expectations arrived too, for Jack's company had been purchased to squeeze it for profits. The old guard felt these new quotas were impossible, but nobody could risk complaining. Upper management was clear: if you weren't a team player, maybe you should find another job where you would be happier. The writing was on the wall. Jack cranked himself into high gear.

For three more years he hustled. Six days a week, ten hours a day. Took work home. He wanted to prove he could outperform anyone around him. Yes, he was having some stress symptoms. He'd dream about work all the time and wake up thinking of things he needed to do. More coffee to keep going. A few drinks at night to unwind. It was only for a while. He had to keep up the pace. Fatigue. Tightness in his chest. Irritability. An insidiously growing, hidden fear that he couldn't keep pushing like this. And depression. This isn't how he wanted to live. But he didn't have time to whine about these changes. Hey, life's tough.

It seemed like it couldn't get much worse, and then it did. A new medication was being marketed. The company wanted sales figures way beyond realistic expectations. The experienced sales people knew it couldn't be done. Ever the trooper, Jack set out to do his best. In addition to sales pressures, Jack was also hearing rumors about this new product. There were side effects that hadn't been described. Some people with complicated heath problems had died. Some of the doctors he had known for years were furious. But the company denied any product problems and there were sales goals to meet. So there it was. In addition to his exhaustion, Jack now had a problem with conscience. He had guilty dreams of dying patients. He felt haunted as if he had sold out to the grim reaper. He was tired and something inside was dying. It was too much.

In a staff meeting, the day after a big promotional conference where sales reps were again harangued to increase sales numbers, Jack began to lose it. He blurted out some angry comments about unrealistic goals. For the first time in his life, he felt like killing people and could picture doing it. Agitated and preoccupied, Jack couldn't sleep that night. He actually dreamed of the grim reaper coming to his bed. Later that day, his chest felt tighter and tighter. He knew the symptoms of a heart attack. Feeling feint and shaky, Jack went to an emergency room. Exam and EKG. Thankfully it had not been a heart attack. The doctor suggested it might be stress. Off on another business trip, Jack found himself in a hotel room with an angry colleague who was complaining vehemently about the company. Unable to stand hearing all his own concerns, Jack ran from the room down to the street outside. Even in his agitation, he noticed something strange: people couldn't see him, they walked right through him, he was invisible. Suddenly it occurred Jack that he'd left is body! The next thing he knew, he was back in his room shaking.

Jack went to the company's Employee Assistance Program who referred him to me. The day he told this whole story, he knew he could not go back. He could not support this product and could not keep up this work pace. He broke down. His emotional symptoms, clinical presentation, and psychological test profile indicated a Major Depression. He was far more depressed than he realized. He had been hiding it from himself a long time. Unable to return to work, I put Jack on disability and we began to explore what had really happened to him. All the way back. His Dad. His "no whining" attitude. His strict work ethic. He learned how his own stern, uncompromising, perfectionistic conscience forbid any signs of weakness or need. He had been seriously depressed but couldn't tell a soul. Not even himself. As so often happens in such cases, Jack's body had to speak the truth he couldn't admit. Physical symptoms often carry this extra baggage.

Jack didn't go back to his company. Every time he tried to talk himself into resuming his career there, his depression and stress symptoms returned and escalated. There are some roads you cannot travel twice. This was one of them. So Jack applied for a disability retirement. It took him two more years to finally understand and dismantle his "compulsive warrior" work ethic and uncover the true self he had betrayed most of his life. As he did this, Jack's depression resolved and he began to rediscover what he loved most: people. All along what he had enjoyed most about his work was the people: teaching, mentoring, supervising, caring. Soon, through involvement's in a new church and a community homeless project, Jack found a way to express this love and turn his high level managerial skills to the service of people. He gradually came back to life and described himself as happier than he had ever been before. Jack's conscience was now clear. More importantly, his new volunteer work expressed the love he had always known in his soul. In his work life, love had to be subjugated to productivity; now love was an end it itself.

Then another phase began. Jack told me one day that something new was happening in his life. He and his wife Betty began taking early morning walks for exercise and companionship. Up before most of the rest of the world, they loved the serenity and beauty of these times. Jack commented that he had never noticed that the world was so beautiful.

One morning they paused to look across a field. Betty was talking about something, neither can remember what now, and she just stopped in mid sentence. They both did. Nothing happened between them for a long time - Jack estimates it might have been 10 minutes. They just stood there: no speech, no thought, no awareness of time, no mind. It was as if, for an endless moment, they had entered eternity. When the "spell" broke, they both knew it.

Another time, on their early morning walk, something else very strange happened. A larger consciousness seemed to envelope Jack, and suddenly everything he had ever done that hurt others raced through his mind at lightning speed. It was faster and wider than thought, yet he could remember every single instance. Jack felt sad for a while afterward, then he found himself flooded with love and appreciation. It was as if he had experienced the Near-Death life review, but he wasn't dead. He was grateful simply to be alive, with the rest of his life now offering a chance to love the whole world unconditionally.

Jack's false self had become so stressful and soul crushing that it broke down. So unbearable was it that he actually had an out-of-body experience to escape the pain. There was no choice but change. Unable to stay in quadrant 3 any longer, Jack gave up the fight and fell into his damaged soul (quadrant 4). As we worked through this pain, he not only recovered his true self, he also found the opening to his soul and in its center, a flood of love, joy, generosity, and wonder (quadrant 1). In moments of spontaneous mystical experience, the world itself seemed filled with the divine. Jack then returned to quadrant 2. Having recovered his soul, he now has a second chance to live the life he had always wanted. He has started the second cycle of life. I always look forward to seeing Jack on his monthly visits - wondering where this journey will take him next.

RESISTING THE FALL AND THE
SPIRITUAL LIFE: STUCK IN QUADRANT 3

Many people resist the spiritual life, even when its call should seem unmistakable. The work that must be done to recover one's true self and connection to soul, however, is sometimes too great or too painful.

Henry had been arrogant his whole life. Full of scathing judgments, he had left his small midwestern hometown to become a very successful West Coast traveling salesman. Like his parents, he drank everyday, drank his lunch and dinner, lived on the road in restaurants, bars and motels. Waitresses were his family. His wife raised their five children and divorced him. He remarried. Didn't miss a beat.

At sixty-five, he got prostate cancer. Surgery. He knew something was wrong. He was being called to look at something deep and fundamental. He abruptly quit drinking. Then he fell into a deep and sudden depression. Looking back, he saw that his whole life had been lived in the service of his arrogance and superiority. He'd argue with people in bars just to make them feel stupid. He'd criticize society. He was above it all. He had a million bar acquaintances but no friendships. He shared his inner life with no one.

Henry was trying to do at sixty-five what he had needed to start at forty: find out who he really was, share himself authentically with others, and search for the spiritual meaning. He realized that he had been putting this off his whole life. He didn't know his kids, had no friends, no God, and time was rapidly running out. This was indeed a crisis of soul.

Although he never resumed drinking, Henry also never returned to therapy or to this struggle with soul. Instead, he gradually reinstated his arrogance, kept busy, and criticized his wife until she needed antidepressants.

Sometimes the emptiness feels too great, or the hope too small, to face the work of healing one's soul. Many people never do it. I often wonder what happened to Henry and what it is that allows some people to bear the pain while others keep it buried.

QUADRANT 1: "I KNEW MOST OF ALL
THAT LIGHT WAS INFINITE LOVE."

Sometimes people have profound mystical experiences that affect them forever. They draw from them over and over in life. This is an example of one that occurred to a friend of mine at the beginning of his career in psychology nearly 40 years ago. He has never forgotten it.

A brand new instructor at the time, Bill was required to teach huge and intimidating psychology classes. The pressure led to an anxiety attack and a colleague encouraged him to seek psychotherapy, which he did. Gradually, Bill felt better about himself. More than that, he felt a level of self-esteem he hadn't known before, and he told the colleague who had referred him for therapy of his growth. For some inexplicable reason, this colleague ridiculed him, saying, "You're not only inhuman, you're dangerous."

That night, something happened. Bill recalled, "I had this feeling in my stomach. My wife was pregnant with our second child. I sat up late wondering what this feeling was in my stomach. I felt like I had been kicked by a mule. I looked inward without knowing what was going to come out. It was an honest self-confrontation. And then this rage came up at him. It was a total new thing for me. I went into the bathroom and looked at my face in the mirror. I was just seething. I could see my lips pulled back from my teeth like a wolf. I wanted to kill this man and it startled me. I had never had a feeling like that before." Becoming teary, he continued, "I went back and sat down, kind of rocking. I asked how can anybody hate someone. And then this inner vision thing started. It was as if I was looking down into this black pit...I felt like if I ever fell into it I would fall endlessly, there would be nothing to hang onto."

Sensing that this image had something to do with God, Bill recalled saying, "I have seen either the black side or the backside of your face." And then he asked, "Is that all there is?" As if in response, another image came- a black cloud floating in front of the moon with its edges lit - and he realized that the pit he had seen was actually contained by a light. Then something even more remarkable happened. "As soon as I saw that, I felt my whole being all the way down to my toes swept upward into this ineffable light. Different than any kind of light available to the senses. And it was indescribable. When I came down, I had no words to put to it but the experience itself...to be in that light, to be ecstatic..."

Bill added, "I don't know how long it was. It could have been one second, thirty seconds, a minute and a half. I have no idea how long it was. It was followed by a rustling sound like dried leaves being blown across the cement of a driveway. It felt like a trillion synapses going off in my brain all at the same time. And then this sense of total conviction. I found myself saying 'I know, I know, I know' over and over again. It felt like I had been in touch with all knowledge." Then, "I came down from it. It was a sense of re-entering my self as an ego'd personality with my own history and inadequacies and aspirations. It was the feeling that I had to come back to earth, so to speak, to my ego life, but that I knew that even though I lived out of touch with the light, that whenever I died I would rejoin it and in fact was never separated from it but couldn't be aware of it when I was alive. At least that was the conclusion."

What happened next? Bill remembers, "It felt absolutely glorious and yet so out of my character or anybody else's I ever heard of I woke up my wife and asked her if I was crazy. She said 'No. The same thing happened to St. Paul on the road to Damascus.' I thought I am no saint but it gave me a frame and perspective." It was, he realized, a moment of mystical enlightenment, a quadrant 1 experience.

About his experience, Bill reflected, "I knew most of all that light was infinite love. That light was the source of all the energy in the cosmos. And the other aspect was that when I came back to myself, I knew that time was a construct. I thought I have a nervous system that experiences things sequentially so we build this idea that time is a thing and that isn't true in terms of the light. It's not germane anymore. Things are eternal. You can't ask time questions of that dimension."

How did he feel afterwards? Bill recalled, "For months after I had this sudden, and to me kind of miraculous, sense of my own feelings. I discovered things about myself. My desire was that my family should be the center and have so much love in it, real love, true love, that it would overflow to other people." He also described some rather extraordinary changes in consciousness, "I was going over with somebody to the university dining room and I was walking in and felt this luminosity, this sense of everything being luminous. I remember walking in the faculty dining room and seeing across this long room a young student waitress, slender and tall. I saw these stars arcing outward and downward from her eyes." Again becoming tearful, he recalled, "So I finagled our table to be in her area. I asked her if she had just had her heart broken. And she said she was just getting over it."

Still, life goes on. Despite this profound mystical experience, Bill's everyday life was no smoother than before. His marital conflicts became severe and he went back into therapy. Even though this mystical experience "...had not taken away my real life concerns at all, I came out of the experience knowing that no matter how young or painfully I died, it would still be all right because I would still be going to the light."

My friend's quadrant 1 experience still brings tears to his eyes. It still comforts, guides, and deepens his appreciation of quadrant 2, that is, living these spiritual truths in the world. It is one of those experiences that teaches profound lessons about life, love, work, and God. It was not crazy.

Understanding it through his own unique blend of psychology and religion grew a soul much deeper than the one he knew as a young man. This, too, is spiritual work.

A FATHER ON FIRST: ONE MAN'S SACRED RITUAL

We all need rituals, ceremonial ways to handle things that are too big for us to bear or resolve individually. But, rituals need not always be formal, mysterious, or intimidating institutional affairs. The best ones, sometimes, are ones you make up yourself, ones that exactly fit what you feel and what you need to do.

Steve grew up in a chaotic family. His mother, sometimes the prima donna, more often the alcoholic, controlled the family with her rages. His father, a nice guy, well liked by everyone in his small hometown, mostly hid out at work. Although he couldn't stand up to his wife, or be home much for his family, he was there for his son in other ways. They shared an avid, almost devout, interest in sports. His father coached Steve's little league teams, they went to Giants' games, Cal games. Their bond was forged around sports.

In fact, one of the proudest times in Steve's life occurred in a little league game. Some of the other team's parents were mercilessly riding the other team's pitcher. The kid was doing the best he could. It was cruel and uncalled for. Finally Steve's dad walked out onto the field, stopped the game, and said to the offending parents, "If you don't like how this game is going, don't yell at this kid, it's not his fault. If you have to yell at someone, yell at me and my son." To be included with his dad like this, as a man taking a man's stand for what was right, was an unforgettable moment of fathering and initiation.

Although things were not so good at home, Steve's relationship with his father and their shared interest in sports somehow made life bearable. At least until Steve's mother finally made good on her oft-repeated suicide threat and literally blew her brains out in the kitchen when he was in high school. Steve helped his father clean up the blood. Another unforgettable male initiation.

Steve went on to become a math professor. His father went right on working up to the age of 75 when his employer finally said "enough." It seems that his father was just making too many mistakes. Being fired, however, was more than his father's pride could face. A man who had never taken two consecutive weeks of vacation in sixty years, a man who loved people and lived for his work, a man whose soul identity was on-the-job, could not be put out to pasture. After his dismissal, nothing seemed to matter to Steve's dad. A year after his termination, he fell and broke his hip. The doctor said it would be easy to fix. Steve's father went into the hospital, stopped eating, refused fluids, and died in two weeks. He had made up his mind.

Steve loved his father. He also respected him. He understood that his father had the right to end his life when it was no longer meaningful. His father was cremated and Steve took the ashes home. What should he do with them? Where did his father belong? Then it all became clear. A deeply personal ritual was born. Steve took his father to one last Giants' game. When it was over, he spoke to a young usher. He explained his need. She told him to wait until the stands were clear and her supervisor was gone. When all was ready, Steve took his father onto the field and rubbed him into the grass of the first base coaches' box. It felt absolutely right. It was sacred and beautiful and right. Professional baseball never had a more moving moment.

Steve's father still coaches baseball and Steve still goes to his games. A father and son bond memorialized for all time. A fitting tribute. A sacred ritual. Divine inspiration (quadrant 1) healing the sorrow of death (quadrant 4), culminating in new life meaning (quadrant 2).

YOU MUST DO IT YOURSELF: ENTERING THE LABYRINTH

After presenting a workshop at a recent conference, a woman come up to me and described her difficulty applying spiritual practices to her everyday work as an art dealer. She seemed burned out by her work yet unable to decide whether to change careers or keep struggling. Frustrated by my answers to her questions, she left the workshop.

Needing a chance to rest and restore myself after the presentation, I walked down to the nearby beach. There, quite by "accident," I met the same lady, though I first failed to recognize her behind sunglasses, scarf and jacket. She asked to talk more about spirituality, and especially the mystical experience I had described in my talk. We conversed for about 15 minutes, but again she was frustrated. Nothing I said seemed to fit her dilemma. Finally, realizing no one can be convinced of anything, I suggested she go back to the conference center and walk the labyrinth.

The labyrinth available in this conference was a replica of the one laid in the floor of Chartres Cathedral around 1220. Its maze fills the entire room. One walks the path of the labyrinth silently, in a meditative, reflective, reverential fashion from the outside through seemingly endless twists, curves, and turns, finally winding up in the center. Seekers are encouraged to contemplate a question of personal significance on this inward journey to the center of the soul.

Later that day, just before I was about to leave the conference, I ran into the same lady in the bookstore. She was so excited! With tears in her eyes, she said, "It worked!" and explained that she had indeed walked the labyrinth and, upon reaching the center, suddenly felt incredibly joyful, light, and free. The room filled with light, the grounds outside the window were exceeding beautiful, and she saw two deer nearby that no one else noticed. Most importantly, however, she felt she had experienced something of her own spirituality, a tangible moment of connection with the sacred universe that finally answered her doubts about the mystical experience and its relevance to her life.

Though not a psychotherapy client in the literal sense, this woman was a seeker who had come to a psychologist asking for guidance. The psychologist had ostensibly failed her, and her questions went unanswered. Yet turning her toward an ancient mystical exercise made it possible for this woman to find the answers herself. You must do it for yourself, when you are ready. But a little guidance can go a long way.

WHEN RELIGION BECOMES A DEFENSE

Ted came to see me because his marriage was in trouble. His wife was a former nun, now very devoted to Buddhism. They had met in Buddhist retreat and originally seemed to have so much in common, especially religion. Extremely interested in Christianity, Ted worked a night watchman's job so he devote himself to translating the original Greek texts of the New Testament through the long quiet hours. He also spent all his spare money on reference books.

Despite their intense interest in religion, Ted and his wife had a spiritually barren marriage. She was cold, distant, and unhappy, and often raged at him. He was forever trying to please her and, and when this failed, he would bury himself in translations. They slept in separate bedrooms, argued about religion, and felt no closeness.

Asked why he stayed with her, Ted rationalized that she was a disturbed individual. He hoped if he stayed and learned how to help her, things would change. They didn't. Ted and his wife were each repeating their early childhood homes filled with distance, criticism, and coldness. Each used religion addictively: to numb pain, blame the other, instill a false sense of order and control, and fill the emptiness. Though steeped in religion, there was no spirituality, no soul, no love in this relationship. Unwilling to confront the descend in to quadrant 4, Ted dropped out of therapy.

WHEN TURNING YOUR LIFE OVER TO JESUS DOESN'T WORK

Paul grew up with a critical, explosive, and violent father, and a mother who was "hurt" by his misbehavior. By adolescence, his emotional pain was raw and terrible. He tried compliantly to do whatever his parents wanted, hoping someday to be seen and loved. Only crumbs. Still he hung on.

At 16, Paul learned about Jesus from other kids at school. If you turned your life over to Jesus, they said, all would be forgiven and you would feel his love. One night Paul found his mother watching a famous evangelist on TV This man promised everyone in the audience that their sins would be forgiven when they turned their lives over to Jesus. Paul walked into his bedroom, got on his knees, and gave his life to the Lord.

It didn't work. "There must be something unforgivable about me," Paul thought. "Why else would Jesus reject me?" Now he was so unworthy, even God couldn't love him. Still he tried harder, becoming actively involved in Christian groups and, for a time, even planning to be a minister. That didn't work either. Eventually, angrily, he turned his back on God.

Twenty years later, in therapy, Paul was struggling to understand his many addictions - smoking, eating, sex - and his self-defeating pattern of challenging authority. He knew there was something he had to face inside, but feared it was too big to overcome. Then one day he broke down and it broke through. Sobbing, Paul recalled the night he saw the evangelist on T.V. and how he desperately wanted to be forgiven to heal his terrible pain. And then he recalled his unbearable conclusion when it failed: "If God couldn't love me, then I am unlovable and my life is hopeless." From then on, he wanted to die. Multiple addictions covered his pain and despair, and defiant behavior toward authority unconsciously expressed his anger.

In therapy, Paul finally understood that all this had nothing to do with God. He had been sold an over-simplified religious solution for a deeply entrenched emotional problem, and it failed. You don't heal this kind of childhood wound with tricks. You have to go back to its origins, feel the pain you couldn't bear then, and work it through. Then it can be over. When pain isn't faced, religion won't work either, but it can become an addiction.

As Paul talked through his wound, and understood its relationship to his addictions and his authority problems, life gradually changed. Pain and anger no longer drove his symptoms, and in time his addictions fell away and his work grew more satisfying. Paul also began to re-examine his relationship with God. He saw that the God he had imagined was modeled after his critical, guilt-provoking father. No wonder this relationship had failed! He realized that it was time for a more mature relationship with a loving God.

Paul's pain had not been healed by religion, it had been hidden and complicated by it. Worse, his relationship with God had been lost in the process. The promise of salvation has this terrible underside: if it doesn't work, what are you then? Are you so bad that you are unforgivable? Religious prescriptions can have this effect when naively, inappropriately, or cruelly applied to emotional problems.

TIM'S NEW JOURNEY: HEALING THE PAST AND GOING HOME

Tim had felt like a robot for as long as he could remember. There had been no warmth in his family. Only duty. He felt mechanical, as if he had never learned the ways of emotion, as if he had been miswired. He was bright and his mechanical aptitude led him to become an engineer. A good one. But there was something dead inside. When Tim's mother died, he never cried. There was no grief. He lost contact with his brother, sister, and father. He saw no reason to see them. There had been nothing but disappointment and coldness in this family. Why subject himself to any more? He had also been in psychotherapy five years when his former therapist died. He still didn't cry. He had no feeling. He didn't know what feeling was. But he was married and this relationship at least brought a modicum of human warmth into his life.

Tim and I worked together for several years. We made some progress, but whenever I tried to help Tim get in touch with the emptiness of his childhood, he would stiffen up. When I encouraged him to reach out to his father, he abruptly quit therapy. He returned a year later to say that his wife had moved out. It seemed that his personality rigidity and his critical nature had done too much damage in the marriage. So at the age of 44, Tim was alone now for real. Then the most amazing thing began to happen. He began to thaw out right in front of my eyes. Hurt, tears, and a hunger for human contact started to melt through this iron man. Tim began to verbalize feelings of warmth and caring toward coworkers, neighbors, and friends. He just had to. More than anything, Tim wanted a kind of closeness he had never known. It was now or never. All his previous work in therapy finally came to fruition.

While helping his wife move her belongings out of the house, Tim told her that he understood what he had done to her. He had shown her what he had experienced as a boy: criticism and coldness. He hugged her and told her he would support whatever she wanted to do. And then, most amazing of all, Tim decided to call his father. When his father answered, Tim asked, "Do you know who this is?" His father replied, "Yes. It is my long lost son."

A new journey began for Tim. Angry and wounded as a child, he had closed himself off to everyone. In the end, he paid the highest cost. Now his wounds were mending. Thanksgiving with his father, letters to his brother and sister, even dating. He got very close to one woman in particular. At 45, looking for the warmth he missed, Tim was finding it. Divorce seemed to have given him a new start.

Then something else happened. One day he missed an appointment - very unlike Tim. I left a message on his home answering machine, but no reply. I wondered if I had done or said something that offended him. Finally his ex-wife called. She said, "Didn't anyone tell you? Tim was killed while jogging with coworkers over lunch. He stepped in front of a car and died instantly."

I was shocked and saddened. Automatically I asked in prayer, "What does this mean? How could Tim die so senselessly just when he was opening to his life? Soon it came to me. I think Tim had finished what he had come into life to do. He had come into this world to face and overcome coldness, to lean how to love, to open his soul. And I believe he had achieved his goals. Tim left because he was ready for a new assignment. He was just moving on. I knew that he was all right.

CHAPTER TWELVE

A MESSAGE TO CLIENTS

Contents: How do you decide between psychotherapy, pastoral counseling, spiritual direction, spiritually oriented psychotherapy, and spiritual teaching? What can you hope for from spiritually oriented psychotherapy?
How do you select a spiritually oriented psychotherapist?
What other issues should you consider?

Much of this book was written with therapists in mind. But it was also written for you, the client. Understanding this material will help you know and get what you want out of therapy. It will also help you on your spiritual journey. This Chapter is intended specifically for people who are in psychotherapy (or plan to be) in order to address questions you are likely to be asking by now. It is also designed to help therapists understand and answer these same questions.

HOW DO YOU DECIDE BETWEEN PSYCHOTHERAPY, PASTORAL COUNSELING, SPIRITUAL DIRECTION, SPIRITUALLY ORIENTED PSYCHOTHERAPY, AND SPIRITUAL TEACHING?

Here are some decisions criteria to help you decide:
* Traditional psychotherapy: If you wish only to work on your emotional problems within a psychological or psychiatric framework, if you have no particular need to talk about religion, spirituality, or God, or if you specifically do not want to address such issues, then you may wish to choose traditional psychotherapy. Be sure to select someone who has experience and expertise in the area of your problem and don't hesitate to speak to several therapists before deciding.
* Pastoral Counseling: If you need support from within your own faith tradition and its resources to get through a difficult life problem, or if you need to reconcile your feelings about God or religion with the formal tenants of that tradition, pastoral counseling with a clergy person from your faith makes most sense.
* Spiritual Direction: If your desire is to explore the meaning and movement of God in your life and in your moment-to-moment experience, if you wish to give your life to God as fully as you can, and if you have no need for concurrent psychological work (or can get it elsewhere), then spiritual direction may be right for you.
* Spiritually-Oriented Psychotherapy: If you feel confused about the overlap of psychological and spiritual dimensions in your problems, if you clearly need to work from both perspectives, or if you feel that your spiritual work has been drawn off course by psychological complications, then a spiritually oriented psychotherapy may be right for you.

* Spiritual teaching: One can receive spiritual guidance and teaching from anyone. Some teachers will come from within a particular tradition, have various credentials, and offer formal training (e.g., meditation training). Others may offer teaching based entirely on personal spiritual or mystical experiences. If you are interested in the classes or material offered by a teacher, by all means pursue it. Keep in mind the potentially dark side of spiritual teachers and cults, and notice the balance between freedom to explore and coercion to believe or join.

WHAT CAN YOU HOPE FOR FROM SPIRITUALLY ORIENTED PSYCHOTHERAPY?

In addition to competent psychological help, spiritually oriented psychotherapy should also provide:

* A chance to have your spiritual yearning accepted, supported, and valued.
* A chance to examine the religious nature of your psyche (e.g., dreams, images, hunches, coincidences, and individuation as a spiritual process).
* A chance to understand your personality and its problems as a spiritual process and explore the spiritual meaning and direction of your life.
* A chance to integrate your spiritual practice with psychotherapy in order to potentate the activity and movement of each.
* An opportunity to depthfully consider both the psychological and spiritual aspects of an important life decision.
* A chance to learn how to sense God's presence in your interior and in your life.
* A place to examine and apply the insights of the world's religions to your own   life experiences.

HOW DO YOU SELECT A SPIRITUALLY ORIENTED PSYCHOTHERAPIST?

There are many things to consider in locating the right psychotherapist for you. Here are some questions you can ask yourself and anyone you are considering as your therapist:

* Compatibility, comfort, and chemistry: Are you compatible and comfortable with this person? Do you feel safe with them? Does the professional and human "chemistry" between you feel right? Is there anything that feels weird or unprofessional to you? Can you talk to this person about your concerns? Does he listen and understand?

* Formal religious background: Do you want a representative of your religious tradition, a professional with the same religious affiliation, or someone outside that tradition? Are you concerned about whether the therapist's religious orientation might get in the way? Would you prefer someone without extensive formal religious orientation? Do you feel you can ask these kinds of questions?

* Spiritual experience and training: What kind of spiritual experience or training do you want this person to have? Is it important for him to have worked on himself? What spiritual values do you wish from a therapist?

* Age: Is age important to you? Do you prefer the therapist to be your own age, older, or younger? Those recently graduated have the latest techniques, those past midlife have the greatest life experience. Older therapists, assuming they have stayed current, may be more capable of spirituality simply because they have lived and experienced the journey for a longer time. They are also less likely to be fooled by spiritual ambition or addiction. Cynicism, however, is the complementary risk, and age by itself is no guarantee of wisdom, maturity, spirituality, or even competence.

* Gender: Are you more comfortable with a man or woman? Some argue that working with someone of the opposite sex allows an experience of the wholeness missing when working with someone of the same sex. There are times, on the other hand, when the same sex is important, especially with sexual or gender issues. Is this important to you? Do you feel safer with men or women?

* Professionalism: Is this therapist respected in the community? Do they present themselves with dignity, humility, and respect? Do they make unrealistic promises? Does the therapist engage in peer consultation in their work? Does such consultation include spiritual matters?

WHAT OTHER ISSUES SHOULD I CONSIDER?

* Length and frequency of treatment: Are you interested in brief, problem-centered counseling or more long term psychotherapy? Do you want to meet occasionally as the need arises or on a regular weekly or monthly schedule? How deeply and intensively do you want to work?

* Cost: Is cost a factor? What can you realistically afford? Have you shopped around among the various professionals to compare rates? Can you value emotional and spiritual growth as much as you would a new car or expensive vacation, and make it a financial priority?

* Proportion of psychological versus spiritual work: Are you more interested in a psychological counseling with occasional spiritual input, or a primarily spiritual format with psychological guidance only when needed? How much do you want immediate spiritual experience, such as prayer or spiritual direction, to be part of your work?

* Trial Contract: Unsure whether a particular counselor is right for you, consider working together for a trial period of one to three sessions to see how it feels. Don't forget that the decision to continue is yours.

* Periodic evaluations: However you proceed, it is wise to set time aside to evaluate your experience. Is therapy feeling authentic, valuable, and alive? Are you sensing progress in your life outside therapy? Are you happy with what is taking place? Do you like and respect your therapist? Does your therapist have the knowledge, caring, and values that are important to you? Is the therapist genuinely sensitive to your spirituality?

PART FOUR

PROFESSIONAL ISSUES

Having argued for a mature integration of psychotherapy and spirituality, formulated a model for this integration, and explored the subjective experience of spirituality in the consulting room, it is time now to ground our discussion in sound clinical and professional practice. Part IV examines the role of the mental health practitioner, the nature of spiritual assessment, diagnosis, management, and referral, the place of spirituality in other helping professions, issues of training and ethics, and how a therapist personally decides to do this work.

CHAPTER THIRTEEN

THE ROLE OF MENTAL HEALTH PRACTITIONERS: PRELIMINARY REFLECTIONS

Contents: Careful Thinking
            Self Assessment
            Client Assessment
            The Client's Developmental Level of Religious and Spiritual Belief

CAREFUL THINKING

Most mental health practitioners have never carefully reflected on the variety of religious and spiritual issues inherent in a psychological problem, or conversely, on the various psychological issues inherent in a religious or spiritual problem. As we have seen, the importance of examining both dimensions is real. In this historically complex and murky area, we need to think clearly, logically, objectively. The following questions are offered to illustrate these complexities and sharpen the reader's clinical acuity in preparation for the forthcoming Chapters on practical and applied issues.

* Can you distinguish between religious, spiritual, mystical, medical, and psychological problems, and if so, how?
* When are the goals and methods of religion, spirituality, mysticism, medicine, and psychology appropriate for a particular problem, and when are they not? What problems are best served by each discipline?
* How is the decision to discuss religion and spirituality influenced by variables such as age, experience, health status, personality, diagnosis, or religious background?
* How do we know when to bring up the issue of spirituality, especially when a client has never initiated the topic?
* What is the relationship between mental illness, religiosity, and spirituality?
* What is the psychological meaning of spiritual crises and the spiritual meaning of psychological and health crises?
* How can medicine, psychotherapy, religion, mysticism, and spirituality complement and serve each other in the service of ameliorating human suffering?

With these questions in mind, we can begin to examine the role of the mental health practitioner in dealing with religious and spiritual matters. What does all this mean to the average therapist and client?

SELF-ASSESSMENT

In Part I of this book, we addressed the first question a therapist needs to consider in this area, "Do you believe it is appropriate to integrate spirituality into clinical practice?" If you answered "yes" to this question, the next logical question is, "Do you feel competent to discuss religious and spiritual matters with your clients?"

Given the enormous range of humankind's religious, spiritual, and mystical experience, it is difficult for anyone to answer the second question with an unqualified "yes." The average psychotherapist still receives little solid training in these areas, and the domain of experience is vast. Later we will discuss the educational and experiential pre-requisites that might begin to fill this void. For now, the goal is to critically examine our own training and experience, and discern its most important gaps. For example, have you read and experienced enough to have a basic footing in this area? Are you sufficiently familiar with world religions, non-ordinary and sacred experiences, and the various pitfalls that exist on the spiritual path? If not, expand your reading, attend relevant workshops or conferences, and pursue your own spiritual practices until that readiness develops. And as you make this turn, remember your limitations, stay humble, and keep learning.

After considering the therapist's intellectual and attitudinal readiness to incorporate spirituality into his or her work, we next need to address the therapist's personal readiness. This area of self-assessment includes the therapist's spiritual feelings, private beliefs, sacred experiences, general comfort level, and maturity. As therapists, we need to expose our basic assumptions, prejudices, positive or negative religious transference, and magical thinking in order to really look at what it is we think we are doing. We should also share our beliefs and assumptions with others to identify erroneous or highly idiosyncratic ideas. Such self-assessment is essential because we need to be clear headed and because the client has a right to expect us to know what we are doing.

CLIENT ASSESSMENT

Like any other sensitive topic in therapy, the decision to discuss spirituality requires the therapist to assess the client's readiness. This readiness is comprised of the following ingredients:

* Desire: Does the client even want to discuss this topic? Has it been brought it up before? What happened?

* Need: Do you sense the client has a need or yearning to discuss or explore spirituality in the hour? Do their presenting problems cry out for a spiritual discussion (e.g., abusive religious training, addictive religious practices, profound loss or life tragedy, non-ordinary states of consciousness, or spiritual despair)?

* Comfort level: Is the client comfortable with spiritual topics or fearful, defensive, and skeptical?

THE CLIENT'S DEVELOPMENT LEVEL OF RELIGIOUS AND SPIRITUAL BELIEF

Desire, need, and comfort level are intimately tied to the development of the client's religious and spiritual beliefs. As discussed in Chapter 7, psychospiritual development tends to follow a common and possibly universal course over the life span with each stage marked by specific growth tasks, characteristics, and problems. The client's beliefs expand accordingly to integrate an evolving depth and diversity of spiritual experience. The therapist's diagnostic competence is especially important here because a client can be hurt or alienated when information from the wrong developmental level is introduced. A therapist, therefore, needs to assess the maturity of a client's belief system relative to the following general stages:

NON-EXISTENT, HOSTILE, OR ATHEISTIC BELIEFS:

Clients who profess non-existent, hostile, or atheistic religious beliefs may be saying they do not want spiritual information and if so often resent its introduction. Their skepticism and disdain typically belie a painful wounding of their religious longing early in life that will eventually need to be sensitively addressed before the spiritual journey can begin. Some have intellectually adopted the culture's views on scientific and economic materialism, viewing spirituality as not provable and unnecessary. For others, the spiritual longing has simply never been named or encouraged.

DOGMATIC RELIGIOUS IDEAS:

When religious ideas are imposed on a young psyche in an authoritarian way (e.g., with rigid, harsh, or punitive early training), dogmatic beliefs form. The believer blindly incorporates and fearfully parrots what he or she has been told. Dogmatic religious beliefs then serve as a security blanket and defense against the fear of authoritarian assault. Confronting such black-and-white, literal, or legalistic religious beliefs, practices, or affiliations too early in therapy usually results in futile debates that quickly compromise or erode therapeutic rapport. The wounding behind these rigid beliefs needs to be healed before the client can explore a more permissive and personally meaningful spirituality.

NAIVETÉ AND GULLIBILITY

When individuals first open to all the possibilities of the spiritual path, they may be especially naive and gullible about even the most extraordinary religious claims. Individuals at this stage accept religious ideas with little capacity for mature discernment and reality testing. Like a child, incredible and impractical notions may be accepted uncritically (simplistic faith in signs, premature dependence on divine providence for survival). Some people make disastrous decisions based on this gullibility (e.g., turning over their savings to cults or believing in false gurus). Most simply outgrow gullibility with time and experience, for the inevitable clash between naiveté and betrayal shatters innocence, launching a more realistic and sophisticated spiritual quest.

CONSTRUCTIVE QUESTIONING

A client at this stage begins to explore his religious assumptions with a more open, experimental, and investigative attitude. He is genuinely interested in examining what he really believes, what his experiences mean, and how to know the truth for himself. A more personally meaningful religious and spiritual orientation coalesces. In this phase, spiritual reading, instruction, and practice can be exciting and beneficial, and should be encouraged. Care should be taken not to present spiritual ideas as conclusions, for clients need to develop trust in their own understanding and will balk when feeling lectured.

ESTABLISHED, COMMITTED, AND INTEGRATED RELIGIOUS BELIEFS

People with well established beliefs often do not bring up religious issues or problems in psychotherapy, but when they do, they naturally prefer to examine them within the existing perspective. They also tend to bring their religious and spiritual concerns to established clerical rather than secular authorities.

THE RELIGIOUS PLATEAU

Well-established beliefs provide a religious orientation that feels comfortable and secure. For those uninterested in mystical experiences, this orientation may last a lifetime. Their beliefs have formalized and provide an enduring structure for accepting life changes, hardships, and existential doubt. But secure religious beliefs can also serve to forbid or suppress authentic spiritual inquiry and growth, for rare is the person at this or any stage who is truly and completely secure. Although the religious plateau may seem well entrenched, sensitive inquiry, particularly at times of crisis, loss, and impending death often yields new questions and a need to search once again.

INTUITIVE-MYSTICAL

For those who feel called to more mystical experience of religious truth, the spiritual path continues. A basic, grounded, and growing trust in personal mystical awareness and intuition grows steadily. Spiritual authority now comes from direct experience, not from experts, although mystical literature from around the world may be valued for its uniformity and universality. All religions are felt to be relative, reflecting differing cultural, ethnic, and personal models of reality and truth. Acting now from mystical consciousness rather than dogmatic belief, clients at this stage benefit more from spiritual direction than spiritual teaching.

THE MYSTICAL LIFE

As the growth of a client's mystical consciousness opens into an ever greater experience of unity, spiritual values begin to be expressed in behavior and life decisions. Some individuals in this phase become the spiritual teachers or counselors, others pursue activities that hold their spiritual truth (e.g., volunteer work, loving attitudes, serving God in a particular way). Personal concerns, even death, become much less important. As the seed of divine self opens, the individual's path naturally replicates stories of all the great religious figures. People at this stage rarely need psychotherapy.

The developmental stages of religious and spiritual belief often occur over the course of psychotherapy. Early inquiry into spirituality may be met with disinterest, hostililty, dogmatic debate, or gullibility. With time and therapeutic progress the capacity for constructive questioning develops. Similarly, comfortable beliefs that have lasted decades may be shaken by difficult or traumatic life events, and for spiritually motivated individuals, the second half of life often quickens mystical interest, experience, and understanding. Assessing a client's developmental level, therefore, is critical to knowing when and how to bring the spiritual journey into the psychotherapeutic process.

CHAPTER FOURTEEN

RELIGIOUS AND SPIRITUAL ASSESSMENT, DIAGNOSIS, MANAGEMENT, AND REFERRAL

Contents: Religious and Spiritual Assessment
             Management, Treatment, and Referral
             Discernment

RELIGIOUS AND SPIRITUAL ASSESSMENT

Following the preliminary reflections in the preceding Chapter on careful thinking, informal assessment, and the significance of our clients' varying beliefs, we can now move into issues pertinent to the clinical and professional practice of psychotherapy. The natural place to start is religious and spiritual assessment.

We take numerous wrong turns on the spiritual path. When we do so, the feeling of connection with God is lost, spiritual understanding begins to seem empty and intellectual, and discouragement sets in. These are normal impasses common to the journey through the Ego-Soul Matrix and resolve with time, patience, discernment grace, and spiritual guidance. When obstacles are more severe, structured religious and spiritual assessment may be helpful in clarifying healthy and unhealthy psychospiritual functioning, particularly with respect to hidden forms of religious addiction and abuse. As discussed in Chapter 8, a client's psychospiritual problems can become serious, and the importance of professional assessment naturally increases with the severity of our client's distress.

An individual's religious and spiritual functioning can be formally assessed by taking a Spiritual History (Appendix G: Some Ideas on Taking A Religious and Spiritual History). Using a structured or informal interview format, the therapist asks probing questions, evaluates the client's responses, considers relevant diagnoses, and reviews options for management and referral.

Using the form provided in Appendix G, the reader is encouraged to personally answer the assessment questions and interview family or friends in order to understand the development of religious belief and become more comfortable and proficient in this area of inquiry. What can you learn about yourself? What role has religion and spirituality played in your life and in the lives of those closest to you? Are you comfortable asking others about their religious and spiritual beliefs and experiences? What do you find most difficult?

The information from a client's spiritual history, in combination with other social, medical, and psychiatric information, allows the skillful therapist to assess the following areas and problems:

ASSESSMENT AREAS	PROBLEMS ASSESSED
Religious Background and Activities	Pathology of the God Image
Religious Beliefs	Dysfunctional Beliefs or Practices
Prayer Experience	Activities that Interfere with Medical or
Spiritual Experiences	Psychotherapeutic Treatment
Spiritual Meaning of Life	Pathological Use of Religion
	Misunderstanding of Mystical Experience
	Contributing Organic or Psychiatric Disorders

FORMAL ASSESSMENT INSTRUMENTS

In addition to exploring a client's religious and spiritual history through interview format, formal psychometric assessment exists, consisting primarily of self-administered paper-and-pencil instruments with simple scoring and interpretive procedures. In contrast to the field of psychology, which range from the differentiation of complex psychopathology to the detection and description of organic brains syndromes, assessment in religious and spiritual areas is still rudimentary but nonetheless theoretically interesting and promising.

Assessment instruments generally fall into three categories. The first includes those evaluating the meaning and place of spiritually in the individual's overall life as one of many values, but more importantly, the one that provides the core, life long context and meaning of existence. Attempts are made to create an inclusive definition of spirituality applicable across traditions and individuals. (e.g., The Spiritual Well-Being Scale, Ellison, 1983; the "Wheel of Wellness," Witmer, et. al, 1992).

A second class of instruments purport to assess spiritual health, maturity, and well-being. These tests attempt to measure the nature, personal value, and coherency of an individual's spiritual belief system (e.g., feeling of love and connection to a transcendent being, ultimate meaning and hope in life, loving connection to others, positive involvement with a religious community, spiritually derived courage to cope with hardship)as well as any spiritual distress, generally consisting of the absence of these faith dimensions often in combination with other acute life problems (e.g., the Spiritual Health Survey, Veach & Chappel, 1992). Similar attempts have been made to assess the healthiness of one's God concept (e.g., Johnson, 1991) or and basic spirituality (Index of Core Spiritual Experience, Kass, et. al., 1991).

A third category of psychometric instruments assesses the health and impact of one's religious orientation (e.g., the Religious Belief and Activity Scale, DeJong, et. al, 1976) or its specific influence on everyday life functioning, such as family satisfaction (Abbott, et. al, 1990). The majority of these tests measure religious maturity within an established system such as Christianity (e.g., Bassett et. al., 1990).

Psychometric measurement can complement but should not replace interview assessment for several reasons. Because of the relatively young status of the field, formal instruments still have relatively limited applicability across the diverse settings, cultures, and religious populations of American (e.g., mental health clinics, private practice, recovery programs, ethnic diversity, church congregations, and faith traditions). Second, psychometric measurement at this stage is primarily a convergent methodology, reducing an individual to categories, concepts, and scores. Clinical interview methods, on the other hand, are primarily divergent, allowing the clinician to explore the expression of a particular theme in an individual's actual experience. On the positive side, this is an area where science, religion, and spirituality can and do meet productively. As we will see, there is a growing body of literature relating religious and spiritual functioning to health, social and emotional well being, and even longevity. Examining the assumptions underlying these tests is also reveals how religious thinkers operationalize concepts most people use with imprecision. At this stage, however, whether a therapist employs formal measuring instruments is a largely matter of personal preference, experience, and specific goals, with practice standards still far in the future.

GOALS OF ASSESSMENT

The goals of religious and spiritual assessment, discussed more fully in the remainder of this Chapter, include:
* Encouraging Clients' Personal Reflection
* Differentiating Healthy and Unhealthy Spirituality
* Recognizing Defensive and Maladaptive Spirituality
* Differentiating Healthy and Unhealthy Religion
* Differential Diagnosis of Underlying Psychiatric Conditions
* Differential Diagnosis of Psychotic and Mystical States
* Differential Diagnosis of Underlying Spiritual Conditions
* Reaching Management, Treatment, and Referral Decisions

ENCOURAGING CLIENTS' PERSONAL REFLECTION

The first, and one of the most important goals of assessment, is client self-awareness. The majority of people have never reflected comprehensively on the impact of religion and spirituality have across their lifetime. They easily recite facts, dates, activities, and official faith convictions, but not the inner story: how they personally feel about God, how their beliefs have changed, their still unanswered questions, or deepest yearnings. A gentle but thorough history taking, with plenty of time for probing, reflection, and free association, can enrich one's faith experience and clarify the current and unfolding spiritual meaning of life. With skillful guidance, it can also identify the kinds of problems described below.

DIFFERENTIATING HEALTHY AND UNHEALTHY SPIRITUALITY

It is not always easy or immediately possible to know if an individual's religious or spiritual interests are healthy or unhealthy. Zeal, glowing reports of progress, and sincerity of spiritual practice sometimes mask serious problems. The following chart provides some relevant distinctions:

Healthy Spirituality	*Unhealthy Spirituality*
Complements therapy by adding a new dimension or stimulating the growth of self and soul.	Avoids or interferes with the work of therapy (e.g., as an escape from painful affects or insights).
Involves an open, flexible, investigatory process.	Pursued in rigid, legalistic or secretive ways.
Helps client grow and evolve his spirituality beyond.	Leaves the client totally dependent on a particular teacher, group, or practice.
Allows client to move beyond ego and false self.	Tied to goals of ego mastery and false self inflation.
Promotes growth in social relationships.	Impedes growth (e.g., self-imposed isolation, cult rules).
Deepens client's capacity to love, serve, and care.	Leaves client more self-centered, grandiose, or controlling.
Does not harm self or others physically, emotionally, or spiritually.	Causes harm or damage to self and others.

RECOGNIZING DEFENSIVE AND MALADAPTIVE SPIRITUALITY

Unhealthy spiritual practices can become frankly defensive and maladaptive. Religious addiction and abuse, two quite common examples, represent the next level of dysfunctionality that therapists working in this field need to understand.

RELIGIOUS ADDICTION

According to Booth (1991), symptoms of religious addiction can include the inability to think or question religious information or authority; black-and-white or simplistic thinking; shame-based beliefs about oneself; magical thinking that God will fix things; scrupulosity (i.e., obsessive adherence to rules); uncompromising and judgmental attitudes; compulsive praying, church activities, or quoting of scripture; unrealistic financial contributions; belief that sex or the body are dirty or evil; compulsive overeating or fasting; conflicts with science and education; progressive detachment and isolation from the real world; psychosomatic illness; manipulation of scripture, feeling chosen, claiming special messages from God; trance-like states or highs; glazed facial expression; and, as the addiction proceeds, eventual psychiatric crisis, breakdown, and behavioral cries for help.

The addictive quality is evident in the client's inability to abstain from such behavior, or when abstinence is temporarily successful, the emergence of acutely uncomfortable mental and emotional states. Religious addiction leads to what has been called "Toxic Faith" (Arterburn & Felton, 1991) and often occurs to people with elevated emotional vulnerability due to illness, infirmity, age, psychosocial disadvantage, or chemical dependencies, and whose vulnerability renders them more susceptible to the magical promises of religious leaders (e.g. televangelist).

RELIGIOUS ABUSE

Religious addiction often has its origins in homes where religious abuse was actively practiced. Children are exhorted to believe they are sinful, that God is powerful, wrathful, and watching them, that the devil can control people, and that they will go to hell unless they scrupulously obey strict religious rules. Religious beliefs are used in punishment, typically combined with other verbal, emotional, and physical abuse. Child abuse and severe family dysfunction are rationalized by scripture, creating fear, guilt, insecurity, codependence, and the defensive adoption of the same black and white belief system for survival. Children from such families frequently exhibit religious anxiety, rigidity, guilt, excessive compliance to authority, and religious addiction as teenagers and adults. Fearing reprisal, they are also deeply fearful of examining their own beliefs.

DIFFERENTIATING HEALTHY AND UNHEALTHY RELIGION

Considerable research over the years into the relationship between religion and health (mental and physical), while still ambiguous in many areas, increasingly suggests a mixture of helpful and harmful patterns. For example, there appears to be a consistently positive association between actual participation in institutional religious activities (e.g., church attendance, prayer groups) and physical and mental health. Religiously committed individuals not only live longer, their incidence of divorce, depression, suicide, drug use, alcohol abuse, and delinquency is lower than the non-religious population (Gartner, 1996). Moreover, religious beliefs and sanctions seem to discourage maladaptive behavior (e.g., violence and promiscuity), encourage positive values (e.g., social conscience, volunteerism, health education), and provide emotional support and direction in times of crisis or hardship (Pargament, 1996a). There is also an increasing body of literature linking measurements of spiritual well-being to real and perceived health status, adjustment, and coping (e.g., McKee & Chappel, 1992; Waldfogel & Wolpe, 1993).

On the negative side of the ledger, however, research suggests that fundamentalist or authoritarian religious organizations can foster or rationalize harmful attitudes and behavior toward others (e.g., prejudice, discrimination, intolerance, rigid and controlling beliefs, perfectionism, legalism, scare tactics, shaming) (Hunsberger, 1995; Johnson & VanVonderen, 1991), child abuse (e.g., harsh or rigid child rearing methods, medical neglect, sexual abuse by religious authorities) (Bottoms, et. al., 1995), and cultic sexual promiscuity (e.g., Gordon, 1987). Anxiety arousing beliefs about God's nature similarly affect mental health. People who view themselves as "sinners-in-the-hands-of-an-angry-God" tend to experience more distress, anxiety, and depression, while those believing in the "loving God" model experience more positive mental health (Pargament, 1996b).

In general, healthy and unhealthy religion can differentiated along the following lines:

Healthy Religion	*Unhealthy Religion*
Presents religious beliefs in permissive, exploratory fashion	Presents religious beliefs in rigid, legalistic, black-and-white, or authoritarian fashion.
Permits and encourages personal interpretation.	Forbids questioning or personal interpretation.
Reveals no indications of religious abuse or addiction.	Encourages or rationalizes religious abuse or addiction.
Views God as loving, helpful, caring.	Views God as demanding, angry, or punitive.
Leadership viewed as emotionally accepting and supportive.	Minister and church viewed as threatening, controlling, critical, shaming, or manipulative.
Personalities of leadership not excessively important.	Accommodating leaders personality eccentricities critical to church functioning (e.g., violent temper, whims, demands for special treatment).
Views self as primarily worthy.	Views self as primarily sinful or damned.
Views hardship as opportunity for spiritual growth.	Views hardship as deserved punishment for evil or original sin.
Selects scripture emphasizing love and forgiveness.	Selects scripture emphasizing fear and retribution.
Integrates psychological understanding emotional problems.	Views emotional problems as of human evidence of sin.
Emphasizes tolerance and inclusion toward problems and diversity.	Harshly judgmental of human problems or differences (e.g., divorce, homosexuality, other religions or practices).
Emphasizes non-judgmental and non-Competitive standards of spiritual worth.	Fosters comparative and subtly shaming standards or community behavior (e.g., perfect church attendance, clone-like imitation, image more important than honesty).
Democratic and open about power, policies, problems and finances in church structure.	Secretive, distrusting, ,or paranoid(e.g., in group has power and important information, serious problems denied or concealed, questions viewed as disloyalty).

Concern for members' well being over rigid submission to rules or authority.	Submission to rules causing hardship or abuse (e.g., pressure to remain with abusive mate).
Spiritual and religious tenants taught in familiar ways.	Twisted and fear-inducing use of spiritual concepts to control others (e.g., subtle witch-hunts, excessive fear of Satan's influence, "spiritual warfare").
Realistic church goals consistent with existing human needs.	Righteous or overly zealous goals (e.g., recruiting quotas, excessive political agenda).
Accepts the reality of emotional problems in life (e.g., marital difficulties, childhood wounds, church conflicts).	Religion used to deny or suppress the psychological reality of emotional problems in favor of scriptural interpretations.

CULTS

Originally, the term cult referred to any specific sub form of established religious worship or devotion, with the additional implication that such worship might be practiced in an unusual or extreme way. Most of the world's religions started as cults, often forming around a highly inspirational leader during times of social or religious crisis. In cults, the sacred is often believed to be literally located in the leader, who may be viewed as possessing extraordinary powers and spiritual secrets.

In recent years, the term cult has taken on numerous and almost entirely negative connotations, implying coercive religious groups that require total commitment and unquestioning obedience from their membership. In such groups, members often voice contempt for traditional church structures, viewing them as too dogmatic, conventional, and democratic, and for the existing social order as ignorant and oppositional to the cult's mission. Closed societies with utopian philosophies, cults are often described as controlling their members with intense peer pressure, an authoritarian power structure, and paranoia toward non-members. Cults are said to attract followers because they appear to offer total acceptance, security and unambiguous beliefs, appealing to people who feel powerless, alone, unworthy, frightened, or outside the social structure. Usually one generational, they are tied to a specific charismatic leader and fall apart in his absence. If they do survive the leader's death, departure, or debunking, however, cults may evolve to take on the characteristics of sects.

The research on cults suggest that they represent highly diverse and complex social and religious movements. Because of many recent and highly publicized cult tragedies (e.g., Jonestown suicides and the Branch Davidians in Waco, Texas), the concept typically stirs heated debate not infrequently leading to sweeping and simplistic generalizations, militant deprogramming efforts, and court room dramas (Saliba, 1995). Given their wide variety of forms and beliefs, each cult should be understood individually at personal, psychological, and sociological levels. In fact, the consequences of cult membership can range from helpful to benign to profoundly destructive. Though much of the rhetoric is negative, focusing on the seduction and control of emotionally vulnerable and alienated individuals, there is evidence that some membership in some cults may relieve stress and anxiety, provide belonging and identity, and serve as a rite of passage for young persons during the difficult time of emancipation. Cults have also been described as a genuine search for alternate spiritual experience, a revival or breakthrough of the spirit, the recycling of neglected archetypal beliefs, and a reaction to the breakdown of traditional religion, and may embody these more positive values.

DIFFERENTIAL DIAGNOSIS OF UNDERLYING PSYCHIATRIC CONDITIONS

Higher level diagnostic distinctions arise when maladaptive spiritual and religious practices develop into, mask, or reflect even more serious psychiatric disturbance. While addictive and abusive beliefs and practices can be incorporated into virtually any psychopathologic process, several diagnostic categories are more commonly represented, including:

OBSESSIVE-COMPULSIVE DISORDERS

Religious ideas and practices are readily assimilated into obsessive-compulsive defenses, evolving into the phenomenon known as scrupulosity. Obsessive, inflexible religious ideas and repetitive, ritualistic behavior are defensively used to ward off or distract oneself from the anxiety of unacceptable feelings and impulses, particularly unconscious childhood feelings of helplessness, guilt, shame, inferiority, or rage

DEPRESSIVE DISORDERS

The deep feelings of worthlessness, failure, or guilt associated with serious depressive disorders are fertile ground for religious addiction. Constant prayer, for example, may reflect desperate or magical attempts to seek redemption from self-perceived unworthiness (i.e., evil, sin, and damnation).

IMMINENT SCHIZOPHRENIC OR MANIC BREAKDOWN

Religiosity and scrupulosity can sometimes represent desperate defenses against imminent psychiatric breakdown. Mobilized by the terrifying awareness of impending structural disintegration of personality functioning and defenses, decompensating patients focus on end-of-the-world religious beliefs, symbolically reflecting their own psychological state. Some have argued that this kind of breakdown reflects a process of deep personality reorganization with archetypal religious themes (e.g., Perry, 1987, 1989).

PERSONALITY DISORDERS

Underlying both religious addiction and abuse are the widely divergent personality problems known as personality disorders. In these disorders, religion may be used to express or justify deeply ingrained personality disturbances. Examples vary widely, including the schizotypal loner with autistic religious ideation, the antisocial or borderline personalities explosively re-enacting their own religious abuse, the narcissistic clergy or cult leader demanding followers exactly mirror their own distorted views, the dependent personality trading abuse for security, and the masochistic personality recapitulating sadistic childhood domination.

PSYCHOACTIVE SUBSTANCE USE DISORDERS

Acute drug intoxication (e.g., LSD, mescaline, or PCP) and end state alcoholism or drug dependence can present with religious or mystical material. Management requires accurate assessment of medical risk and psychological stability. Legitimate mystical experience can also be evoked or associated by these states, though the ego may not be capable of assimilating it.

CHRONIC AND SEVERE PSYCHIATRIC CONDITIONS

Some of the more chronic and severe pychiatric conditions can present with religious hallucinations, delusions, or exaggerated ideation, including acute psychotic, paranoid, or manic states, and major depressive syndromes. In the majority of these cases, the use of religion becomes unhealthy and defensive.

DIFFERENTIAL DIAGNOSIS OF PSYCHOTIC AND MYSTICAL STATES

As the reader can see, multiple diagnostic possibilities need to be considered when a client is disclosing unusual or highly charged religious experiences, ideas, or symbolic processes. Differentiation between psychotic and mystical states can be especially confusing. Agosin argues that this distinction is often difficult because psychotic and mystical states share many common features (Agosin, 1992), including:

* Intense subjective experience and inward focus
* Sense of noesis, involving illuminations and revelations of seemingly profound importance
* Ineffable quality that defies language
* Loss of ego boundaries with others, nature, or the universe as a whole
* Distortion of time sense with only the eternal present seeming to exist
* Heightened perception in all sensory modalities along with hallucinatory phenomena
* Intense affective experiences such as joy, ecstasy, terror
* Altered state of consciousness with profound disruption of normal consciousness
* Implicit attempt at renewal and healing

Agosin also points out, however, that there are several important differences between psychotic and mystical experience, including:

* Self-image: mystical experience involves a loss of self; grandiosity and self-centeredness characterize the psychotic
* Ego-identity: mystics shed their identity; psychotics cling to whatever fragments of identity they can
* Serenity: mystics find increasing serenity, peace and tranquilly; the psychotic has little serenity
* Change: mystics welcome change; the psychotic is terrified of anything new
* Thought processes: the mystic generally shows no obvious thought disorder; the psychotic shows typical loosening and fragmentation of thought
* Aggressive or paranoid content: mystics manifest very little aggressive or paranoid material; psychotics frequently do
* Hallucinatory experiences: more visual and positive in mystical states; more auditory, negative, and terrifying in psychotic states

* Self-limiting: the mystical state is typically short-lived and reversible; psychosis can become chronic
* Consequences: the mystical experience leaves the individual more connected and involved in the world, expanding his capacity for love, service, reverence; psychosis, leaves the individual more self-involved and anxiously self-protective

David Lukoff (1985) differentiates psychotic states in need of medical attention from those with more mystical significance, which may be positively transforming even when associated with psychotic features. This latter category, "Mystical Experience with Psychotic Features," is characterized by both psychotic process and mystical experience (e.g., ecstatic mood, a sense of newly acquired knowledge, some perceptual alterations, delusions with mythological themes, and no conceptual disorganization). It is also associated with more positive predictors (i.e., a good history of social and vocational functioning prior to episode; acute onset; clear evidence of a precipitant leading to the episode; positive exploratory attitude toward experience; and little evidence of risk factors suggestive of suicide or homicide).

In his pioneering work on Psychosynthesis, Roberto Assagioli (1965) described the stages and complications involved with the breakthrough of the superconscious reality into an individual's customary psychological experience. Some problems were said to be directly associated with spiritual awakening, others arise in reaction to it and during the often long process of personality re-integration. Each stage can evoke symptoms that mimic psychiatric disorders, but careful assessment will reveal a precipitating transpersonal process typically associated with intense mystical themes, illuminations, visions, voices, and energies. The accompanying excitement, confusion, misunderstanding, and personality changes often require spiritually informed professional guidance. Regarding differential diagnosis, Assagioli states that psychiatric problems commonly demonstrate regressive characteristics while mystical states more often reveal a progressive process. Treating mystical breakthroughs as psychiatric disorders is not only contraindicated but also often destructive to the process and the individual.

Grof and Grof (1990) also differentiate spiritual and psychiatric disorders. In contrast to organic and psychiatric disorders, spiritual emergencies are said to show negative clinical, neuropsychological, and laboratory findings for organic disease; intact intellectual, memory and orientation functions; adequate ability to communicate and cooperate; adequate pre-episode personal history and adjustment; genuine spiritual themes and synchronicities; awareness of the intrapsychic nature of the process; sufficient trust in caretakers to accept help without persecutory delusions and hallucinations; the ability to honor the basic rules of therapy; and good cooperation with regard to physical health and hygiene.

DIFFERENTIAL DIAGNOSIS OF UNDERLYING AND SPIRITUAL CONDITIONS

Mystical states are not the only spiritual condition that may be mistaken for a psychiatric disorder. Other distinctions include:

DEPRESSION VERSUS THE "DARK NIGHT OF THE SOUL"

May (1992) notes that the "Dark Night of the Soul," an experience of God's personal abandonment described by the Christian mystic St. John of the Cross (also discussed in Chapter 15), may have many features in common with depression. Both can involve feelings of hopelessness, helplessness, agitation, emptiness, poverty of thought, absence of motivation, and loss of self-confidence. The "Dark Night," however, is not usually associated with 1) significant loss of effectiveness in life and work, 2) loss of humor, 3) negative self-absorption, 4) diminished compassion, 5) tremendous frustration, or 6) struggles with despair. In fact, May points out that many people at this stage, despite their suffering, recognize a kind of "rightness" about the experience and, understanding this, would not choose to have it otherwise. The "Dark Night" occurs more often among sincere and long practicing religious individuals.

KUNDALINI

Kundalini is a process of psychospiritual awakening in which spiritual energy or currents are said to rise from the base of the spine through the seven chakras, or energy centers, occasionally producing enlightenment. Signs of Kundalini include spontaneous motor movements (e.g., spasms, jerks, vibration, unusual breathing, paralysis), sensory phenomena (e.g., lights, sounds, heat, cold, tickling), mental and emotional experiences (e.g., feelings of ecstasy, peace, love, or fear, confusion, and depression; accelerated, decelerated or irrational thinking; visions; and dissociation), and nonphysiological phenomena (e.g., out-of-body experiences, psychic abilities) (Sanella, 1992). These signs can easily be mistaken for psychiatric and organic disorders and thorough medical and psychological examinations are necessary for proper diagnosis. Though comparatively rare in western culture, this experience has been particularly well described by eastern writers and gurus.

NEAR-DEATH EXPERIENCES

The Near-Death Experience, discussed earlier, has easily identifiable signs. It is an experience of profound spiritual and mystical significance, though the unexpecting and unprepared individual may be frightened by its extraordinary and "impossible" nature. Voluntary or involuntary psychic phenomena sometimes follow, including extrasensory perception and out-of-body experiences. Near-Death Experiences occur in perhaps a third of those people medically resuscitated from clinical death, and are not characteristically associated with mental or emotional disorders, unless the individual has been made to feel "crazy" or sinful by others.

OUT OF BODY EXPERIENCES

Some people, during times of acute distress or physical exhaustion, or in moments of altered consciousness (e.g., the twilight state before sleep) discover their consciousness to be literally outside the body boundary. Some actually learn to evoke this state, others dismiss it as a dream. A variation of this experience occurs in Lucid Dreaming, a learned state in which an individual becomes competent at maintaining and directing consciousness while dreaming, sometimes traveling to other places or dimensions while the body sleeps. Like Near-Death Experiences, out of body experiences are not by themselves indications of mental or emotional disorder.

EXTRASENSORY PERCEPTION

Intense transpersonal experiences often expand consciousness, sometimes resulting in extrasensory perception (e.g., pre-cognition, remote viewing, mind reading). For others, ESP may develop naturally and gradually, often being present since early childhood. Authentic psychics tap into a larger consciousness in which temporal-spatial dimensions (i.e., past, present, and future; near and far) co-exist. Violating our rules of ordinary reality, such perception is often dismissed despite sometimes-remarkable evidence. ESP is not by itself a sign of mental or emotional disorder.

THE SHAMANIC CRISIS

The Shamanic Crisis has been described by anthropologists the world over and generally begins with a profound (and often psychotic) breakdown or illness. Accompanied by other worldly visions or experiences, it is commonly interpreted by indigenous peoples as an initiatory experience into non-ordinary states of consciousness, mystical experience, and soul travel later associated with the gift of psychic healing, identifying the individual as a shaman or spiritual medicine man. Western culture has no acceptable category for this experience, tending immediately to pathologize it. How often psychiatric breakdowns in young adults actually reflect this process is unknown.

GHOSTS, SPIRITS, DECEASED RELATIVES

People not only believe in ghosts, spirits, and visitations by deceased relatives, they experience them, sometimes quite distinctively: an apparition in a doorway, a message from a spirit or spirit guide, a recently deceased loved one at the foot of one's bed (Guggenheim & Guggenheim, 1996). These phenomena are common, often very important to the experiencer, and rarely associated with psychopathology. More controversially, some people profess the ability to channel disincarnate beings. With our increasing understanding of dissociative states, particularly Multiple Personality Disorder, the line between spirits and split off personalities is sometimes difficult to determine. Channeling, common with New Age practitioners, may represent a variety of possibilities, including the capacity to access to non-ordinary reality, the evocation of split off personalities, active imagination, or intentional fabrication.

A NOTE ON FORMAL PSYCHIATRIC DIAGNOSIS

Many of the foregoing mystical and spiritual processes are not explicitly included in American Psychiatric Association's *Diagnostic and Statistical Manual* used to codify mental and emotional disorders. When presenting signs and symptoms conform to a standard psychiatric diagnosis, conventional categories apply. Until recently, non-ordinary states had no appropriate section. A diagnostic category entitled "religious or spiritual problem" was introduced by Lukoff, Lu, and Turner (1992) and included in the latest revision (DSM IV). It reads, "This category can be used when the focus of clinical attention is a religious or spiritual problem. Examples include distressing experiences that involve loss or questioning of faith, problems associated with conversion to a new faith, or questioning of other spiritual values that may not necessarily be related to an organized church or religious institution." (APA, 1994). The initiators of this diagnosis indicate that many non-ordinary experiences would now fit in this category (e.g., mystical experience, spiritual emergence or emergency) (Lukoff et. al., 1996).

MANAGEMENT, TREATMENT, AND REFERRAL

Ideally, differential diagnosis should lead to differential management, treatment, and referral. For the average therapist or health care worker, the range of possible treatment options and decisions would usually include:

* Management of any acute medical or psychiatric crisis surrounding the presenting problem.
* Psychiatric or psychological treatment for diagnosable disorders.
* Spiritually oriented counseling for unhealthy or maladaptive spirituality, or non-pathological spiritual conditions causing emotional concern.
* Spiritually oriented psychotherapy for individuals seeking to integrate personal and spiritual growth.
* Explanation and reassurance when treatment is not necessary
* Possible referral to an appropriate::
    a. Mental health professional for psychiatric medication consultation, psychiatric hospitalization, psychological testing or social work assessment
    b. Medical professional for physical exam, laboratory testing
    c. Educational forum for classes, reading, study groups
    d. Church or church groups for prayer or study
    e. Clergy professional (e.g., priest, minister, rabbi, pastoral counselor, spiritual director)

MANAGING MYSTICAL AND PSYCHOTIC STATES:

Drawing from Agosin, Lukoff, the Grofs, and personal clinical experience, the following general decision rules and issues should be kept in mind when addressing conditions with mixed mystical and psychotic features:

* Determine whether the person is truly psychotic. If not, the individual's experience may simply be extraordinary rather than pathological.
* If psychiatric symptomatology is present, rule out organic disease with appropriate clinical and laboratory tests.
* Properly diagnose any ongoing psychiatric condition or process of decompensation, and treat it if possible without altogether suppressing or pathologizing any concurrent mystical experience.
* Sensitively confront pseudo-religious material directly (i.e., hallucinations, delusions, and obsessions) that represent defensive attempts to appear special or superior amidst catastrophically collapsing personality and self-esteem.
* Be very careful in working with mystical consciousness in serious psychiatric conditions (e.g., schizophrenia, paranoia, and major depressive episodes) to ensure that fascination with numinous content does not result in postponing appropriate psychiatric treatment, for the traumatization and damage of a prolonged breakdown can far outweigh momentary glimpses of eternity.
* Assess pre-morbid functioning very much the way you would any psychotic disorder, because prognosis is better if the patient has had a productive and functional ego structure in the past.
* Assess the client's ability to productively process their mystical experience (i.e., confusion, reality testing and insight) and their capacity for communication, cooperation and self-control.

*   Differential Crisis Management: If the patient is experiencing some level of mystical or spiritual crisis, determine which mental health, religious, or spiritual resources are most appropriate:
    1. Ascertain whether this is a medical, psychological, or spiritual emergency, or all three, and which strategies from each specialty are most appropriate.
    2. Balance psychotropic medication with the value of experiencing mystical phenomena with guidance.
    3. Decide whether the client should be hospitalized or placed in some other safe environment with responsible,, caring, and skillful supervision.
    4. Decide whether to use traditional psychotherapy or some form of spiritual guidance through the emergency.

DISCERNMENT

A special and very different kind of decision making occurs when a therapist uses what religious practitioners call discernment. Considered a spiritual gift or skill, discernment is a capacity of intuition in which the will, operation, or movement of the divine is sensed within one's own life or interior, or in the experience of another person. In clinical practice, it can also be a highly intuitive perceiving of the sacred nature of the client's presenting problem.

At one time in western Christianity, discernment focused primarily on determining whether one was being moved by good or evil spirits. With the advent of modern depth psychology, this classical tradition, called "discernment of spirits," evolved toward differentiating positive spiritual energies or promptings (those that bring one closer to God) from negative ones (those that block genuine spiritual growth, e.g., fear, guilt, pride, selfishness). Some argue that discernment is a divinely placed talent that can be developed but not routinely trained, though this argument could apply equally to psychotherapeutic talents, for some people are simply better suited to be therapists by temperament and native ability than others.

Qualities traditionally felt to underlie the capacity for spiritual discernment include humility and pureness of heart, personal spiritual experience, and openness to God. Tools of discernment emphasized in the religious literature consist of prayer, spiritual reflection, guidance from one's religious community, and analysis of the effects ("fruits') of a chosen path or decision. At the center of the discerning process is a prayerful reverence which intuitively and unselfishly seeks whatever is truly intended for the individual's soul and its growth in God.

Therapists blessed or trained with discernment sensitivities often utilize them during diagnosis and treatment, shifting from the clinical to the spiritual realm in determining whether a course of action is truly in the client's highest interests. Used sensitively, discernment can be genuinely beneficial, particularly when one has the courage to support a client's spiritual growth amidst contradictory medical, psychiatric, or family opinion. Its practice, however, should not replace sound clinical judgment but instead complement and extend it, particularly in distinguishing among psychological, spiritual, and mystical phenomena and their hidden purposes.

Chapter Fifteen

SPECIAL PROBLEMS IN A SPIRITUALLY ORIENTED PSYCHOTHERAPY

Contents: Client Problems
               Therapist Problems
               Clinical Problems
               Spiritual Problems

Spiritually oriented psychotherapy presents a unique set of problems. Understanding them will help therapists avoid a variety of complex, sometimes serious, and often unexpected pitfalls. These special problems fall into four areas: Client Problems, Therapist Problems, Practical Problems, and Spiritual Problems.

CLIENT PROBLEMS

Problems originating from clients include transference distortions, resistance to spiritual inquiry, unconscious ambivalence toward spiritual practices, the use of spirituality and religion to resist psychological work, and conflict between the drive for spiritual completion versus the psychological need for belonging.

TRANSFERENCE DISTORTIONS

Transference refers to a client's unconscious projection of original parental attributes and experiences onto the therapist, a process that is both normal and ubiquitous in and out of therapy. The analysis of transference, that is, bringing the related distortions into consciousness and uncovering the hurt that they hide, represents one of the most important tasks of therapy.

Transference distortions complicate the psychospiritual journey in numerous ways. They may inflate the perceived power, knowledge, or importance of the therapist until the client becomes more concerned with winning the therapist's approval or avoiding his criticism than confronting underlying wounds. Sometimes a client, longing for parental love to make up for childhood deprivation, will develop an idealizing transference, viewing the therapist as an all loving or "spiritually advanced soul." Excessive love, devotion, clinging, or dependency warns that such defensive transference is taking place.

An identical process happens in the relationship between spiritual teacher and student or aspirant. Spiritual seekers universally project their unfinished parental needs and fears onto religious leaders or teachers. When a parent has been violent, judgmental, uncaring, manipulative, or absent, the same characteristics will be found or projected onto both God and God's representatives. One of the basic causes of cult formation is the unconscious replication of dysfunctional parental relationships with the leader and the cult family. Devotees with histories of seriously dysfunctional family relationships are unable to recognize dangerous and manipulative leaders; worse, they are often drawn directly to them, falling prey to their disguised psychopathology. Though common in authoritarian religious communities, similar though more subtle and benign transference distortion often colors the average parishioner's relationship with their clergy, whom they also tend to unconsciously idealize or fear.

Many gurus from eastern traditions encourage a kind of idealized positive transference, explaining that loving them is a means of loving God. With 6000 years of Hindu religion, culture, and mythology to support and manage this model of "union with God through the teacher," the eastern guru-seeker relationship comes with various built-in corrections. In the west, however, this model can provide a foundation for enormous spiritual abuse and exploitation. With little or no comprehension of eastern culture and religious tradition, western seekers take the guru's word and behavior literally, naively overlooking the transference experience. Indeed, the seeker may explicitly be told that failure to submit to the guru is tantamount to failure to progress on the spiritual path. Complicating matters further, many transposed gurus, enamored by western material riches, succumbed to their own unrecognized conflicts surrounding greed, lust, power, or childhood deprivation. In a dysfunctional religious community, their subsequent acting out is ignored or rationalized as divinely inspired teaching behavior. There are accounts of such spiritual abuse in nearly every religious tradition and community (Simpkinson, 1996).

Loving the therapist or spiritual teacher "as God" may be appropriate at an advanced stage of the spiritual journey; encouraging it from the start, on the other hand, more commonly evokes the kind of idealizing transference that leads instead to cultic worship and exploitation. While an individual's deep longing to love God may underlay the entire spiritual journey, the transference desire to merge with an absent, cold, or unnourishing parent renders this longing highly susceptible to manipulation.

RESISTANCE TO SPIRITUAL INQUIRY

Some clients have a deeply ingrained reluctance to discuss spirituality in psychotherapy. Authoritarian religious teachings in childhood have left the whole subject of religion and spirituality frightening and uncomfortable, evoking unconscious fear of renewed chastisement and punishment. A history of religious abuse, including threats of hell and damnation, the manipulative use of guilt or humiliation, and harsh parental punishment rationalized by religious doctrine, can understandably instill in the client tremendous resistance to exploring their relationship to God in the therapeutic hour. As with any resistance, the therapist proceeds with caution, sensitivity, tact, and persistence to expose its roots and damage, and to promote healing of the associated traumatic ideas and emotions.

UNCONSCIOUS AMBIVALENCE TOWARD SPIRITUAL PRACTICES

For many people, the idea of doing spiritual practice is fraught with unconscious ambivalence. Some clients may resist contemplative practices or spiritual direction fearing an actual encounter with a God. Certain fundamentalist Christians believe that meditating may even allow Satan to slip into an unprotected mind. Others view meditation or contemplation as passivity or laziness, violating childhood standards of industry, ambition, and performance. Loss of control is yet another fear, particularly for people with rigid defenses. Perfectionists and over achievers, worried about whether they are practicing correctly or progressing rapidly enough, find spiritual practices frustrating, particularly when it has no "goal." Those with authority issues may resent being instructed to practice at all. Finally, the transcendence or dissolution of self, the ultimate destination of many spiritual techniques, is itself a terrifying idea to people overly attached to the security of the false self.

Such ambivalence is, of course, found in all religious communities and clergy are often called to advise struggling practitioners on their problems. The depthful and highly personal orientation of psychotherapy, however, creates an additional opportunity to expose, understand, and overcome ambivalence in a safe and supportive context.

THE USE OF SPIRITUALITY AND RELIGION TO RESIST PSYCHOLOGICAL WORK

Spirituality may itself be used as resistance. Some use prayer or spiritual practices to avoid examining underlying psychological wounds, naively hoping God will simply fix them. Others use religious dogma to rationalize their severely rigid conscience or need to control the behavior or feelings of others. Still others turn to spiritual "highs" or pollyannaish beliefs to deny the dark side of life, with its suffering, depression, danger, loss, unfairness, and cruelty. Religious addiction, the compulsive use of religious ideas or practices to defend against unconscious wounds, similarly obstructs the hard and painful work of uncovering and healing emotional injuries. A spiritually oriented psychotherapy must deal with such self-deception, confronting the client with the necessity of facing underlying psychological problems before spiritual movement can occur.

THE DRIVE TO COMPLETION VERSUS THE NEED TO BELONG

An important and recurrent conflict on the spiritual path pits the calling to complete one's spiritual destiny against the human need to belong. The drive to completion is a relentless search for the experience of holiness and union. We also experience the psychological need to have a place in family and community, a need which draws us into the social milieu for security, identity, and self-esteem. But belonging will never bring spiritual wholeness, and time spent socializing, even in rich and authentic human relationship, will not complete the journey. Seekers arrive at this crossroads when their need for divine communion, whether in contemplation, meditation, service or solitude, runs counter to their social or involvements. Genuine spiritual maturity requires finding a balance between these conflicting drives, often one that increasingly tips toward the spiritual as one ages.

THERAPIST PROBLEMS

Problems also originate from the therapist's side of the equation, including limitations of spiritual training and awareness, covert proselytizing, therapist fascinations, and difficulty releasing the traditional psychological mentality.

LIMITATIONS OF SPIRITUAL TRAINING AND AWARENESS

Requiring a high level integration of clinical and spiritual skills, spiritually oriented psychotherapy demands special competencies of the average therapist. For example, limitations in spiritual training and awareness can impair a therapist's capacity for contemplative attunement, causing him to avoid the Presence with easier psychological talk, or result in feeling responsible for making something spiritual happen in the hour. The ever-present risk of self-inflation similarly arises when the therapist believes that spiritual knowledge gives him special power or authority. These kinds of problems not only make spiritually oriented psychotherapy unique and challenging, they represent the personal and ongoing spiritual work required of the therapist.

COVERT PROSELYTIZING

One of the obvious hazards of doing spiritual work with clients is covert proselytizing. Every spiritually oriented therapist runs the risk of imposing personal beliefs on the client. Some do this subtly, some forcefully believing the client should have their views, and some do so without even realizing it. Many therapists, critical of the abuses of institutional religion and borrowing freely from eastern or New Age religions, amalgamate their own personal spiritual belief system and want the client to believe likewise. Though well intended, the therapists subtle pressure may violate the client's need to form their own spirituality or return to their original faith tradition. Until the therapist addresses his personal religious prejudices and preferences, the risk of such proselytizing will be great and paradoxically impede the very spiritual growth sought by the client.

THERAPIST FASCINATIONS

The therapist, too, can become fascinated by issues unrelated to the client's genuine psychological and spiritual growth. Entranced by dream symbols, extraordinary experiences, esoteric practices, or the spiritual meaning of signs and life events, therapy can be distracted from the psychological work of uncovering repressed emotional issues or the spiritual work of entering the Presence. The therapist needs to examine whether the client's material feels psychologically and spiritually alive, or whether spiritual talk has simply become a metaphysical fascination or distraction. The value of any spiritual discussion may be found in its consequences: Does it truly expand the client's capacity for spiritual practice and awareness, and does it lead to genuinely positive changes outside the session?

DIFFICULTY RELEASING THE TRADITIONAL PSYCHOLOGICAL MENTALITY

Moving into the spiritual dimension of psychotherapy, a therapist must release the traditional, well disciplined problem-solving orientation. Instead of focusing on psychological problems, states, and interventions, attention shifts into a very different consciousness, one that does not seek to fix anything but rather opens itself to the presence, guidance, and reality of the divine. The therapist's goal here is to support and maintain sacred consciousness, for now God becomes the therapist and the therapist becomes a midwife to this higher consciousness. It is difficult for most therapists to yield the need to offer interpretations, give direction, or draw conclusions, and trust instead that the spirit will find its own way to insight and action. The spiritual journey is not a problem to be fixed, it is a process of revelation, and a slow one at that. The traditional psychological mentality, while valuable in the psychological phases of the work, can actually serve as an impediment to the client's spiritual evolution.

CLINICAL PROBLEMS

Clinical problems involve decisions about how to conduct therapy within a larger psychospiritual format, including when to invite spiritual discussion, how to protect the sacred, the assessment of spiritual progress, comfort versus the spiritual value of pain, strengthening versus surrendering ego control, confidentiality and the transmission of spiritual information, resistance from family, and individual versus group therapy.

WHEN TO INVITE SPIRITUAL DISCUSSION

When are discussions of spirituality indicated and when are they contraindicated? The answers are practical, clinical, and spiritual, and do not easily reduce to simple principles. As discussed previously, the therapist's decision is based on assessment of the client's personality and readiness along with prayerful discernment of the client's spiritual needs. For some clients, the presenting problem is itself an immediate opportunity for spiritual learning, enrichment, and healing, and many are far more ready to discuss their spirituality than their therapists realize. It is often the therapist's lack of awareness or readiness that stands in the way. For others, talk of spirituality will need to wait until their presenting psychological problems are resolved, until they are emotionally ready, or until something about the problems under discussion simply cries out for this dimension.

PROTECTING THE SACRED

Even when spirituality has become an integral part of psychotherapy (i.e., the Pure Spirituality in Psychotherapy end of the Integration Continuum, Chapter 9), it is important to safeguard the sacred dimension. Over-reliance on God's presence in problem solving, excessive frequency of spiritually oriented sessions, or intellectualized spiritual discussion can dilute and trivialize the divine dimension. Simple rituals such as lighting a candle, saying a prayer, or sitting in silence, may be used to create a boundary between psychological and spiritual modes of work. Limiting the frequency of direct spiritual experience also heightens its intensity, meaning, and specialness.

ASSESSMENT OF SPIRITUAL PROGRESS

Given the numerous ways religion and spirituality can be defensively misused, the client's spiritual progress should be periodically reviewed. As we have seen, assessment focuses on the quality of the client's prayer experience and felt relationship with the divine, and involves a thoughtful discrimination between healthy, unhealthy, defensive, and maladaptive forms of spirituality. Such assessment may be formal or informal and initiated at the request of therapist or client. In fact, periodic standardized review can assist the client in objectively assessing their spiritual progress over time. The client's progress should also be reviewed within the context of the specific developmental stages of the spiritual journey, for the issues and criteria change significantly along the way.

COMFORT VERSUS THE SPIRITUAL VALUE OF PAIN

People bring real and often deep pain into therapy, and therapists work sincerely to help them experience and complete it. When the client's suffering does not remit with appropriate treatment, or when it worsens, and when alternative forms of treatment have been unsuccessful, the task of therapy may instead be to help the client simple bear the pain, find its spiritual meaning, and eventually surrender it to God for resolution. Too much support and comfort, too many attempts to fix the pain, often driven by feelings or failure on the therapist's part, rob the client of this important "soul work." Hidden in the deepest suffering can be profound (though often slow) emotional and spiritual growth. This kind of pain becomes a fire that burns away years of buried cancerous torment, finally opening up space within for genuinely new emotional and spiritual growth. Not all pain can be cured; some is meant to transform the one afflicted.

STRENGTHENING VERSUS SURRENDERING EGO CONTROL

In traditional psychotherapy, and expressed in the rugged individualism of western culture, the goal of psychological development and life itself is to form a strong and confident ego. There are times in the spiritual journey, however, when the drive to overcome, master, or conquer problems must be surrendered to the will of God. Irreparable catastrophes, unremitting hardship, and aging, with all its defeats and losses, undermine the heroic attitude of western man. People who only value strength and ego-mastery either ignore spirituality or desire to meet God on their own terms. Unwilling to give up the false self of quadrant 3, they resist the necessary spiritual growth found in the descent in to quadrant 4. Psychotherapy moves from traditional to spiritual goals when it arrives at this crossroads, addressing the value of surrender, the growth of the soul, and the priority of spiritual union over the ego's desire for solution, control, and domination.

CONFIDENTIALITY AND THE TRANSMISSION OF SPIRITUAL INFORMATION

While therapists often need to exchange clinical information with other therapists or health care providers (with formal authorization, of course), a particularly delicate problem arises when spiritual information is shared. By its very nature, such information is sacred and can lose its immediacy, poignancy, meaning, and beauty when diluted in casual or intellectualized secular discussion. If other professionals need to know something of a client's spiritual life, it is often best for them to address this need directly with the client, who in turn can decide when and what to reveal. For the same reasons, it is important that the client not casually or indiscriminately divulge his personal spiritual experiences or insights to family and friends. Spiritual information is best communicated, in a protected and sacred space.

RESISTANCE FROM THE FAMILY

The emotional and economic security of both family and friends is invested in their familiar relationship with the client. When a client begins to make important life changes, when the drive to completion begins to overshadow the need to belong, this familiar enmeshment and interdependence may feel threatened. Spiritual change in particular, often creates irrational fears that the loved one will quit work, become a religious fanatic,or join a cult. Criticism, non-support, or discouragement from family and friends can profoundly discourage or undermine a client's spiritual journey. Education, skillful guidance, and emotional encouragement from the therapist are especially important in minimizing familial distrust and alienation. Because most people do not, in the end, go off and do what their family fears most, this resistance can usually be managed until it dissipates. When it does not remit over time, the psychological problems of others in the environment must be identified and understood (e.g., co-dependence, enmeshment, fusion, and merging defenses) for such resistance may be warning signs of more serious dysfunction.

INDIVIDUAL VERSUS GROUP THERAPY

Spiritual direction and spiritually oriented psychotherapy can also be done in groups (e.g., Dougherty, 1996). In fact, group work has certain advantages, including a greater range of client experiences for the group to learn from, discernment and corrective feedback from other members, and deeper experiences of prayer and meditation that can occur in-group settings. The advantages of individual work, of course, include greater individualized time, attention, and depth of focus. Therapist comfort, training, and preparation are central factors in this decision. While therapist can refer a client to a spiritual group and continue individual therapy, it is probably not appropriate for spiritual work to be done in both places at the same time.

SPIRITUAL PROBLEMS

Some of the problems encountered in a spiritually oriented psychotherapy are unique to the spiritual journey itself, including fear of spiritual growth, or major changes in life goals, the melancholy of releasing attachments, declining defenses against the awesome reality of God and death, the "Dark Night of the Soul," religious conversion, coping with altered states, and limitations in spiritual capacity. Rather than being automatically reduced to psychopathology, spiritual problems need specialized attention, discernment, and management.

FEAR OF SPIRITUAL GROWTH

Despite our professed longing and motivation for spiritual growth, we all carry secret resistance to the spiritual journey and its revelations. Genuine spiritual progress is frightening, especially when we realize it may require: 1) yielding the false self with its grandiosity, attachments, addictions, and illusory security; 2) making the time, energy, and financial commitment to psychological healing and spiritual progress; and 3) confronting the moral issues associated with increasing spiritual awareness (e.g., recognizing that one's job or lifestyle is spiritually harmful or socially unjust). We repeatedly turn away from the spiritual path when its insights and implications seem to demand too much. Sometimes we avoid our fears by escaping into spiritual techniques where the "highs" of a practice become more important than the immediate reality of God in one's life. At times of fear and doubt, our beliefs or techniques can insidiously become more attractive than their goal - knowing God.

MAJOR CHANGES IN LIFE GOALS

The growth of spiritual awareness is often accompanied by significant changes in life values and goals. False self, money, power, and success diminish in importance, replaced by a desire to spend more time in spiritual practice or serving God. Along with these new values come many anxious questions: How do I know if my desire for solitude and contemplation is healthy? Is my desire to serve God truly a calling? Should I give up all the accumulated material possessions I no longer value? Am I foolishly risking financial security by following this path? What about my obligations to family and friends? Such questions also arise in traditional long-term psychotherapy, where deep personality changes lead to reconsideration of numerous occupational, marital, and personal values. With spiritual progress, the changes may simply be larger.

The prospect of significant change naturally evokes fear. In fact, fear may be a warning that we are not ready. Rather than acting impulsively, the desire for radical change should be explored practically, psychologically, and spiritually until its basis and validity are truly understood. Extensive discussion in therapy, conversations with friends and family, prayerful discernment, experimental but low risk steps in the desired direction, and patience are all important resources during times of decision. Eventually the next genuine step in our spiritual path usually becomes clear, though its final concrete form is not infrequently quite different than first imagined.

THE MELANCHOLY OF RELEASING ATTACHMENTS

Desiring the life of the spirit very often leads people away from material and relational attachments. Anytime attachments are lost, however, there are feelings of sadness and melancholy. We love the gratification of relationships and the conveniences the modern life. Giving up attachments does not necessarily mean choosing a bare and Spartan life, it means giving up those attachments that are most clearly addictive. Addictions by definition lower consciousness and the time comes when the cost of this diminution is too great. In the end, all must be given up anyway, but as so many religions teach, it is the act and process of releasing attachments that result in the most profound spiritual transformation.

The melancholy we feel as attachments are left behind is appropriate. It is a sign to go slowly, to feel and understand the meaning of what we are doing. Real spiritual growth is not about forcing oneself to be ascetic. Genuine asceticism flows from a joyous release of things no longer valued. Melancholy is also a manifestation of our own humanness and how deeply we bond to people, places and things. Without opening to this feeling, we cannot know the nature of the heart and what it is to be fully human. Clinging to things, however, we cannot know the reality of the spirit.

DECLINING DEFENSES AGAINST THE AWESOME REALITY OF GOD AND DEATH

For the unenlightened, belief in a fixed, concrete reality, whether full of satisfactions or sorrow, is itself a defense against the unfathomable and awesome reality of God and death. We are not ultimately in control of our destiny. We cling to reality comforts and fantasies to escape the knowledge that one day we must leave this world and face the Creator. While death is easily romanticized with comforting religious images, its imminent realization is more often terrifying and catastrophic, at least at first.

Spiritual practice can bring us to this same point, for as the penetration into the dark nothingness of God deepens, and as the world of attachments increasingly falls away, the terror of personal death emerges and must be lived through. Sometimes this terror actually represents an old emotional issue in disguise (e.g., repressed childhood fears of dependency loss); sometimes it is the fear of losing everything that is familiar. The anxieties in this category are primarily psychological, for the instinctive fear of dissolution and non-existence is staggering, evoking all our survival issues. But when the fires of terror finally burn out, what remains is God, whose love allows us to releases the attachments of this world and move on.

THE "DARK NIGHT OF THE SOUL"

In the "Dark Night of the Soul," described by the Christian mystic St. John of the Cross (St. John of the Cross, 1990, Welch, 1990), one feels profoundly abandoned by God. Spiritual deadness, emptiness, and decay grip the soul, which can be especially distressing after earlier experiences of divine love and ecstasy. Said to be a natural and inevitable stage on the spiritual path, the "Dark Night" serves the profound purpose of dissolving ego-centered desires, attachment to God images rather than God, and even our experience self. With the complete frustration of the ego, the individual has no choice but to surrender. Broken and powerless, emptied of self-centered desires for God, one is gradually albeit painfully purified of pretension, fantasy, and grasping. The surrender is to what God wants and is.

While anger, depression, and despair often occur in this desolation experience, it should not be mistaken for a mood disorder. Nor should more everyday life disappointments, losses, or melancholy be mistaken for this experience. The "Dark Night" is said to be a specific God-given experience with tremendous healing hidden within its profound suffering. As such, it needs to be recognized and handled from a spiritual perspective rather than reduced to a psychological or psychiatric disorder.

CONVERSION

Another experience commonly connected to the spiritual journey is religious conversion. In Christian parlance, the term implies a profound and abrupt metamorphosis of belief and personality, from a secular, self-centered life to one devoted to and centered in the figure and experience of Jesus. The term can really be applied to any profound religious experience (e.g., the Kundalini or Shakti phenomena, moments of mystical awakening, the Near-Death Experience) that profoundly reorganizes an individual's inner life, value structure, and outer goals.

Examples of dramatic, instantaneous conversion abound in religious literature, creating the impression that it is the normative means of spiritual change. By far the more common experience however, is a gradual, up-and-down process of endless small and large events, all contributing to a progressive spiritual evolution. In fact, the process of religious conversion typically goes on for a lifetime, with the most profound progress often occurring in those painful life experiences that disrupt our convenient religious beliefs and security, and call instead into a naked, direct, and authentic confrontation with God. Each conversion, whether small or large, is also a mini-death and a passage from one life form to another. In this sense, life is potentially a series of religious conversions, each taking us more deeply into the reality and experience of the divine acting in our lives.

A spiritually oriented psychotherapist needs to understand the difference between the "big" conversion (i.e., satori, enlightenment), and this slow, ongoing accretion of smaller conversions. Even those mystical experiences that carry transformative teachings do not typically result in a permanently enlightened religious life. Nor do they eradicate pre-existing life problems and suffering. Instead, it is the infinite series of little conversions whose summation constitutes our most profound movement into God. This kind of spiritual growth requires, and in time provides, courage, surrender, and faith. Looking back on the path we have taken, we see that the little steps were more important as the big ones.

COPING WITH ALTERED STATES

Sometimes along the spiritual path, whether from intense spiritual practice or unexpected epiphany, a seeker may experience states of mind and energy unlike any previously encountered. Infusions of powerful or ecstatic energy, swooning states of bliss, inner light shows, metaphysical revelations, openings to other realities, holy visions or encounters, heightened consciousness of the immanent divine, psychic perceptions, past-life remembrances - saints, mystics, and even everyday people have described such phenomena for centuries.

Not only are these altered states commonly mistaken for psychiatric disorders, they can be frankly disabling to conventional life adjustment, sometimes for extended periods. People absorbed in the power of such non-ordinary consciousness sometimes require prolonged support, protection, supervision, and guidance. Some are frightened by what is happening and equally frightened to tell anyone. Others are able to conceal their experience and simply withdraw until it ends. Here the skills of a spiritually sophisticated therapist are particularly relevant, for the problems caused by altered states are a part of the spiritual path generally unknown to conventional therapists.

LIMITATIONS IN SPIRITUAL CAPACITY

Human nature is clearly limited in how much love, transcendence, joy, and ecstasy the nervous system and personality can incorporate before cutting it off. Moments of mystical enlightenment, the alterations of consciousness that can arise during a prolonged spiritual retreat, or the bliss of deep contemplative union exceed not only our everyday capacity for spiritual experience but the limits of our psychophysical make-up as well. It is far easier to engage reactive emotional distress (e.g., anger, conflict) or be seduced by low levels of consciousness (e.g., television, movies, gossip) than a sustain life transforming awareness of the divine Presence.

Limitations in spiritual capacity are the rule rather than the exception. Not only do they reflect the countless barriers to expanded consciousness inventoried by every religion and metaphysical system (e.g., greed, lust, laziness, ignorance), these limitations are consistent with the present state of psychospiritual evolution. The human personality is simply not capable of holding the power, consciousness, and intelligence of the Divine Being. This realization sets an important reality limit on our spiritual fantasies and aspirations: no one in this lifetime gets there. Temporary states of union, yes. Life altering revelation, yes. Permanent enlightenment, no. Our goal is not be master the spirit, but to open to its ubiquitous presence and be changed in accordance with its will. What that means must be discovered by each.

CHAPTER SIXTEEN

SPIRITUAL PRACTICES AS ADJUNCTS TO THERAPY

Contents: Selection of Practices
             Client Preparation
             Therapist Skill and Experience
             Description of Selected Spiritual Practices
             A Note to Clients on Experimenting with Spiritual Practices

If we are serious about bringing spirituality into psychotherapy, then we need to consider bringing it directly into the therapy hour and into the client's life. The range and variety of spiritual practices is rich and nearly endless. Spiritual techniques introduced need not be elaborate or complex. Their success, however, depends on appropriate selection, the client's preparation, the therapist's skill, experience, and informed consent, and a thoughtful review afterwards.

SELECTION

Spiritual techniques can be used in the treatment of specific emotional problems or for spiritual growth, with the selection depending on the client's place in the Ego-Soul Matrix.

QUADRANT 3: DISMANTLING THE FALSE SELF

As discussed earlier, psychotherapy typically begins in quadrant 3 or 4. Techniques in quadrant 3 are few. Here the client is still holding onto the false self and often resists attempts to unmost or unmask or dismantle it. In fact, most spiritual practices will merely be assimilated into the false self in this stage.

QUADRANT 4: COLLAPSE

Much of a client's initial healing occurs in quadrants 4. With the breakdown of the false self comes acute distress and the need to manage, contain, or work through that distress. Much of this distress is also historical requiring a return to buried wounds.

Sometimes clinical problems can be helped by spiritual or religious methods. For example, considerable experience and literature support the use of meditative techniques in the treatment of various medical and psychological conditions, including psychophysiologic disorders, chronic pain, and historical trauma (Bogart, 1991; Kabat-Zinn, et. a., 1986; Kabat-Zin et. al., 1992, Urbanowski & Miller, 1996). The use of prayer, guided religious visualization, and scripture have similarly been used to treat traumatic memories (Tan, 1996). Imaging a religious figure interceding in a painful memory can reduce anxiety and promote comfort, healing, and forgiveness, as can pray or reassuring passages of scripture. Techniques that allow the client to express, discharge, or give form to this distress can also be helpful (e.g., journal writing, exercise, artwork) with or without a spiritual basis.

With the collapse of the ego's control over life comes the opportunity to learn about surrender, for it is surrender that opens the door to the sacred dimension of quadrant 1. Many clients, however, view surrender in negative ways, as giving up, failing, being weak, or worse, being unprotected from more assault. Although surrender is more an attitude than a technique, it can frame much of the healing achieved in quadrant 4. Indeed, any attitudes and techniques that support and validate this stage will be are also helpful (e.g., prayer, contemplation, or collective worship).

QUADRANT 1: REVELATION AND HEALING

In quadrant 1, we seek spiritual meaning, revelation, contact, healing, and growth. This work can begin whenever a client's acute distress has been sufficiently contained and understood to begin exploration of the spiritual dimension.

Meaning and revelation can be found in writing a spiritual autobiography, exploring one's life and problems in spiritual direction, beginning to interpret dreams, or through more active searching outside the hour via religious study, ascetic practices, or some form of vision quest. Revelation comes in many forms through spontaneous insights, intuitions, images, dreams, synchronous life events, or the continuum of mystical experience.

Direct sacred contact often happens within experiences of prayer, sacred space (e.g., rituals, spiritual retreats, solitude, nature mysticism, and formal worship), and activities that invite spirit directly into being (e.g., ecstatic dance, song, chant, creativity and art, contemplation, and body practices such as yoga or tai chi). Spiritual healing and growth occur anytime we are in direct contact with the living divine Presence.

QUADRANT 2: LIVING A SPIRITUAL LIFE

With the growth of spiritual contact and awareness comes rebirth and renewal, and the desire to bring this growth into life. We can express our increasing spirituality in numerous ways, including formal worship, a commitment to living spiritual values, deeds of compassion or social justice, or simply bringing our work into the spirituality we feel. In fact, the spiritualization of everyday activity can itself be practiced by repeatedly bringing consciousness back into the Presence during ongoing thought, intention, and behavior.

Each client has a unique spiritual path. On the path, practices will feel right and useful, off the path, they will feel sterile and empty. The authenticity of the path depends on which quadrant the client is operating in. For example, when practices are performed with an excessive concern for correctness and success, ego has become too important and authenticity is lost. (quadrant 3) On the other hand, dogmatic rules and expectations imposed in quadrants 1 and 2 will injure the religious experience and its expression.

CLIENT PREPARATION

Preparation and informed consent are not only ethically mandated, the effectiveness of spiritual techniques depends heavily on the client's understanding, acceptance, and congruence of values. A skeptical engineer may need a scientific or mechanistic explanation for the value of meditation before he would be willing to consider it. An individual hurt in the past by dogmatic religious behavior may need a lot of preparation before she can consider any healing images from that tradition. And because religious beliefs are both deeply personal and irrational, sensitive understanding of a client's faith is critical to the therapeutic power of these deep images.

THERAPIST SKILL, EXPERIENCE, AND INFORMED CONSENT

Therapists should only introduce techniques and practices with which they have sufficient skill and experience. Using a technique beyond the scope of one's training and experience is a little like practicing a new surgical procedure for the first time without the requisite training. Fully informing the client about the technique, its nature, purpose, assumptions, and outcomes, and one's own experience with it, is ethically necessary and allows the client to decide whether they believe it is in the best interests.

REVIEW

Anytime a spiritual technique or experience is introduced into the therapy process, some review of its meaning and impact should take place to ensure it is having the desired or efficacious effect. Clients are usually interested in debriefing an experience, and the information they provide can be invaluable in determining whether and how to proceed with a technique. In fact, they are often most creative in guiding the therapist in how the technique might be modified to best suit their needs in the future. Similarly, unspoken blocks and reservations are often exposed in the review.

Relevant and penetrating questions can focus this review process, including: Is this portion of our work helping you? Is it getting in the way of our psychological work? Is your life changing as a result of your spiritual practice? Do you feel you are growing in your relationship to God? Are you feeling grounded, real, and nourished in this experience? These kinds of questions ensure that the spiritual portion of the client's ongoing therapy is constructive and genuinely helpful. With such thoughtful assessment, and the client's honest feedback, the therapist become a close and valued assistant on the client's spiritual path rather than its director.

DESCRIPTION OF SELECTED PRACTICES

While it is impractical and virtually impossible to describe every spiritual practice of potential value to psychotherapy, some deserve attention here because of their immediate value and ease of integration.

SPIRITUAL AUTOBIOGRAPHY

One of the most revealing and catalytic exercises, especially early in the spiritual journey, involves simply asking the client to write his spiritual autobiography. It can include descriptions of formal religious instruction, very personal spiritual experiences and realizations, changing beliefs, and current status. More than a objective history, it can tell the story of the client's religious longing and the journey taken to meet it. The spiritual autobiography nicely complements the process of spiritual assessment, often covering many of the same areas and providing information that can then move naturally into the more formal evaluation discussed in Chapter 14.

LEARNING TO BE QUIET

A client may be asked simply to be still, quiet, and patiently open for several minutes. The goal is a non-intellectual openness, one in which active thinking and analyzing are replaced with a calm, centered, receptive or expanded awareness. Without specific effort or intention, it is a quiet that gradually changes one's consciousness, resulting in softening and relaxation, heightened or clearer self-awareness, and a sense of one's own "ground of being." As the Tao teaches, muddy water, let stand, becomes clear. With this kind of awareness, whatever is truly important about the client's issues will come into focus. Quiet can also be used as a bridge into specific exercises or skills, or the more spiritually attuned consciousness associated with contemplation or spiritual direction.

PRAYER

Prayer, of course, is a vast and multifaceted religious practice, and can only be addressed briefly here. Its personal and subjective value, however, has always been enormous.

Though it may seem strange or alien to a secular therapist, a spiritually oriented psychotherapy will sometimes include prayer. It may consist of a shared experience of coming into the divine Presence, formal prayer, verbal or silent, addressing the problem at hand, or simply talking out loud to God. Times for prayer may also be set aside during the day and many people feel their lives are better balanced when prayer is practiced regularly. What is most important is the individual's actual experience of prayer and its effect or influence in his life.

Discussion of prayer may be helpful or necessary, for many clients hold simplistic beliefs that limit the value and experience of prayer in their lives. Some believe that God is too far away to hear their prayers, that they do not know how to pray properly, or that they are undeserving of God's individual attention. These and other misconceptions need to be identified and corrected. The variety of prayer forms should also be discussed so that the client can discover what feels most natural and comfortable. Prayer, is a learning experience that will change over time, and periodic discussion of a client's prayer experience is suggested.

Prayer need not be petition only; it can also include simply sitting in the Presence, spiritual focusing, chanting, contemplation, meditative walking, journal writing, reading inspirational material, dialogues with God, working in the garden, ecstatic dancing, or listening to music. The essential idea is that prayer is a way of making conscious communion or relationship with the divine in whatever form feels most immediate and authentic, for such connection is central to spiritual growth.

At its deepest level, prayer is not about getting or fixing something. It is beyond problems. Prayer is an end in itself: an opening to the energies, love, or holy silence of the Divine Being. It is the ultimate relationship, and needs to be treated with the deepest respect, honesty, and intimacy.

For the deeply religious, this relationship is the very reason for existence, and for them life becomes an ongoing prayer.

The therapist may also feel called to pray for his clients, both during and after the hour. It need not be formal or acknowledged. It is the therapist's private communion and his heartfelt desire for the client's highest good. The therapist's prayer serves as a humbling recognition of the real source of healing and growth in psychotherapy.

SPIRITUAL DIRECTION

While Spiritual Direction has been previously discussed, it is mentioned again here as a particularly natural complement to psychotherapy. Learning to experience the Presence is one of the most rewarding spiritual practices a client can learn, and teaching it through the process of Spiritual Direction fits beautifully with the therapist's already developed skills of active listening, empathic attunement, and trust in the client's core experience. With thoughtful explanation, many spiritually motivated clients take readily to Spiritual Direction. Although it need not be a frequent activity in therapy, devoting an occasional hour to it can provide a rich and sacred complement to the more conventional therapeutic work. Again it should be emphasized that the therapist should have some personal experience in and training Spiritual Direction before they can assume competence.

A whole or part of a session may be devoted to Spiritual Direction, bracketed by a ritual that invites, contains and amplifies the Presence. It often begins with simple ritual demarcating the movement into sacred space, and may involve lighting a candle, sitting in quiet or silent prayer for a few minutes, and then talking in a simple and centered way about the client's experience of God in his life, problems, or the here-and-now moment. Creating ritual space for exploring personal mystical experience keeps the focus explicitly on the sacred itself, preventing by mutual agreement lapses into conventional psychological talk or problem-solving.

CONFESSION, ATONEMENT, AND ABSOLUTION

Historically viewed as a solely religious activity, the psychological and spiritual benefits of confession, atonement, and absolution are not limited to religious institutions alone. Alcoholics Anonymous for example, relies heavily on a foundation of confession, penitent restitution, and forgiveness. Psychotherapy, too, asks clients to confess what feels painful, shameful, or unforgivable, and helps them work through the underlying anguish to become more forgiving of themselves and others. In the healing experience, atonement often emerges naturally, for clients long to heal the wounds they inadvertently inflicted on others. The therapist's deep and unconditional acceptance then becomes a kind of psychological absolution.

Confession, atonement, and absolution can also be taken into the spiritual dimension of the psychotherapy hour. A client may prayerfully acknowledge past cruel, ignorant, or hurtful behavior, and ask the divine for forgiveness and release from its karmic consequences. It is not about shaming or punishing an individual that we encourage confession, it is for that person's healing in God.

A NOTE TO CLIENTS ON EXPERIMENTING WITH SPIRITUAL PRACTICES

In experimenting with spiritual practices, keep in mind the following principles:

* Trust your interests. If you find an area stimulating and meaningful, immerse yourself in it. When you begin to lose interest, back away and let this new material settle. The religious psyche needs time to digest and evaluate what it has experienced. There are even times when a seeker needs to take a break from seeking altogether. Then, when the time comes, spiritual hunger will arise anew and the next step will appear.

* Don't be afraid to explore new ideas and move among various spiritual paths. Find out which paths really speak the language of your soul.

* Though it may sound contradictory, understand that jumping around among many different traditions also prevents you from going deeply enough into the wisdom and experience any particular one. When you are ready, therefore, study and practice within a specific tradition until you have fathomed its depth and breadth, often within a community of believers.

* Integrate your spiritual interests and experiences into therapy. Use therapy as a place to share, understand, and examine your journey, and to see how it reflects, complements, or undermines your psychological growth.

* Always remember the old adage that the finger pointing at the moon is not the moon. God is more than any technique, system, or experience. Becoming too fascinated by any activity is itself an attachment that will only divert you from the far more important goal: the immediate, here-and-now, experience of God.

* The whole point of the spiritual path and its practices is to experience God's presence and activity in our lives. It is an ability that we learn gradually over a lifetime, carrying us through our hardest times and giving to life its finest and highest meaning.

CHAPTER SEVENTEEN

EDUCATION, TRAINING, AND PERSONAL PREPARATION: A NEW SPECIALIZATION?

Contents: Professional Preparation: Education and Training
             Personal Preparation: The Calling of Spiritual Psychotherapy
             Spirituality in Other Helping Professions

What does a therapist need to do to bring spirituality into the consulting room? Is specialized training or supervision required? Should there be professional certification in the practice of spiritual psychotherapy as a subspecialty?

In religious circles, there has always been debate regarding the selection and training of spiritual guides and directors. Some argue that special training is necessary, others that such skill is a God-given talent, a Charisma, that can only be discovered, validated, and encouraged as a ministry. Some religious communities encourage lay people to provide such direction if they feel called, and believe that the calling is far more important than the training. In psychology and psychotherapy, on the other hand, certification has become increasingly important because of the complexity of the problems being addressed, the rapidly growing sophistication of knowledge in the behavioral sciences, and therapists' responsibility to the public. In this professional climate, most practitioners in the field would argue that therapists wishing to practice a spiritually oriented psychotherapy should receive additional training and supervision in it.

PROFESSIONAL PREPARATION

There is a tremendous diversity of religious and spiritual information available nowadays. The sheer number of offerings in spiritual courses and programs is incredible: everyday spirituality, vispassana meditation, Rumi poetry, Jewish mysticism, Enneagram as a spiritual path, kundalini yoga, Native American spirituality, journal writing, drumming, mystic spirituality, biospiritual focusing, centering prayer, lucid dreaming, art as divine expression, Jungian spirituality, psychosynthesis, and volunteer service as spiritual practice. One must be cautious, on the other hand, of this contemporary supermarket approach, which often offers quick serve, superficial packages of spiritual instruction and techniques by relative beginners. Mix and match spirituality means sampling many wells and never going to the bottom of any. It also means incorrectly believing one has attained significant spiritual understanding from what is really a shallow exposure.

As noted earlier, professional training in spirituality has historically been quite limited and most currently practicing therapists never took a psychologically relevant course in the fields of religion or spirituality during their graduate studies. Recently, however, graduate programs specializing in blending psychology and spirituality have begun to appear, offering fairly depthful and advanced course work leading to certification as well as masters and doctorate degrees (e.g., California Institute of Integral Studies, Institute of Imaginal Studies, John F. Kennedy University, Shalem Institute for Spiritual Formation, The Haden Institute, Institute for Transpersonal Psychology, University of Santa Monica Center for the Study and Practice of Spiritual Psychology, The University of Creation Spirituality). Because these programs are relative few in number, this trend still leaves the majority of well trained practitioners with no formal exposure to religion and spirituality, and a handful with a lot. Unfortunately, state licensing exams also place such a high demand on clinical and technical knowledge that graduates of spiritually oriented professional schools often must set aside much of what they have learned in order to pass the exam.

It can be seen, then, that the professional preparation of psychotherapists is still uneven and uncertain, particularly for those trained one or more decades ago. A fundamental assumption of the present work, however, is that therapists are uniquely skilled to work with a client's spirituality; in fact, our reluctance in this area borders on professional negligence akin to the days before mandatory training in sexuality and substance abuse. It is not that each therapist should practice spiritual psychotherapy, for the field of psychology like medicine is too large for everyone to know everything, nor does everyone feel interested or called. But every therapist should know enough to inquire and refer, and those interested in practicing a spiritually oriented subspecialty of psychotherapy should be sufficiently prepared to conduct themselves in a professional fashion. Therapists can learn much about religion, spirituality, and mysticism that will benefit their clients. Those able to incorporate the skills of spiritual practice, direction, and discernment will contribute even more.

With this proposition in mind, exposure to the following areas of knowledge, personal experience, education, supervision, consultation, professional associations, and participation in a faith community are recommended:

Knowledge:
comparative religion
the psychology and history of religion
stages and trials of the spiritual journey
familiarity with the symbols of the sacred journey in myth, legend, and folk tales
shamanism, faith healing, indigenous spirituality
mysticism

Personal
Experiences:
personal spiritual work and practice
initiation, ritual, ceremonial practices
experience in spiritual direction or spiritually oriented psychotherapy
discernment of personal readiness

Education:
workshops and conferences on spirituality and spiritually oriented psychotherapy
academic courses in religion outside the major of psychology

Supervision:
ongoing supervision or apprenticeship with a spiritually experienced therapist

Consultation:
peer review groups of spiritually oriented psychotherapists

individual consultation as necessary

Professional Societies:	relevant professional societies and their newsletters (e.g., Division 36 of the American Psychological Association: Psychology of Religion and its newsletter)
A faith community:	participation in some kind of faith community for feedback, sacred experience, support, deepening practice, the understanding of religion

Should spiritual psychotherapy be a specialization within the field of counseling and psychotherapy? I think the time has come to answer affirmatively. It is too risky to practice in this area without meaningful preparation and ongoing review. We expect this level of professionalism in all other areas of specialization, and spirituality, with its many unique pitfalls, should be no exception. It is also time for all psychological and medical graduate programs in counseling, psychotherapy, and psychiatry to provide course work in religion, spirituality, consciousness, and mystical experience.

PERSONAL PREPARATION

The most important preparation is also the most personal. It may come from individual contemplative experiences, Sunday afternoon reading, Spiritual Direction, great sermon, a spiritual journal, one's own spiritual autobiography, hiking in the woods, applying a sacred story to life, a religious dream, or a conversation with a friend. It also comes in the feeling of being called to this field, a requirement rather unlike any other specialization.

In Chapter 15, we discussed some of the questions therapists need to ask themselves in determining their readiness to explore religious and spiritual themes in psychotherapy. This section asks a more personal and simple question: Do you feel spiritually drawn to this kind of work? Education, experience, and motivation are basic pre-requisites, but there is one more: *Calling*.

If one is to move into direct spiritual work with clients, opening their awareness and the therapy hour itself to the very presence of God, the therapist needs to know whether this kind of work truly emanates from a personal calling or natural gift. Consistent with its sacred origin, this question cannot really be answered logically; instead it should be the subject of introspection, prayer, spiritual direction, and consultation with one's psychological, spiritual, and religious community. Rather than impulsively rushing into spiritual practices in therapy, the question of "vocation" should be patiently contemplated until a deep and soulful answer begins to form. Then the answer needs to be re-explored and the question asked again in light of new experience. In time, through these cycles of discernment and experimentation, personally valid answers take shape.

Self-reflective questions a therapist might ask include: Is spiritual work an extension of my indwelling nature? Has this calling emerged gradually and steadily over time as an integral part my spiritual development and wholeness? Does my interest suggest a gift ready for development at this time? Does it flow from God's presence in my life? Does it fit with my other values and community commitments? Am I old enough, humble enough, wise enough? What specific problems or doubts come up for me when considering this work? What else do I need to consider in approaching this work?

Filled with hallowed consciousness, spiritual psychotherapy is a rich and beautiful work even in the midst of suffering, hardship, and pain. More than techniques, it is an attitude, an awareness, and a communion with the Presence for the benefit of the other. When a therapist feels drawn to this kind of consciousness, then a spiritual psychotherapy may be his calling as well.

SPIRITUALITY IN OTHER HELPING PROFESSIONS

A wide range of professionals could benefit from education and training into the spiritual nature of the health problems and crises, including doctors, nurses, physical therapists, occupational therapists, chiropractors, hospice workers, emergency room staff, EMT's, prison staff, probation officers, pharmacists, and nursing and convalescent home staff. In fact, the overarching principles discussed in this book may apply to any helping profession, though the unique opportunities and applications will vary.

With medical practitioners and emergency workers, for example, the spiritual energy conveyed through prayer, touch, and loving-kindness should never be underestimated. In prisons, where brutality often crushes spirit and hope, the needs of the soul are especially great. There are times, also, when we are all called to be priests, that is, to witness the holy, confront sacrilege, or transcend the small, personal self in the service of others. Such callings frequently occur in extraordinary circumstances (e.g., war, civilian disasters, medical emergencies, and family crises). Once our clinical responsibilities are disposed of, the discerning heart will reveal the emotional and spiritual needs of the situation as well.

Anyone, who cares for others, personally or professionally, can learn to in prayerful, reverential, and loving ways. Remaining in communion with the sacred Presence while ministering to others widens the opportunities for service - not so much in the practice of specific clinical skills, but in the spiritual consciousness brought to the work. Not only does our own spirituality grow, but we become open conduits for the flow of love into the world. Whatever the setting, this extra step often leaves the most lasting impact.

For all human services professionals, therefore, the following basic principles and recommendations would seem to apply:

* Everything we do has a spiritual dimension. Learn to feel the presence and intentions of the divine in whatever work you do.
* Be especially aware of the spiritual dimensions in your work setting. Learn where the spirit can come through, where it is being suppressed or twisted, and who needs spiritual support the most.
* Trust your own spirituality and help others trust theirs. This is not about changing or convincing people, it is about discerning the movement of the spirit within and empowering others to act with the wisdom of the heart.
* Give people a chance to talk about their spiritual concerns. Take the risk of asking them what their concerns are.
* Learn the patient's religious language and their particular use of its symbols, for spirituality is not always communicated explicitly or in ways consistent with your own vocabulary.
* Be aware of the spiritual power of touch in helping and healing.
* Grow your own spirituality and spiritual practice. Everything you do can be part of that practice.

CHAPTER EIGHTEEN

PRACTICAL, ETHICAL, AND MALPRACTICE ISSUES

Contents: Practical Issues
Ethical Issues
Malpractice Issues

A variety of practical, ethical, and legal issues arise when one begins to bring religious and spiritual themes, problems, and experiences into the psychotherapy process. These issues include the appropriate physical and social environment, the ethics of charging and advertising for spiritually related services, and the risk of malpractice allegations.

PRACTICAL ISSUES

Practical issues revolve mostly around the physical and social environment in which therapy is conducted. While most therapists have pleasant offices, they are not always appropriate for work that becomes increasingly spiritual. The most important physical and social parameters for spiritually oriented work include:

QUIET

Spiritual work (especially prayer, spiritual direction, ritual, and meditation) thrives in a space that is peaceful and insulated from the noise of traffic, loud music, or people working nearby.

SECURITY

The office environment needs to be secure from interruption and distraction (e.g., telephone, office staff, or other therapists) so that the sacred space created can also be protected.

SOCIAL SUPPORT

It is helpful if colleagues and employees can also to be attuned to the spiritual dimensions of the psychotherapy environment. In fact, where appropriate, even professional meetings (especially client staffing related to spiritual work) can be conducted in sacred space created with simple boundary rituals (e.g., holding hands and saying a prayer). Additional emphasis should be placed on creating a general social or office atmosphere conducive to the presence and movement of the spirit.

FURNISHINGS

Though it need not be fancy or elaborate, a spiritual decor helps create a sacred atmosphere. Wall hangings, candles, flowers, and tasteful religious figures support this atmosphere, with simple furnishings preferable to ostentatious ones.

ETHICAL ISSUES

INFORMED CONSENT

A prospective client has the right to receive enough information to make an informed choice about whether to seek services with a particular professional. There are three elements that customarily constitute informed consent: information, competence, and voluntariness. The client must receive sufficient information to understand any proposed treatment (including its nature, duration, cost, side effects, and alternatives) and be legally and cognitively competent to truly make an informed choice about the services in question. Finally, there must be a free volitional choice about proceeding with any proposed services, that is, there should be not be undue influence or pressure brought to bear on the client from the therapist, church, or family. Providing the client with a formal consent form detailing the nature and available alternatives is recommended.

ECONOMICS

When psychotherapy moves away from the treatment of psychological problems and into the spiritual realm, does the therapist charge for his services? Historically, and still in many traditions, spiritual direction has been a ministry rather than a paid profession. Some have suggested, however, that spiritual counseling might be a salaried position in a church setting (Edwards, 1980) and certainly ministers and pastoral counselors are paid for their services. Indeed, the clergy is a profession and a job, and most clergy persons need to economically support themselves and their families through their work.

While the issue of fees should be first and foremost a matter of the therapist's individual discernment, a case can be made that charging customary (or perhaps reduced) fees is ethically legitimate. First, to do this specialized work, one has to invest considerable time and money developing the requisite knowledge and skills. A spiritually oriented psychotherapist offers a highly skilled service. Second, in this work, one's psychotherapeutic training is neither retired nor irrelevant; to the contrary, the therapist is always checking in with his psychological training and intuition to be sure the spiritual focus is not dysfunctional or defensive. Third, the spiritual portion of this work usually alternates with other ongoing or emergent psychological goals. Finally, repeatedly deciding when therapy time should be free or charged would complicate not only bookkeeping but the therapeutic relationship itself, restimulating complex issues (e.g., conflict of interest, secondary gain, feelings of entitlement, covert resentment) that have already been worked through in the traditional psychotherapeutic manner.

An alternate resolution to the fee question is possible. The shift from psychotherapy to spirituality can be accomplished at the termination of formal treatment, with the client moving into a separate program of spiritual direction in an established religious setting. This transition would mark a graduation from one format to another, with the economic basis of the spiritual direction being either renegotiated or established by the ministerial setting.

The issue of money can be troublesome in virtually any setting. In the case of spiritual psychotherapy, peer consultation, personal discernment, and ongoing spiritual guidance are advised to address and confront these potential issues.

INSURANCE BILLING

A related and equally complex ethical and economic question involves billing third party payers for services of a spiritual nature. The answer to this question depends partly on where the work is being performed on the Integration Continuum described in Chapter 9 . If the primary work in therapy falls in the first three cells, that is, when the work is focused on the client's psychological problems, including those arising from religious abuse, addiction, and unhealthy spirituality, and assuming that diagnosable emotional disorders are associated with this work, then billing the third party insurance carrier would be consistent with established psychodiagnostic and therapeutic protocols.

When the work in therapy moves in the fourth and fifth cells of the Integration Continuum, it may or may not be part of a formal treatment regime. Though not yet recognized as a common, customary, or empirically established treatment modalities, adjunctive spiritual practices can be valuable and professionally responsible approaches psychological problems. When utilized as part of ongoing psychotherapy, spiritually focused work would, in this psychologist's opinion, be a legitimate and billable service. Whether the insurance carrier was legally responsible, however, would depend on the mental health services covered in its contract. Finally, when the work in therapy becomes purely spiritual and no longer connected with diagnosable emotional problems, the third party payer would bear no contractual responsibility to underwrite it.

ADVERTISING

Advertising is yet another complex issue. Existing laws in many states actually encourage psychotherapists to advertise as part of free enterprise competition to prevent industry-wide price fixing. Professional associations of therapists provide guidelines to ensure that skills, training, and services are truthfully represented. Advertising oneself as a spiritually oriented psychotherapist, therefore, would be lawful and professionally ethical assuming it is consistent with professionally attained competence.

The ramifications of advertising oneself as a spiritual psychotherapist, however, should not be minimized, for it affects one's professional image in the community, the kinds of clients referred, and the expectations the advertisement engenders. Clients can respond to the word "spiritual" with idiosyncratic and sometimes irrational assumptions, requiring careful inquiry early in the therapy process. Therapists generally agree that the most successful advertising comes from satisfied clients and referral sources, where good will is at a maximum and confusion at a minimum. In the practice of psychotherapy, integrity, competence, character, and caring are the most important elements, and when practiced by these standards, a spiritually oriented psychotherapy will flourish by itself without excessive marketing.

THE MEDICALIZATION OF PSYCHOTHERAPY

The medicalization of treatment can take the form of psychotropic drugs, shock treatment, or the narrow medical definition of what constitutes appropriate treatment for each conditions. Psychoactive agents certainly have a place in mental health care, and sometimes even shock treatment may be appropriate. But there are occasions when the medical model defines treatment in ways that conflict with spiritual goals, requiring personal soul searching and discernment. For example, if we view depression solely as an unwanted biochemical disorder, providing medication without therapy, then we miss its deeply important psychospiritual etiology - the betrayal of the soul. Viewing a mystical experience as fantasy or psychosis may similarly cause us negate a spiritually valuable experience, producing shame, self-doubt, and further self-betrayal.

For these reasons, it is important for a therapist to maintain multiple standards of care - medical, psychological, social, and spiritual - and to determine which standard is the most important at any point in time with respect to the presenting problem. The client, of course, must have the last say and, with informed consent, have the chance to struggle openly with these issues for his own growth.

MALPRACTICE ISSUES

Because there are not yet formal legal or professional standards of care for spiritual psychotherapy, the issue of malpractice must be considered. New treatment modalities in a field are appropriately considered experimental and questionable. Healthy skepticism and professional debate, however, do not prevent their exploration.

Introducing spiritual insight, information, and processes into the psychotherapeutic domain at this time is legitimate but needs to be done in careful and thoughtful ways that complement rather than replace established treatment approaches. The therapist should be clear with the client about the distinctions between psychotherapy and spirituality, and spiritual themes or practices should never be forced. The best insurance against malpractice is openness, informed consent, personal competence, ongoing personal and peer review, and caring.

PART FIVE

SACRED PSYCHOLOGY:
SUMMARY AND IMPLICATIONS

To Dr. John:
Ego to spirit, is a long hard trail
We both are taking:
(And so is every man).
And are we "making it?"
Or is it making us?
And is making, and being made,
The same?

Congratulations, Dr. Robinson
Your earthly span is young,
The years will come and take their toll:
And when they do -
At the far ending of the whole -
You will have met, at last, your soul.

Agnes Claflin Adams

This poem was written by my 83 year old grandmother in celebration of my doctoral degree in 1973 two years before she died. I continue to be amazed how much she tried to teach me a quarter century before I began writing.

CHAPTER NINETEEN

SACRED PSYCHOLOGY

"The spiritual life is nothing else than God himself struggling to become more God within us; spirituality is the awareness of this process, shattering our self-deceptions and overwhelming us in its simple truth: we belong to God, not to ourselves, and God loves us beyond anything that we can know or hope for. Experiencing this truth daily is the inner secret of the spiritual life, emerging from the center of oneself and encompassing all of one's world."
Frederick Parella

Contents: Summary
Final Implications of the Ego-Soul Matrix
Psychotherapy as a Model and Preparation for Meeting God
Conclusions: *But Where Is God?*

SUMMARY

But Where Is God? argues that it is time for a mature integration of psychotherapy and spirituality. Religious and spiritual issues have always permeated psychotherapy. Blinded by historical prejudice and prohibition, and entranced by the glamour of twentieth century scientific materialism, psychotherapy turned its back on the sacred. But like the Prodigal Son, psychology has since grown up and experienced enough in the past decade to return home; mature and ready to restore, renew, and celebrate the spiritual dimension of its healing art.

We began our integration of psychotherapy and spirituality by blending their vocabularies to build a psychospiritual model of personality. It had to be large enough to embrace the "Varieties of Religious Experience" through which the sacred reveals itself yet personal enough to be applicable to the individual entering psychotherapy. With an expanded model came additional goals: psychotherapy's task was not only to treat emotional problems but to understand their connection to self, soul, divine self, God, and the sacred journey of life. Determined not to be naive, however, a wide range of objections and liabilities were addressed along with all the clinical, professional, educational, ethical, and practical issues associated with a spiritual psychotherapy. Faith and careful thinking were joint architects of this synthesis which will be extended with each new generation of searchers and builders. We turn now to some final implications of the Ego-Soul Matrix.

Final Implications of the Ego-Soul Matrix

In its essential structure, the Ego-Soul Matrix summarizes the integration of psychology and spirituality pursued throughout this book. The ego, a psychological structure, and the soul, a spiritual one, interact in the ongoing relationship between the individual and the divine that constitutes the journey of life. We return to this model one last time to illustrate some final and broader implications of the psychotherapy-spirituality integration in the religious search. Delving deeply for final insights, we will be superimposing the transparency of the Ego-Soul Matrix on the following topics: Spiritual Health and Healing, The Sacred Journey of Life, The Value of Ego, The Role of the Therapist, Universal Religious Symbolism, the Stages of Culture, and the Archetypal Religious Psyche.

Spiritual Health and Healing

The spatial topography of the Ego-Soul Matrix confirms what religion has universally taught about our relationship to God: It is our woundedness, collapse, and surrender that brings us close to God, and it is our closeness to God that heals our woundedness and restores balance to the ego's journey home. Each quadrant of the matrix clarifies this truth.

Ego

False self Unhealthy personality	True self Healthy personality
3	2
	Soul **Spirit**
4	1
Darkness The broken personality The wounded self	God No ego healing

The false self (quadrant 3) has the least contact (i.e., common boundary) with the sacred (quadrant 1). Even when pontificating on divine matters, people functioning in this quadrant are really the most distant from the divine, and can as a result perpetrate terrible atrocities in the name of religion. The sacred dimension (quadrant 1) is, on the other hand, very close to people in pain (quadrant 4). Those who are psychologically broken, whose wounds are bleeding, or who are most devalued by society (the poor, the weak and helpless, the abused) are, as the New Testament proclaims, closest to the sacred. This is because the collapse of the false self disorganizes the ego's defensive barriers to the inflowing spiritual dimension. Finally, the true self (quadrant 2), positively balancing ego and soul, is naturally close to God and brings the divine into the world. Neither damaged nor divided, it has no discarded parts, no buried pain or shadow material, and hence no common boundary with the dark, unconscious repository of woundedness (quadrant 4).

Psychological healing and healthy personality functioning, therefore, are intimately related to our closeness to God, and dysfunction to our distance. The more we exist separate and independent from the sacred consciousness of quadrant 1, the more secret damage is occurring to the self-soul connection. Seeking only a successful ego, we become more spiritually estranged than we know, yet descending into our universal woundedness restores the path back to God. In this sense, healthy psychological breakdown is an essential spiritual practice and a movement into the realm of sacred healing. To be healthy, however, this descent must still involve the ego, for the buried grief and suffering of a self torn from its soul must be admitted into consciousness, understanding, and compassion. Then, with the total surrender of the false quest for independence, power, and control, the naked self is moved by soul and touched by spirit, and healing happens.

The most important developments in the field of spiritual psychotherapy will come as we learn more about the experience of bringing quadrant 1 into the everyday life of quadrant 2. Exploring this forgotten yet richly porous connection may be one of psychology's greatest achievements. The ultimate purpose of healing woundedness is not simply to feel better, but to engage the spiritual life, to marry spirit and soul, and awaken the sacred dimension of human existence. In bringing sacred consciousness into quadrant 2, we are healing the world.

The Sacred Journey of Life - Two Cycles of Spiritual Transformation

Our distance from God creates and fuels the Sacred Journey of Life. Urged by the dynamic stages of spiritual growth discussed in Chapter 7, the journey potentially moves through the numbered quadrants twice. By now, the reader should be familiar with the first cycle. Born from the sacred, the young self tacitly knows its natural relationship with soul, and this connection thrills the ego with a magical flow of energy, inspiration, and excitement. Unfortunately, the wounds of childhood, the uncompromising standards of society, and the ego's own quest for autonomy and competency cause it to abandon the true self on the journey through the spring and summer seasons of life. Traveling an arc as the sun moves, from east to west on the soul continuum, we arrive at midlife, which not surprisingly turns out to be the farthest distance from our soul.

At midlife, we unconsciously struggle to dismantle the false self (quadrant 3), descend into the healing grief and ashes of the betrayed true self (quadrant 4), and then, in this profound and complete surrender of pride and control, enter the realm of the sacred (quadrant 1). In this descent, we travel to the east, back through our original woundings to the sacred source of being. Touched by the spirit, filled then with the energies of true self and soul, and supported now by a healthy and more mature ego, we are "reborn" in the world (quadrant 2). The fall season of life then becomes a time of harvesting the gifts the true self and all that has been learned along the way. If we fail to take this journey to the east, the brittleness and sterility of the false self petrifies steadily until death literally shatters us back into the sacred (quadrant 1).

The Journey of Life: First Cycle

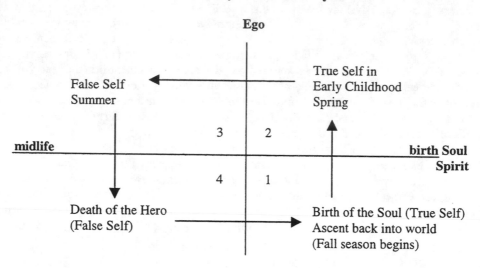

For the spiritually mature individual, there awaits a second cycle through the Ego-Soul Matrix The true self of quadrant 2 flowers in the fall of life, manifesting its intrinsic beauty and disseminating its gifts (i.e., its spiritual seeds) into the world and the next generation. Thus the fruit of true self fully ripens, sweetens, gives itself to the world. We do the work of our soul in the fall, whatever that turns out to be, and it is perhaps the most loving, generous, and precious time of our journey. We give ourselves completely: all we have and all we are.

But the cycle continues. Beginning in the early winter season of quadrant 3 and culminating in its depths in quadrant 4 is a process that, as much as any, deserves the phrase memorialized by St. John of the Cross: it is the "Dark Night of the Soul." Caused by the losses, disappointments, and defeats of aging, this deep passage into the black emptiness of God's vacuum sooner or later strips away all remaining illusions and attachments, our precious individuality and identity, and sometimes even our experience of closeness to God. Everything is dismantled in this descent, not just the false self. When the anguish of loss seems insurmountable, when all seems empty and gone, when the seasoned journeyer has given up all hope, suddenly or gradually the light of quadrant of 1 returns. It is everywhere. Radiant with the immanence of God, the world is once again beautiful beyond measure and the joy of being breaks through again. Awakened to mystical wonder, we return to the Edenic world of early childhood (quadrant 2) filled with sacred consciousness. With no separate individuality, the ego experiences God as the whole of existence.

An 82-year-old friend of my mother, legally blind for over twenty years from a botched cataract operation, wrote this poem during her husband's terminal illness. She is talking about this very process.

> Suddenly
> I must call
> a number of friends
> to say
> that after an overcast day
> the sun has emerged
> and that late light
> is striking everything in sight,
> and to add
> that this last light
> has me twirling

and clicking my heels
and shouting
"Alive, Alive-O"
Ruth Biemiller

The second half of life, then, moves us through the cycle again, yet in a more profound and transformative way. For those rare individuals capable of such enlightened consciousness, it culminates in a new and mystical relationship with reality.

The Journey of Life: Second Cycle

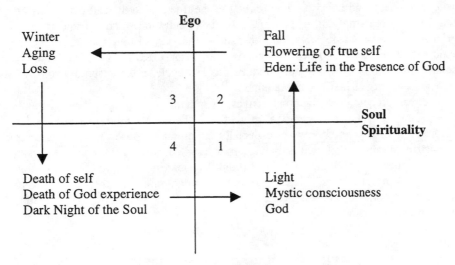

These cycles also occur in countless lessor ways in everyday life anytime we pursue goals that takes us away from God (cycle 1), and every time surrender identity to know the divine as our true ground of being (cycle 2). These two great life cycles also define the essential stages and tasks of spiritual psychotherapy. This great journey, we understand, is the very nature of our psychotherapeutic work.

THE VALUE OF THE EGO

Another important implication of the Ego-Soul Matrix is the value of the ego. The ego has been necessary all along, for without it, there would be no learning, no progress, and no real capacity for spiritual growth.

Ego, then, has many important mediating functions. Through ego we first learn to know the self and soul; later it dismantles the false self and tolerates the grief of its failure; then it learns to support the true self again and open to soul; and finally, it is the ego that becomes capable of holding mystical consciousness. The religious prescription to rid oneself of ego actually refers to shedding the false self in the first cycle, and overcoming the attachment to identity and control in the second cycle. The great mystics had egos all the way to the end of their lives, there was simply little or no separate personal self directing them any longer. The small, separate, individual self gives way to the divine Self.

THE ROLE OF THE THERAPIST

The Ego-Soul Matrix also shows us that the role of the therapist changes through the quadrants and cycles of both therapy and life.

In the first cycle, a therapist's job is to help the young person grow their ego competencies without losing too much of their true self (yet recognizing that self-betraying worldly quests are the inevitable price of summer's enticements). In midlife, the therapist's task is to help the individual face the emptiness of false achievements and descend through the wounds of spring and summer to find the true self again. Regarding quadrant 1 work, the task is to provide spiritual guidance so holiness can enter the client's consciousness and inform their life. In the second cycle, the therapist's role is to affirm and nourish the unfolding of the true self in the fall (quadrant 2), guide the individual through the emptying of self and identify (quadrants 3 and 4), and then help the client experience and trust the mystical apprehensions of Divine Being (quadrant 1), and the world's Edenic nature (quadrant 2). Eden, as we have seen, symbolizes the world saturated with the divine Presence. Only a few rare souls fully realize this last cycle, often assuming roles as social activists and teachers for the benefit of humankind.

In this cyclical process, the therapist strives to remain psychologically, spiritually, and professionally grounded, integrating personal growth with theory, training, practice, and clinical experience. The tools of psychotherapy are especially important because the barriers to spiritual growth are primarily psychological, that is, barriers to feeling, consciousness, and relationship born of psychic trauma, ignorance, and fear. Finally, it should be clear by now that this work aims not at withdrawal from the world, permanent bliss, or retiring in enlightenment; rather, its goal is to come home to the sacred as our lives and our world. Here we build loving and inclusive relationships, healing communities, and a new order.

UNIVERSAL RELIGIOUS SYMBOLISM

It is interesting to note that archetypal religious symbolism is also evident in the Ego-Soul Matrix, validating the inherent equivalence of the psychological and religious paths.

For example, from the Judeo-Christian story, Eden is found in the experience of quadrant 2 in early childhood before the ego learns to perceive only the world defined by materialistic culture. Sin and evil, meaning egoic behavior estranged from sacred awareness, arise in quadrant 3 and result in humankind's "fall from grace" and the hellish conditions we create on earth. Where ego's spiritual consciousness is absent, the dark forces of shadow and pain can fuse with the false self in myriad forms of violence and warfare. Hellish experience deepens in quadrant 4 as one descends inwardly to experience the personal devastation that such falseness has wrought. This is, indeed, the "end of the world" prophesied by apocalyptic religions, symbolizing the end of the false world built on soulless ambition. Absolution and healing from this terrible mistake require the absolute surrender of false self to enter the religious life. The longing for salvation associated with quadrant 4 is for the "second coming" of sacred consciousness (i.e., quadrant 1 consciousness symbolized by figures like Christ, Buddha, or the Great Spirit) to redeem humankind and the world from its sinful ways. Finally, if one has truly gone through the second cycle to find mystical consciousness, the "Kingdom of Heaven" on earth becomes the sacred reality of quadrant 2.

Religious Symbolism in the Ego-Soul Matrix

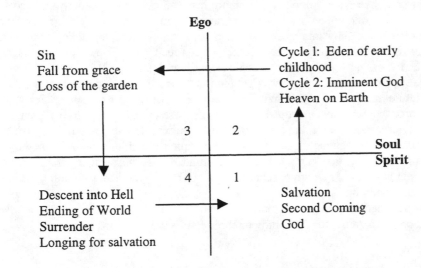

The symbolic equivalence of psychological and religious matrices reflects the unifying archetypal structure of the religious psyche underlying both the process of individuation and the spiritual journey. In reaching this level of correspondence, we are touching humankind's deepest structures of myth and meaning. Using the language of religion in psychotherapy, therefore, is not only valid, it can provide powerful images and metaphors for psychological experience, especially for the client with natural access to mythic imagination. Shifting from religious to psychological language, on the other hand, can ground the more concrete or naïve client swept away or inflated by archetypal symbolism.

THE STAGES OF CULTURE

The archetypal religious symbolism structuring human consciousness also contributes to the development and cycles of human culture, which in turn create the collective stresses clients bring into therapy.

When a culture trades its soul (quadrant 2) for material symbols of the false self (quadrant 3), that is, when greed, power, fame, and lust are collectively prized as more important than soulful relationships and sacred consciousness, then that culture becomes increasingly bankrupt and in time begins to collapse (quadrant 4). Helpless and bereft, people `then turn again to God (quadrant 1) and a new beginning is inspired, envisioned, and pursued (quadrant 2). In this stage, what we seek to build is holy, but gradually loses its truth and beauty as ego becomes inflated once again with its handiwork and forgets the true source of its vision. What is built eventually becomes false (quadrant 3) and must be dismantled (quadrant 4). Family, community, and society perennially go through this cycle of inspiration, growth, decay, collapse, and renewal. Collectively, we try again and again to correct our failings only to find new falseness has grown up again. The cycle continues as each individual and humankind at large struggles to align more with the sacred than with false self.

It is also clear enough that we are in a larger time of cultural transition between quadrants 3 and 4. The world created by our species is in deepening trouble: population, pollution, hunger, economic disparity, war. The patriarchal false self is breaking down. On his deathbed in 1961, Jung shared one final vision: that tremendous world disorder and destruction would occur approximately 50 years after his death, roughly 2011. This corresponds to the beginning of the Age of Aquarius, by the water carrier. Psychologically understood, the image of Aquarius suggests that each individual must take the responsibility of containing his own consciousness, symbolized by the water in the container carried on the head. It can be further argued that a rocky transition from the current world order is not only imminent but necessary, for our reigning institutions (i.e., financial markets, government, healthcare) have largely lost touch with God, replacing sacred consciousness with an increasingly soul-less ego and its technology (quadrant 3).

At the ending of the twentieth century, this "post-modern" time of chaos, deconstruction, and disorder, western culture seems to be in frenzied arrest on the precipice of change. For those individuals able to drop consciously into quadrant 4 of the first cycle, and bear the pain and insecurity of large scale social change, the boundary with quadrant 1 will become increasingly permeable. Psychotherapists are uniquely qualified to help people through this death of the heroic patriarchy. Along with the clergy, they can serve as priests of a new psychospiritual paradigm. The clergy has already taken in much of modern psychological thought and practice, psychology is now taking the corresponding step into the spiritual and religious domain. A psychology of personal and cultural change grounded on the integration of true self, soul and spirit, can provide a wise, loving, and compassionate container for those moving through this cultural transition.

THE ARCHETYPAL RELIGIOUS PSYCHE

The whole argument for an integration of psychology and spirituality leads inevitably to the archetypal nature of the religious psyche.

The Ego-Soul Matrix is essentially a representation of the archetypal religious psyche, encompassing the fundamental realms of experience known to the spiritual journey. Its quaternity reflects the wholeness of being and all its dualities: true and false, conscious and unconsciousness, positive and negative, light and dark, heaven and hell, good and evil, authentic and inauthentic, constructive and destructive. Each quadrant is one of the basic lands of the religious psyche, and the journey must go through them all. The youthful intention to stay in quadrant 2 of the first cycle, and "live in the light" for ever, is not only unrealistic, it invariably produces the false self it was determined to avoid.

Central to this entire argument is the basic religious nature and function of the psyche, that is, its deep abiding interest in ultimate questions, spiritual intimations, religious symbols, and mystical communion that appear everywhere in human experience: fantasy, dreams, psychosis, myths, yearnings, intuitions, ritual, and enlightenment. This is the religious psyche and its desire for sacred consciousness. It is driven by the urgency of individuation, that profound psychological process which asks each of us to become conscious of who we really are and why we are alive. As the saying goes, "Who you are is God's gift to you; what you do with it is your gift to God." Rephrased in the concepts of this book, the saying might go, "Your soul, and its psychological awakening as the true self, is God's gift to you and the world; how you (i.e., your ego) nurture, support, and engage this process is your gift to God." The saying might then be extended one more step: "Through spiritual learning and practice, you (i.e., your ego) must consciously hold the inner wedding of soul and its lover, the indwelling spirit, in order to catalyze the birth and growth of a new and cosmic consciousness, for it is this consciousness that holds the new world experience." The Ego-Soul Matrix suggests that the human personality literally opens to the consciousness of God, and that this consciousness will take us through the second cycle of change.

The implications of this furthest expression of the religious psyche may seem "far out" to many readers, but they are neither new or insupportable. Such intuitions are part of its deep mythic structure. For example, the ancient Hindu scripture, the Bhagavad Gita, anticipates the final transformation, advising:

Let your thoughts flow past you, calmly;
keep me near, at every moment;
trust me with your life, because I
am you, more than you yourself are.

With this final transformation, the world itself is imbued with immanence. As Firdausi, another Sufi poet, proclaimed:

If on earth there be
a Paradise of Bliss,
It is this,
It is this,
It is this.

The mystical experience fully contains these realizations (Robinson, 1995). The awakened individual knows with certainty that the ground of experience is God, and that when the lens of human perception is wiped clean (as William Blake described), the Divine Being and its consciousness is everywhere. The religious psyche contains this seed of enlightenment, and spiritual psychotherapy, skillfully practices, can water its growth.

PSYCHOTHERAPY AS A MODEL AND PREPARATION FOR MEETING GOD

In the final analysis, the whole project of life is about meeting God. Yet so confused are we about what this means, and so fearful of censure, ridicule, or failure, that the project is commonly abandoned. We will get back to it later, rationalizes the ego. Though the sacred will be met at death, if we are to grow spiritually in this life, the encounter must be sought in the present, directly opening the psyche to the sacred consciousness informing it and the world. Interestingly, a model for this encounter can be found in the stages of the therapist-client relationship, which reflect and symbolically replicate the journey toward God.

In long term psychotherapy, the client's view of the therapist evolves naturally over time. In the beginning, the therapist is known only as a fixed and one-dimensional object: the "expert." As time passes, the therapist is next experienced as a parental figure, that is, a transference object, both positive and negative. Working through this transference is one of the principle healing tasks of psychotherapy. But real maturity does not fully arrive until the therapist is no longer an object, but can be seen as a unique and very human person, trained in psychotherapy but neither superior to nor fundamentally different from the client.

After the presenting problems have been worked through and the therapy relationship has become deep and meaningful, the client eventually discovers an interest in knowing the therapist as a person. His attention, freed from his own problems, shifts to the other. This interest is not essentially in the therapist's personal biography or circumstances (though some of this may occur), but in his nature, being, and humanness. The client realizes that this has become a relationship of love and commonalty, and in knowing both himself and the therapist, a universal human isomorphism is discovered: the other is really not other than oneself. Indeed, client, therapist, friend, neighbor, male, female, this race or that - at the universal level, we are one, both in our essential human nature and in the fundamental unity of creation. Rare is the long term client that reaches this level of realization, but it is there nonetheless.

Understanding this human microcosm of relationship stages in therapy helps us understand the corresponding macrocosm of coming to know God. At first, God is experienced as a fixed, one dimensional object. The seeker believes what he is told about this object and tries to change himself to be acceptable to it. He asks God for help, but like therapy the focus is primarily and urgently on himself. Sooner or later, the seeker begins to explore his image of God and discovers how it has been greatly but subtly shaped by parental and cultural attitudes, limiting his first hand religious experience. After working through these transference distortions of the God image, there comes a time when the seeker wishes to know God directly, not abstractly, not as a distant or parental authority, but intimately, personally, and authentically - as the Other.

As with therapy, the process of meeting God starts with a movement beyond self into a readiness to know the other. We eventually approach God with a desire for a real relationship. At first, the focus may still be on the seeker, who asks of God: "Are you interested in me? Do you look for me? Do you really care about me? What do you want from me? Then, increasingly, the attention turns from these self concerns to the Other, and the seeker asks: "God, who are you? Where are you? I want to know you. I want to feel you. I want to hear your voice." Gradually the seeker begins to find this Other and a relationship with God actually happens; it is not a metaphor, not a guided imagery, not a pleasant fantasy. We know the Presence as a real relationship. And eventually it is everywhere. For the great saints and mystics, this expanded awareness is the purpose of life, and along with it comes the final isomorphic realization that the Other is not really other than one's own nature. We are one and the same, for unity can only mean one substance of being and consciousness everywhere.

There is one last comparison between psychotherapy and the religious search. In the former, the therapist must psychologically bear the client's pain in the same way a mother must bear the pain of an injured or ill child. As the client gets stronger, he becomes capable of holding, feeling, and finally healing this pain. In the religious search, God holds our pain. Especially in devastating times, when the most precious aspects of our life seem to be threatened or annihilated, we continue to exist because God is here, holding us in consciousness, showing us the value of love, teaching us what we must know and do to grow spiritually. A psychotherapy that understands this, and trusts the sacred Presence, can open client and therapist alike, in good times and in bad, to a larger reality whose infinite, loving magnificence dwarfs personal problems, holds the entire universe in its consciousness, and returns the original joyous splendor of divine life to this world. Here psychotherapy and the religious search converge into a single journey, and into a single One.

CONCLUSIONS: BUT WHERE IS GOD?

Like us, most of our clients are so unknowingly crushed by the unfaced wounds of the past, the stresses of modern civilization, the distractions of a soul numbing culture, and the tragic burden of myopic beliefs, that they have little authentic conception of the spiritual life. When asked about their relationship to God, they make a few assertions of faith, change the subject, or lecture defensively about their creed. This avoidance is partly because their presenting psychological problems deservedly warrant our primary attention, but it is also because the subject has either become personally irrelevant or too threatening to discuss. The tragic result is that sacred consciousness lies buried beneath layers of religious confusion, ignorance, fear, or abuse.

A spiritually oriented psychotherapy seeks to restore the quest for sacred consciousness. The "average" problems of life are rarely recognized to be spiritual in nature. Yet, as we have seen, unhappiness, stress, marital or family problems, illness, and even diagnosable psychological disorders always have an additional spiritual dimension. Seeming to lack the drama of religious visions and visitations, we minimize the spiritual value of our everyday problems, forgetting that they are really the staple of religious growth through the life span. God is found in living here and now far more often then in otherworldly experiences. When reviewing their lives during NDE's, people invariably discover that their greatest achievements, failures, and learnings came from the simple human struggle to love. It is clear, then, that psychological and relationship problems *are* spiritual struggles; the religious psyche, with its openness to sacred consciousness, can provide their larger meaning.

As we have seen, there is still a higher step. Spiritual growth is not just another self-improvement exercise and therapy is not merely about feeling better. If it goes far enough, this work is literally one of spiritual transfiguration, that is, the awakening of our inherent mystical capacity to experience the present, this place, oneself, and life as the radiant, joyous, infinitely loving Divine Being. Emotional problems and psychological symptoms identify knots where the process of spiritual unfolding is blocked, betrayed, or wounded; psychotherapy strives to untie these knots. As the Ego-Soul Matrix outlines, the religious psyche organizes the structure, images, and stages of this transfiguring process, for these phenomena are the ways we learn to know the sacred, until the time comes when there is no need for further mediation.

So, how do we actually meet God? In the inner darkness of prayer and meditation? Through the language of life's problems and events? In a dream or vision from beyond? A near-death experience or mystical rapture? In the extraordinary nature of "ordinary" experience? In scripture, dogma, and faith? Through creativity and the arts? In learning to love unconditionally? In times of desolation and hardship? Through the interventions of angels and guardian spirits? In church or wilderness? In the immediacy of childbirth and death? Through icons, symbols, and ritual? In the questions we ask? To the enlightened, God is met in all these ways and countless others. A spiritual psychotherapy, bringing life into the sacred and the sacred into life, values such myriad forms of divine revelation and interpenetration while at the same time recognizing the inherent cycles of self-deception and betrayal that appear on the journey back to God.

In the final analysis, meeting God is a personal experience. The stages of spiritual growth tell us that this encounter happens as we consciously and intentionally explore our personal, subjective, immediate, literal, and radical experience of the divine. No one can do this for you, no one can tell you exactly how to do it, and each person's experience will be unique to them. Asking sincerely for divine guidance, we must enter the sacred encounter alone, wide awake, and experience it as fully as possible. Just as we learned how to swim in water, discovering the magic of sensation, buoyancy, movement, and trust, we must also learn how to swim in the divine. It is here now. Both religion and spiritually oriented psychotherapy bring us to the water's edge. The next step is ours.

THE VARIETIES OF RELIGIOUS EXPERIENCE: A SAMPLING

Presented below is a survey of the kinds of answers mankind has found to its great and eternal questions. Borrowing William James' famous title "The Varieties of Religious Experience," we will briefly explore answers from multiple sources (see insert in Chapter 5) Our goal is not to reduce these diverse traditions to over-simplified religious formulae but instead to appreciate, with awe and wonder, the astonishing beauty each displays. Every religion is, in truth, one facet of a perfect diamond: the mystical nature, structure, and consciousness of the universe.

THE JUDEO-CHRISTIAN-ISLAMIC LINE

Judaism, Christianity, and Islamic religions grew from the same original revelations and have much in common. Each is monotheistic; each overcame enormous religious persecution to become world religions; and each has a tremendous commitment to morality and social justice. Before Judaism, the many gods of the Mediterranean world were not only indifferent to mankind but often immoral, exploitative, and self-centered as well. In the Hebrew Scriptures (the "Old Testament"), the New Testament, and the Koran, God is considered the ultimate reality of goodness and love, and mankind's morality and virtue derive from emulating or embodying God's nature. Hence, love, charity, compassion, goodness, wisdom, peace, truth, joy, and beauty become the highest human values. The purpose of life is to realize these sacred qualities in human life, and to those who do comes a happiness and joy that exceeds any material or self-centered gratification. The purpose of life is to do God's will (not man's) and to love and glorify God who has given all to humanity and the world. Purpose thus flows directly from God and, to the extent man fulfills the divine plan, humanity itself is sanctified.

Judaism, Christianity, and Islam represented an enormous development in the meaning and morality of civilization. Believing that God had personally chosen one's people was a powerful motive for social and political consciousness. Man and God now worked together in the world to build a moral and religious community founded on the Ten Commandments. Struggle and suffering were no longer viewed as bad luck or the perverse play of the gods, they held meaning in world history. They were the price of deviation from divine law. For previously persecuted peoples, this call to morality translated into ideas about social justice, progress, and hope, and motivated a search for the sacred meaning of life events: personal, historical, and worldly.

In this tradition, human beings contain the indwelling Spirit of God. Man, created in the image of God, potentially manifests his character, motives, and spirit. The attachment to worldly ends (fame, fortune, power, reputation) prevents man from experiencing God's spirit and unconditional love. It follows that the central problem of man is his separation from God. Whether this is conceived as "Fall from Grace," "Original Sin," self-centeredness, or ignorance, it is agreed that mankind has forgotten the original, sacred purpose of existence, and instead placed himself at the center of the universe. Ignorance, pride, egoism, desire, greed, and false teachings constitute sin, representing willful barriers that separate man from God. Human nature has degraded toward a state of spiritual corruption and depravity, forgetting its original holiness. How one handles this conflict determines his spiritual growth.

Salvation, the solution to this central problem, lies in returning to God. Whether found in grace, forgiveness, or mystical consciousness, reunion requires mans' willingness to surrender the aspirations of the errant ego to divine will. Help is available through prayer, study of scripture, and grace. Suffering in this context is also viewed as a manifestation of God's grace, showing the error of one's ways, purifying faith, and refining character. Conversion, the return to the ways of faith, is often symbolized as the death of the old, corrupted self and the birth of the new, God-centered one. Conceived of as entrance into eternal life, one moves from existence solely defined on the physical plane to existence on the spiritual one. For the spiritually mature, such a transformation may arrive before actual bodily death, leading truly advanced souls into the unitive state described by the mystics.

The founder or savior plays a special role in western religions. Whether, Moses, Abraham, Jesus, and Mohammed, he is given, often against his will, God's directions for man and must accept a life of communicating these truths to others. The savior or prophet invariably encounters resistance and rejection, but what makes them great is their persistence and devotion in the face of terrible personal costs. These individuals both teach and embody the teaching, serving and manifesting the original values and consciousness God intended for the world. Judaism, Christianity, and Islam differ on whether prophets are themselves divine and who represents the final coming of the Messiah.

From these ultimate teachings flow the religious life. For the individual, it often begins with the conscious, personal decision to take the spiritual path. Supported with divine grace, the spiritual aspirant's journey moves into a life of loving service, selflessness, sincerity, and worship. Spiritual growth rather than material advancement becomes the goal and various methods of self purification, study, worship and devotion are undertaken. Eventually a life of loving service matures, the fruit of which is seen in the joy of caring for others and the work of sanctifying humanity.

The end of the world as we know it is foretold in western religions, signaled by turmoil and tribulation, after which a golden age is expected to flower. The Messiah will come (or return) to finally establish the Kingdom of Heaven on earth, that is, a world without evil, suffering, or death; and in its place, a life of love, brotherhood, joy, and divine communion. Many feel this time is coming in the near future, evidenced by the ecological, political, and population problems seen in the world today.

There are, of course, differences between Judaism, Christianity, and Islam, and it is remarkable how much distrust, distance, and even violence have been spawned between them. More interesting, however, are the unique contributions of each. Judaism emerged as a monotheistic religion with tremendous interests in history, justice, meaning, and progress. Christianity continued these themes but introduced the idea of a personal incarnation: that God so loved humanity he gave birth to himself in the world through Jesus. This birth dramatically symbolized the value of suffering for spiritual transformation. Mohammed, building on Judaism's foundation, devoted himself to overthrowing an overwhelmingly corrupt Arabic world, eventually integrating socially progressive religious themes into everyday life, so much so that nearly every aspect of Muslim society now is predicated on and governed by religious principles.

COMMENT

The above themes, arising from these three inter-related traditions, penetrate western culture and society to its bedrock. Though we take them for granted, these religious values form the very infrastructure of our social and moral beliefs. It is hard to imagine a meaningful life without them, at least in their secular and ethical forms. These are also the themes that provide some of the deepest values for our psychotherapy clients. Failure to understand or evoke this mythic ground of consciousness ignores the sacred meanings that underlie all life in the west, limiting therapy to technical, problem-focused counseling only.

EASTERN RELIGIONS

The eastern religious experience tends to mix ancient traditions into an ageless and somewhat amalgamated philosophical, metaphysical, moral, social, and spiritual belief system. Many Asians comfortably blend Buddhism, Taoism, Confucianism, and even older indigenous beliefs. The numerous forms of each tradition have also evolved and interacted over time to produce an amazing range of ideas, doctrines, and practices. Less driven to analyze and reconcile contrasting points of view, divergent beliefs co-exist rather peaceably in the permissive understanding that each carries part of the truth. A similar situation exists in India, with the blending of the Hinduism and Buddhism.

HINDUISM

Hinduism, unlike many other religions, has no specific historical founder and is often said to be little interested in history per se. Developing in and around India around 1500 B.C.E, it assimilated many disparate religions that came before it and is generally described as more concerned about discovering spiritual truths than recording or sacralizing its history. There is no established church and one is generally free to choose what to believe and which deities to worship.

Hindu scriptures depict the purpose of human life to be realizing the bliss of the Absolute and escaping the Karmic cycle of reincarnations. Hidden beneath the individual self is the divine Self: a deathless, eternal being of infinite consciousness and bliss. This hidden Self is God and it is each person's true identity. There are many paths or yoga's to this realization and its goal, divine union, including knowledge, love, selfless work, and psychophysical exercises (e.g., meditation, breathing, postures). In fact, all religions are considered alternate paths to the same goal for the infinite God cannot be the sole province of any single religion. The end of the journey is opening to the timeless bliss of existence and the realization that the phenomenal world is but a dream. The intoxicating joy of spiritual realization can only be attained with the renunciation and cessation of the self and self-centered living, that is, the ending of desire for worldly goods and experiences.

Hinduism recognizes that life is lived in stages. One begins as a student, learning the knowledge and ways of Indian life, and then becomes a house-holder with interests turned to the practical world of family and vocation. When these responsibilities are completed, one retreats from the world to pursue the spiritual meaning of life. For those who get this far, there is a final stage of returning to the world without a self, and living without goals or belongings in the world as Self that is now known to be everywhere.

God, to the Hindu, is Brahman, the one who is infinite being, infinite consciousness, and infinite bliss. At the personal level, God may be experienced as the Creator (Brahma), the Preserver (Vishnu), the Destroyer (Shiva), or the God within (Atman). Each human soul (Jiva) comes into the world taking a form based on the behavior and level of consciousness from its previous life. Karma, the moral law of cause and effect, regulates this process of reincarnation. Its very existence reflects a universe structured by spiritual laws, with consequences to every act and decision. Overcoming attachment to self and sense pleasures over countless lifetimes moves one toward God. Arriving, the personal and separate self dissolves into God as a drop of water merges totally into the sea.

There are many worlds to the Hindu, and earth is the middle one. Life on earth does not fundamentally change over time nor is there a belief in social progress. Instead it is the self that changes with spiritual progress so that future reincarnations take place in more heavenly worlds, and ultimately in God. But even this world, from an unenlightened consciousness, is an illusion of mind, like a dream, from which we must awaken. Reality is God's joyous, creative, spontaneous play that we misunderstand from our limited perspective. Upon awakening to the superconscious mind, reality is seen to be uniform, infinite, and singular - it is everywhere God. It is the prism of the our mind and senses that split this unalloyed oneness into duality and multiplicity.

COMMENT

Many Hindu concepts now permeate western culture, including karma, reincarnation, enlightened teachers, and the possibility through practice of the direct realization of God. Clients often think in these terms or search for gurus to help them reach enlightenment. Western naiveté, gullibility, and ignorance, however, have also led to tremendous misunderstanding, exploitation, and suffering at the hands of less-than-realized teachers. Despite this cross-cultural confusion, Hinduism provides an enormously rich mapping of the paths and possibilities of mystical union, a union sometimes denied or forbidden in western religions.

BUDDHISM

Buddhism formed around the historical figure and enlightenment experience of Gautama Buddha around 500 B.C.E., and then migrated from India across China into Japan, Korea, and southeast Asia, continually evolving along the way into numerous forms.

Like Jesus and Mohammed, Buddha, saw the corruption of existing religious practices. He felt the Hindu Brahmins, the upper caste of spiritual teachers, had been perverted by superstition and empty rituals. After an enormous and life-threatening spiritual search through all the existing ascetic practices, the Buddha finally "woke up" and saw the true nature of reality. From this enlightenment, he outlined and tirelessly taught a most practical strategy of spiritual practice. Its goal is the extinction of the individual self so that the pure nature of existence can shine through. Known as Nirvana, such purity consists of an emptiness beyond all duality and human conception. Because it is beyond anything that can be known, Nirvana is incomprehensible to the conventional mind and hence indescribable. Buddha did acknowledge, however, that it was a state of bliss and later Buddhists texts suggest that it is imperishable, timeless, deathless, and good. Though there is no personal God or Creator, Buddhist descriptions of Nirvana are not inconsistent with impersonal notions of God.

The Four Noble Truths are an excellent summary of the Buddhist way. After his own arduous spiritual search, Buddha concluded that 1. we are born into suffering, 2. that desire, craving, and attachment to existence and worldly pleasures are the cause of this suffering, 3. that cessation from craving and attachment is its cure, and 4. that this cure is possible from following the noble eight fold path: right views, right intent, right speech, right conduct, right livelihood, right effort, and right mindfulness. The purpose of all this practice, however, is to extinguish mind and self.

For Buddhists, mind is the central problem of man. It is the mind that generates and elaborates the phenomenal world into being. Everything arises in the mind: self, ideas, body, world. One who adopts Buddhist teaching understands that he is neither body nor mind, neither observer nor observed, but simply awareness in which the play of imagination creates scenarios of existence, unhappiness, and suffering. A most practical and empirical individual, Buddha avoided metaphysical speculation, which he considered mental distraction. He also avoided religious authority, which he felt violated the importance of first hand learning, and ritual, which was viewed as superstition. Buddha taught instead that each must do the work of enlightenment on his own.

In Buddhism, quieting the mind, overcoming self-seeking motives and fantasies of past and future, and opening to mindless consciousness are the primary means of achieving enlightenment. Searching for "truth" simply creates more mind forms; ceasing the search, the underlying nature of reality eventually shines through. Transcending mind and emotion, like clouds clearing, reveals the spacious and unalloyed nature of being. Salvation (i.e., Nirvana) can be attained even in this life by subduing mind, with meditation as the main route to dismantling its illusions, attachments, and distress.

Buddhism does not posit a God or a soul but does acknowledge a karmic process of reincarnation. What transcends death, however, is not one's spiritual essence but mental and emotional habits such as desire, attachment, and emotional reactivity. Sometimes the one who is finally enlightened may remain in this world to guide others; he is called the boddhisattva.

COMMENT

In many ways, Buddhism is as much a psychology as a religion, empirically examining the operation of thought and imagination in the creation of suffering and reality. Buddha's "religion" was realistic, objective, psychologically sophisticated, and without a deity (though some later divisions of Buddhism have deified him). Objective and nonauthoritarian, Buddhism naturally appeals to westerners who feel wounded or mislead by institutional religion, who wish to examine higher states of consciousness for themselves, or who learn techniques of mindfulness and meditation to combat the accelerated pace of American life.

TAOISM

The final teaching of the mystic Lao Tzu, Taoism is a highly metaphysical religion. The Tao is considered "The Way" of ultimate reality and the very source of the universe. Spirit rather than matter, it is inexhaustible, flowing, life giving, and balanced with positive and negative elements (yin and yang). It is the order and energy force of the universe. Beyond the capacity of ordinary human knowledge, it can, however, be sensed through intuition, and when directly experienced, is the highest state of consciousness attainable. It functions without personal will or purpose, and hence is not like a deity with intentions for man. As a religion, Taoism generally has little interest in life after death; rather believing that human life is the highest value and should be extended as long as possible.

A concept central to Taoism is *ch'i*, which translates to breath but is more accurately suggestive of vital energy. One can not only feel the *ch'i* moving in the body and the world, one can increase and direct it with practice. Practice involves self-purification and self-transcendence, returning the mind may to its essential purity, stillness, and clarity. The Tao cannot be controlled but one can come into harmony with it. Like Luke Skywalker's "force" existing everywhere in the universe, or like energy itself, the *ch'i* can neither be created nor destroyed, but when correctly realized, is known as the power of being and a kind of magic that reaches everywhere. To align one's whole life and being with the Tao is the way. When done successfully, all things happen as they should with no specific effort, emotion, or activity. Attuned to this power, everything flows naturally, spontaneously, and gracefully. Competition, aggression, struggle, and determination are replaced by serenity, stillness, and humility for the Tao cannot be conquered. Like a river, it is easier to go with the current than against it.

Anyone reading the Tao Te Ching quickly recognizes it to be a mystical and metaphysical work of remarkable depth and insight. It is about individual spiritual balance and flow, attunement to what is eternal and needs no correction, and about peace, simplicity, moderation, freedom, and immortality here and now. Knowing oneself, one knows the world as a continuous birthing of creation. Taoism is about living with neither identity nor ego, neither emotion nor ambition, beyond distinctions or preferences. It teaches the nature of inaction as a most natural source of all action. Within these simple, sometimes paradoxical words, lies a profound metaphysical wisdom and a harmonious view of social life.

COMMENT

Does an action feel natural or forced? Do we feel moved in ways we cannot understand, beyond ego's goals and ambitions? Is there joy and spontaneity in the experience of being? These are questions about the *ch'i* and the way of the universe. Invisible, indescribable, without odor or taste, yet everywhere and capable of being sensed and known, the Tao is a way of experiencing the rightness and flow of the universe in one's personal life. As such, it is a valuable concept for psychotherapy. More than getting in touch with one's feelings, it is learning to discern and flow with the natural energy of being.

CONFUCIANISM

There is another element of eastern religion that contributes heavily to its social form. Originating from the teachings of Confucius, it emphasizes the social expression of spirituality through the continuous improvement of the self-in-relationship. Guided by idealized cultural values, folksy maxims of proper behavior, and a strong commitment to tradition, Confucianism aspires toward, and indeed prescribes, morally enlightened social participation and an ever-expanding web of correct and beneficial human relations. Cultivation of the social self, then, is the essential work of spiritual development.

In the time of Confucius, violent warfare and tremendous social anarchy existed everywhere. Warring states, exaggerated displays of chivalry and bravado, and mass slaughter were common. The prescriptions for mature social behavior Confucius taught became a healing and stabilizing response to this incessant unrest, providing the balm of tradition, propriety, and interpersonal respect. The innumerable sayings ("Confucius says") provided the rules and the encouragement for decency in social life, with virtually all aspects of community behavior and relationship carefully choreographed. With this emphasis, some have described Confucianism as more of an ethical system and social philosophy than a religion, for its goal was to overhaul and civilize society and restore the value of human life.

Confucius argued that our highest potential is found within and through communal participation. Self was conceived as primarily a social experience, a nexus where connecting relationships of family and society take place. Overcoming egotism and pure individuality encourages moral community and proper social order. Education and the arts provided further resources for developing the self and its cultural manifestation. Finally, the transcendent realm also contributes to the worldly order, for the ancestors in Heaven maintain their interest in earth's problems and can be called upon, through sacrifices and divining methods, to guide its inhabitants. The purpose of life, then, is a balanced, harmonious, and humble adjustment in the everyday web of community life.

COMMENT

Though the endless sayings of Confucius sometimes seem trivial or obvious, they are nonetheless eloquent reflections of a most civilized way of life. They teach that there is a higher social nature available to us that can transcend violence, egotism, and greed. When viewed merely as face-saving rules of social conduct, these axioms lose their value; when elevated to spiritual language, they light a way of refinement, decency, and responsibility that western society sorely needs.

REFLECTIONS ON EASTERN RELIGION

As noted earlier, discrepancies between religious systems in the east do not produce the kind of theological debate so common in the west. The differing definitions or significance of self, soul, heaven, and God are discussed but not fiercely contested, for it is understood that all things and ideas coexist in life, just as all members coexist in a family. In the west, on the other hand, it is virtually impossible to be both a Christian and a Jew, or even a Protestant and a Catholic. In traditional Chinese culture, however, Buddhist, Taoist, Confucian, and folk religions naturally commingle without conflict or contradiction, a way of life the west could well emulate.

In a sense, this difference between eastern and western cultures reflects a balance in the larger human psyche between feminine and masculine energies: the feminine expressed in eastern values of interdependence, union, balance, inclusion, co-existence, equality, and nurturing, and the masculine in contrasting western values of separation, analysis, comparison, exclusion, opposition, hierarchy, direction, and dissection. Eastern philosophy and religion, therefore, offer us an invaluable and balancing gift of non-competitive inclusion, for, as we know, religious ideas are often paradoxical and contradictory to the finite human mind.

A second gift available from eastern metaphysics is a profound psychological and spiritual understanding of the mind. Hindus and Buddhists argue that we are responsible for our suffering and that the work of spiritual realization is to face this victimization. Meditative practice reveals that we are not who we think we are, and that attaching to erroneous ideas of self is a curable cause of stress and suffering. They further demonstrate that an empty and quiet mind, an awakened compassion for all beings, and a gradually dissolving belief in self and individual survival are the means of release. Man is like an idea that takes itself too seriously, proliferating into a whole world of thought, identity, divisions, duality, and problems. To achieve ultimate spiritual realization, one must face the illusions of self and personality and open instead to the void, the universal mind, or cosmic consciousness. The ideas and methodologies developed in these religions have many powerful implications for psychotherapy.

Westerners have been increasingly drawn to eastern religions since the late 1950's. Buddhism has been particularly appreciated because it avoids the rigid, authoritarian notions of God that have alienated so many in recent decades. In Buddhism, people find a warm welcome that does not conflict with any pre-existing religious orientation. In fact, Catholic and Episcopal priests have been studying and integrating Buddhist teachings into their lives since Zen was introduced into America nearly half a century ago. Buddhism's emphasis on "mindfulness," a way of observing mental activity and its effects in meditation and everyday life, is also valued as an eminently practical means of living in the present and practicing peace and equanimity in the real world. Buddha's sensitive and loving nature, and his focus on kindness and compassion for all sentient beings, similarly touch our western longing for these virtues in a culture so focused on competition, aggression, and violence. Finally, Hindu, Buddhist, and Taoist religions emphasize that salvation is up to the individual, a very empowering message in a culture that has sometimes been told one cannot know God directly, must defer to religious authority, and must wait to meet after death.

But there is one more reason for the west's growing interest. In eastern religions, the split between psychology and spirituality never materialized as it did for Western man. Buddhism and Hinduism, utilizing meditation and ancient yogic practices as instruments of insight and spiritual transformation, created what is really a spiritual psychology that carefully and ceaselessly examines how the mind creates reality, how it encases the eternal mind, (God or "Buddha consciousness) and how this false construction can be penetrated. Confucian and Taoist religions, calling for outer and inner spiritual balance respectively, teach that spirituality is a matter of everyday social and metaphysical life.

It is not surprising, therefore, that eastern religions have become so popular in America, meeting as they do important spiritual needs under emphasized in many western traditions. It would seem, then, that mixing these eastern ingredients, despite their apparent contradictions, is not a bad idea at all, and in recent years westerners are doing so more often than ever before.

WESTERN PHILOSOPHY AND PSYCHOLOGY: OUR FORGOTTEN SPECULATION ON SOUL

Though we are apt to forget, fundamental to western philosophy and its evolution into psychology has been the concept of soul. Interest in the soul was woven deeply into the religious and philosophic system of the Greeks in the millennium before Christ. Plato argued that the body and soul were fundamentally different entities, the latter being immaterial and capable of apprehending the pure world of universal and ideal forms behind imperfect reality. Aristotle, Plato's student, conceived the soul as immanent in an organism's form and functions. In the twelfth and thirteenth centuries, the Catholic Church revived Aristotelianism to cope with its despair about the material world, its need to separate man from animal, and its preoccupation with sin. In the seventeenth century, Descarte, further developed the matter-spirit duality by arguing that animals, unlike men, were merely machines without souls. How the soul acted on the body became the subject then of considerable philosophic and scientific debate in the seventeenth and eighteen centuries, with Leibnitz, for example, arguing that soul and body operated in parallel fashion, and Berkeley arguing that the soul was the background of all experience.

While later philosophers and scientists tried to mechanize mental processes into conditioned associations, German philosophers reasserted that it was actually soul that makes use of the faculties of mind. Kant claimed that deductive methods can never prove the existence of soul, yet it exists in each act of will. His philosophy eventually led to the school of transcendentalism, which flourished in nineteenth century America with Emerson, Thoreau, and Whitman, and posited that ultimate explanatory principles lie outside of that which is experienced, a position which opened the door to romanticism and its mystical intuitions about nature and spirit.

The scientific revolution challenged the invisible world of the soul, winning victory after victory in its quest to measure and lawfully explain the material universe in purely empirical ways. Experimental psychology grew from the same philosophical roots, with Weber applying the scientific method to the physiology of human sensation and Fechner establishing the arithmetic relationship between sensation and mental functions. Thus the field of psychophysics was born, paving the way for Wundt to found the science of experimental psychology. Interestingly, the soul, though banished, was not forgotten. Fechner, for example, was also passionately interested in its study. Sounding much like a mystic, he believed the universe to be a unitary living organism, including even the stars, planets, and stones, with each and every part alive with consciousness. The mystical and the scientific were for him neither incompatible nor exclusive; they were part of the whole.

Then along came the Harvard professor, William James, the father of American psychology. His textbook, *Principles of Psychology*, was enormously influential in establishing the general foundations of psychology as a science. Yet he, too, was drawn to religion and his work *The*

Varieties of Religious Experience remains a classic. Fascinated by mystical experience, he discussed the struggles of the soul to reconcile good and evil and the role of conversion experiences in resolving this tension. He argued further that mystical experience is genuine rather than pathological, providing man with a vision of a higher reality. James also expressed interest in psychical research and the study of ESP.

More recently, Carl Jung and his followers have renewed psychology's interest in the soul. Despite viewing himself as a scientist, the word soul is used freely and frequently in Jung's work. God, too, found a place in his psychology. The Self, defined as the central archetype of the collective unconscious, is the psyche's repository of the God image. It was further argued that man's psychiatric symptoms reflect his struggle to find a religious orientation to the universe. The Jungian myth, as elaborated by Edinger, Jaffe, and others, views individuation as the process of becoming a conscious individual, not just for its own sake, but for the purpose of incarnating divine consciousness in the world. Theorizing on the epochal changes occurring in our time, Jung suggested that mankind was moving into a period in which each is called to undergo the incarnational experience of Christ, who is described as the first truly individuated man. It was also felt that man serves God by generating consciousness; more than that, it is felt that God, too, evolves as a result of his dialogue with man. Jung's work has influenced numerous psychological and religious writers, many of whom further developed the concept of soul and its place in a psychology of everyday life (e.g., Hillman, Moore).

We can see, then, that the ideas of soul and divine influence in our mental and emotional functioning have never fully left psychology. Though some recent trends, such as behaviorism, sought to exclude any such non-observable phenomena from the field of psychology, man's intuition and interest in the divine were never permanently excluded from his science.

INDIGENOUS RELIGION

Creation mythology the world over, coded in the language of symbol and metaphor, speaks of a time before time, shortly after creation was completed, when man and the gods either lived together in paradise or could travel between heaven and earth. At that time, all men, the gods, and even the animals spoke a single language. Men were of higher character then and often possessed god-like qualities of goodness, holiness and immortality. Despite these virtues, somehow man changed, his character became corrupt, he broke the unity of heaven and earth, and the worlds separated. Disobedience, willfulness, arrogance, wickedness, worldly desires, selfishness, or greed are usually said to be behind this change. In time, man forgot his original god-like nature though he still longs to return to his original home. Many myths also say that the world man created, filled with depravity, must be destroyed by the creator, saving only the obedient so that the paradisal world can be restored again in its wake.

The shaman is the primary healer of aboriginal and non-industrial peoples, and shamanism is the oldest healing form known to man. This term (originally *saman*) originated with the Tungus people of Siberia and meant "one who is excited, moved, raised" (Walsh, 1990). The shaman's trance has been described as religious ecstasy. Amazingly similar across cultures and eras, shamanism continues to be practiced in virtually every primitive tribal society. With the introduction of larger, and more complex social structures, the tribal "medicine man" evolved into several specialized roles, including the priest, sorcerer, witch, seer, diviner, magician, medium, and eventually the physician, psychologist, and psychotherapist.

In the shaman's world view, illness is related to the spirit realm, where the medicine man must travel to locate its source and meaning, and bring back medicine for its cure. Because the link between this world and the original one was broken, the shaman must travel between them. His journeys take place in altered states of consciousness, often at great peril to himself, in order to help his fellow beings. Sickness is always a spiritual matter: the sick are felt to have lost their personal or power animal, their soul has been taken, they have been invaded by an evil spirit or power, they disobeyed the ritual requirements of life, or they forgot to honor the gods. Illness, depression, and misfortune are signs that a person can no longer ward off the negative forces arising from this misalignment, and a correction in one's relation to the spiritual world must be achieved for healing to occur.

There are countless ancient, native, and indigenous religions. The majority show great concern and interest for the soul's existence in an after life. Burial practices and art work emphasize this universal focus, and in many religions, tremendous preparations are made for the dying to cross safely into the other world. Divination and sacrifice serve as means of communicating with the spirits and ancestors, who populate heaven and may contribute to man's welfare on earth. Tenure in the worldly plane, therefore, is considered temporary. Finally, indigenous religions still view the world as a spiritual realm as much or more than a material one. Spirits influence and animate all living and non-living things, events, and processes. In fact, all causes are essentially spiritual ones, and a man's first and foremost duty is to the sacred realm where he receives all that he needs. The material realm is but a manifestation of the supraordinate spiritual one.

COMMENT

Indigenous religions sometimes appear superstitious and barbaric to western man, characterized by endless spirits, animal sacrifices, peculiar divining strategies, and unscientific approaches to illness. But they still remain the dominant worldview for the majority on earth and remind us that life and healing were originally spiritual processes. Pre-industrial man depended on his religious practices for meaning, survival, and healing, and as ways of energetically or spiritually influencing the transcendent order. Moreover, despite our advanced science, these ancient ways continue to live in the psyche. Archaic religious reactions (e.g., petition, superstition, sacrifice) still represent natural responses to distress and are evident in dreams, prayer, and even current metaphysical speculation.

THE NEAR DEATH EXPERIENCE: MEETING THE TRANSCENDENT GOD

Though not a religion, the Near-Death Experience (NDE) is clearly a religious experience. The now voluminous writings on the NDE suggest that the ending of life, far from being simply a termination of organic activity and consciousness, is actually a profoundly meaningful spiritual transition. The dying individual finds his consciousness leaving his body, moving through darkness into another dimension where he may be welcomed by predeceased loved ones, and encountering a loving and all knowing presence recognized to be God. In communicating with this presence, the individual comes to understand, in a lightning fast replay of his entire life, how well he has learned to love, what he has done to benefit or harm others, and how he has contributed to advancing the human race. Although there may be individual differences in the duration and extent of a NDE, its basic form and sequence is remarkably consistent.

Recorded in man's earliest writing and well documented in recent years (e.g., Moody, 1975, Ring, 1980), the NDE provides spectacular data challenging so many of our scientific assumptions about the ending of life. The modern medical-scientific paradigm views consciousness as merely an epiphenomenon of biological activity. After a NDE, however, individuals universally assert that consciousness not only continues beyond the cessation of measurable bodily functions, but does so in lucid, meaningful, and life-transforming ways. Its subjective reality is incontrovertible to the individual, who recognizes the NDE as a powerful spiritual experience rather than a dream, hallucination, or delirium. Numerous astute observers, including Carl Jung, described this experience and its profound personal validity.

The only explanatory model sensible to NDE'ers is a spiritual one. The experience simply demands a religious language for describing the celestial light, transcendental consciousness, heavenly after-life environment, contact with the divine being, and deep spiritual meaning. It can only be described as a profoundly sacred experience. The NDE appears to be a cosmic-archetypal process of transformation of extraordinary beauty, sublimity, power and wisdom that confirms to the individual the spiritual nature of existence, the reality of an afterlife, and the authority of a unconditionally loving, omniscient supreme being. The NDE also demonstrates universality, occurring independent of gender, race, personality, lifestyle, cause, religion or religious beliefs, socioeconomic level, or culture. It plays no favorites and, as the Amazing Grace refrain suggests, requires no personal greatness or elevated spiritual worth.

Not surprisingly, chroniclers of the NDE's report numerous positive changes in the individual's personality, values, and attitudes toward death. Not only do people feel more loving and alive, they have increased self-acceptance, greater appreciation of life, and a desire to understand the inherently spiritual nature of existence. Many report a kind of mystical perception in which the world is seen anew as both infinitely beautiful and immanent with sacred presence. The fear of death is greatly diminished; in fact, many look forward to death as a return to the wonder and joy of the next world. Though some lament the loss of the afterlife experience after resuscitation, most people return to life thrilled with the spiritual possibilities of living and grateful for the opportunity to continue learning and growing.

COMMENT

The Near-Death Experience appears to be a transition from earthly existence into another dimension. It does not tell us much about what happens beyond the threshold (though some religions provide intriguing answers, such as the Tibetan and Egyptian Books of the Dead or eastern theories of re-incarnation), leaving us to wonder, philosophize and extrapolate the possibilities of the next life. The NDE is, however, as close to the immediate first hand contact with the transcendent God and the secrets of life and death as one can get. With medicine's increasingly ability to bring people back from clinical death, it is estimated that millions have now had this experience (Gallup, 1982). Given its profundity and frequency, it is not surprising that the NDE has received so much attention.

MYSTICISM: MEETING THE IMMANENT GOD

Fundamental to religion of every type and time is the mystical experience. It may be called enlightenment, satori, rapture, nirvana, ecstasy, union, or countless other names. As discussed earlier, all religions, simple to complex, are born from this immediate and astounding experience, with subsequent theology representing attempts to understand its purpose and sacred teachings.

To summarize, the mystic vision involves a direct and unmediated communion with the divine. It is beyond the scope of language to describe and beyond the grasp of personal will to evoke. The mystical experience is luminous, timeless, ecstatic, and joyous, revealing a resplendent world saturated with a loving divine presence, as well as authoritative revelations of ultimate knowledge and a life-affirming world view. After this experience, arid philosophical speculation ceases, for the world and one's own nature are known to be the sacred itself. The divine being, centered everywhere and animating everything, becomes the true source of happiness while on earth. As with the NDE, fear of death recedes afterwards because divine union is realized to be the destination of life.

COMMENT

In *Death of a Hero, Birth of the Soul,* I recounted a number of mystical experiences and summarized their common features. The reader is encouraged to review this material for it is of profound and still unrecognized importance to our understanding of religion, spirituality and life itself. Though less understood by the popular culture, the mystical experience, like the NDE, is a life-changing, first hand experience of the sacred, most frequently in its imminent form. Equally important, it teaches us what God is *not*: God is not coercion, proselytizing, dogmatism, religiosity, guilt, shame, blame, sin, judgment, cults, brain washing, control, abuse, psychosis, war, or threats of hell and damnation. God is love.

RECENT RELIGIOUS DEVELOPMENTS

NEW AGE WRITINGS

New Age writings offer a fascinating array of theories, beliefs, and assertions that often fall outside our culture's prevailing materialistic, scientific, and religious paradigms. Included are propositions about energy, auras, spirits, angels, channeling, extraordinary mental abilities, non-ordinary healing, the occult, and God. Unproven by scientific standards and not infrequently viewed as heretical by western religious dogma, these are by archetypal standards beliefs found recurrently throughout the spiritual history of mankind. Ostracized for some years by the scientific and religious establishments, these cyclical archetypal forms are presently making a comeback in the popular counterculture. In their current guise, they postulate the coming of a "new age," an evolutionary breakthrough when people will be able to experience and participate in divine reality more directly. We are on the edge of this new time, they say, and for those who study such beliefs, many can begin to experience this new age already.

New Age teachings assert that humans are primarily spiritual beings who have lost or forgotten their connection to their original divine nature. More than that, human beings are literally manifestations of God, or at least part of God, and hence are viewed as immortal, angelic, and capable of far more than they realize. The core problem of human beings, according to most New Age writing, is their erroneous and limiting beliefs. Convinced instead that they are mortal, helpless, and insignificant, people experience their lives as a chronic struggle for survival.

Central to New Age philosophy is the conviction that the determinants of one's life are free will, belief, thought, imagination, and visualization. These are God given powers that we use to create reality just as God does, only we fail to realize or use them out of ignorance or wrong beliefs. Visualizing and thinking about hardship, unhappiness, or disappointment, for example, is said to create these outcomes. The individual is also the source of his or her own life, and life problems are said to be chosen or created as learning experiences in the continuing pattern of spiritual evolution known as reincarnation. A soul experiences all the facets of life here on earth until it has finally understood the spiritual nature of life, undoes its limiting beliefs, comes to know its spiritual identity, and achieves co-consciousness with God in the creation of this realm of existence. During our sojourn on earth, there are no "accidents" because everything that happens is intended for the soul's advancement.

In New Age theology, life is not meant to be difficult, painful, and disappointing. Rather it is a gift full of love, joy, abundance, and fulfillment, assuming we can overcome our negative beliefs. Change your thinking and your life will become abundant. New Age writers also believe that there is always help and guidance available in this realm, one needs only to access and trust it. Guidance can take the form of spirit guides, teachers, angels, channeled beings, the higher self, or direct contact with cosmic consciousness. Higher wisdom pours through the universe. The human mind, like a radio receiver, can tune into this wisdom when obstructing negative beliefs and emotional reactivity ("static") are overcome.

New Age writers often enumerate spiritual laws or principles responsible for one's life experience. Such principles involve learning to use the powers of love, gratitude, intuition, higher self, inner peace, visualization, and energy dynamics. It is also commonly felt that God does not judge, punish or condemn; man does. Similarly, hell exists only as a state of mind created by individuals ignorant of their real identity and power. Death, too, is an illusion, for consciousness transcends this sphere and moves into the next where learning is incorporated and new incarnations chosen so the journey to God can continue.

COMMENT

Some argue that New Age beliefs represent the beginnings of a new religious paradigm triggered by the unprecedented changes in human life in the past 50 years. Old religious forms, they say, are no longer relevant to the complexities of twenty-first century life. From "postmodern" chaos comes a yearning for a renewed and personally relevant spiritual orientation, requiring in turn the re-invention of religion. Neglected religious needs and archetypes are being mated into a belief system whose presence is felt in churches and synagogues across America. Particular appeal is found in its beliefs that the average person can contact the sacred dimension directly (e.g., through divination techniques such as angels, Tarot cards, or canneling), that life can be positive and joyful rather than filled with pain and struggle, and that we can heal ourselves and the world through loving intentions and attitudes. Some have criticized New Age believers for wanting to live only in the light, avoiding the dark side of life, and for making people feel ashamed when their problems are not solved by positive beliefs (e.g., cancer). Such criticism is not unique to New Age beliefs, and can be applied to any religion. What is probably most important here is the human need to restore an active and personally relevant spirituality in a time of unsettling intellectual, social, and religious deconstruction.

12 STEP SPIRITUALITY

The Alcoholics Anonymous program, and its many 12 Step offspring (e.g., Al Anon, Narcotics Anonymous, Overeaters Anonymous, Sex and Love Addicts Anonymous) arose, much as a religion, from a mystical experience. Bill Wilson's life was being progressively destroyed by alcoholism. One day, in the throes of hopelessness and despair, he cried out to God to "show Himself." The mystical experience that followed changed his life and gave A.A. its spiritual core (Wilson, 1984). AA's spirituality found surprising assistance from Carl Jung who advised another alcoholic that his only hope lay in having a "vital spiritual experience" and consequent transformation of personality. Jung's letter to this man is quoted in the A.A. Big Book. This connection between helplessness and surrender to a Higher Power became the cornerstone of A.A.

Even cursory examination of the 12 Step program reveals a highly spiritual format, which includes admitting personal powerlessness over the symptom in question, belief in a Higher Power that can restore health and balance, the decision to turn one's personal will over to that higher power, a commitment to improving one's relationships, and a desire for conscious contact with God. Meetings typically begin and end in prayer and members are urged to turn their problems over to their Higher Power, however it is conceived.

The core message of A.A., that we must turn our lives over to God and learn to live in greater experiential contact with the divine will, puts spirituality into the center of its healing philosophy. In its structure and bylaws, A.A. tries to avoid the authoritarian paradigm in which experts or institutions interpret, direct, and certify spiritual growth, encouraging instead a democratic and highly personal spirituality. Other religious elements of A.A. include a gospel of hope, scripture like writings, and a community of believers.

COMMENT

The popularity of this self-help program has not only been phenomenal, it has served as an acceptable doorway into spirituality for many people alienated from institutional religion. The 12 Steps offer a spiritual practice with a depth and sophistication exceeding their simple appearance, and anyone working these steps sincerely should find their lives changed in numerous positive ways, including feeling closer to God. In essence, A.A is an eminently practical religion, one that recognizes the importance of honesty, confession, and restitution, as well as the value of suffering, surrender, failure, community, and faith in the healing of a damaged life. Combining psychology, group support, spirituality, and a permissive and personally interpreted religion, it offers a program of progressive personal and spiritual growth.

RECENT SCIENTIFIC SPECULATION: MYSTICISM REVISITED

Current theories and speculations of physics are re-inventing ancient religious models of the universe. The cosmologies of current astronomers, physicists, and astrophysicists sound downright metaphysical, and their work is often metaphorically described as deciphering the mind of God as reflected in the principles of the universe (Davies, 1992). Previously disdainful of speculation in favor of positivism and precise mathematical science, current theoreticians are suddenly interested once again in metaphysical conjecture on the nature and origin of the universe.

The actual lack of perfect predictability and causality in the laboratory and the impact of the scientist's consciousness of what is being studied have undermined the reductionistic assumptions of earlier science. Moreover, the cosmos is increasingly being viewed as a highly complex, interdependently functioning whole that is more than the sum of its individually operating parts. The model that is emerging describes the universe as infinite, acentric (or centered at every point), and possibly even aware - a self-organizing cosmic mind! These conceptions, of course, are very similar to the metaphysics of Eastern religions. Compared to such remarkable revolutions in scientific thought, the return of concepts like soul and God to psychology need not be considered particularly unexpected, or unacceptable.

COMMENT

Science is once again opening its eyes to the awesome marvel of existence, allowing speculation to flow into the mystery of the unknown. In this intersection of wonder and speculation, science stands shoulder to shoulder with religion, and each can complement the other. Here, too, the split between science and soul can be healed. Characterizing the universe as an infinite supermind also has implications for psychology and psychotherapy, including permission to loosen its rigid positivism to explore other ways of apprehending existence. Higher states of consciousness that link the individual and the cosmic minds, long known to religion as mystical experience, can be psychologically examined and experienced via religious technologies such as meditation, yoga, and fasting. Previously condemned as unscientific, the new physics now seems to encourage such experimentation and speculation in the service of a more holistic and integrated model of the universe.

SCIENCE AND RELIGION: THE MYTH OF OPPOSITION

Science and religion actually have many similarities. At the most abstract levels, scientific questions are essentially the same as the religious ones posed in Chapter 5. In addition, science, like religion, is based on commonly held articles of faith (e.g., the search for truth through the scientific method, the belief in natural causes and an objective, external, material world) and spirited debate among adherents with various "religiously" held positions. Finally, scientists, with their remarkable technology and far ranging theories, now evoke the same kind of awe previously associated with religious masters or priests, as if their penetration of ultimate mysteries gives them a kind of magic or numinous aura.

The stereotypical conflicts between science and religion are also coming into question. For example, their principle difference has always been presumed to be the objective data base and experimental methods of science. But objectivity is not the sole domain of scientists. Eastern practitioners, who meticulously examine their own phenomenology and its principles, would argue that their data base is equally and perhaps more profoundly objective, for it looks not only at the observed, but how the observer creates the observed experience (and its science). Another historical distinction between science and religion is in the sphere of ultimate purposes. Science desires to be independent of teleological statements while most religions directly and intentionally postulate and search for divine purposes. Yet some of the new cosmologies describe ways the universe regulates itself, suggesting a kind of purpose and intention very close to the mystics' apprehensions.

But there are good reasons to view science and religion as complementary (rather than identical) forms of learning, for they potentially assist, correct and support each other. For example, science has taught us that many of man's early religious beliefs were wrong, or at least, overly concretized. Illness is not exclusively about spirits, sin, or disobedience, it is also about viruses, toxins, genetics, and objectively definable disease processes. In the medical model, illness loses its religious stigma. But the scientific model of illness also loses its concern for divine etiology and meaning, which the religious pole of the psyche seeks to restore. In this way, science and religion provide a balance of skepticism and faith, objectivity and intuition, ego (with its analytic tools) and soul (with its indwelling sacred knowledge and search for transcendence). Historically the pendulum between these poles swings back and forth, for science *and* religion comprise the whole.

It is the religious nature of the psyche that drives man's search for the sacred. The scientist's wonder at the vastness of the universe is no less religious than the awe of the believer beholding the unfathomable mystery of God. Conversely, it is the scientific, skeptical nature of the psyche that drives man's search for testable truth, and the scientist in the mystic who wants to know God's nature in a practical, empirical, and confirmable manner. Authentic religious teachers will always say "Don't believe me, find out for your self." The activities and goals of science and religion, then are two sides of a single desire to really know the nature of being.

GLOSSARY OF ADDITIONAL VOCABULARY

PSYCHOLOGICAL TERMS

Psychology: The etymology of psychology combines the Greek roots of logos and psyche, literally meaning the reasons, arguments, and discourse pertaining to the soul, spirit, and mind of man. In modern terms, however, psychology refers to the scientific study of human mental and emotional phenomena. As a discipline, it has numerous sub fields that investigate normal and abnormal individual and social behavior, cognitive and intellectual processes, mental and emotional problems, and the biologic substrates of behavior. As a science, it has well prescribed methods of research and theory building, including direct observation, hypothesis formulation, controlled experiments, and the publication of findings in professional books and journals.

Mind: We are born into a developing mental apparatus, the mind, and learn to use it just as we learn to use our body. The mind consists of the total organization of cognitive functions that you, the ego, have available (thought, perception, intuition, memory, action, thought, ideas, beliefs, meanings, perceptions). We use these ego functions to map and interpret reality, provide responses to reality issues, understand and cope with inner events (i.e., thoughts, feelings, and dreams) and address the spiritual universe. One can use the functions of mind to adapt creatively to inner or outer reality demands, or to defend the ego against ideas or experiences felt to be intolerably frightening, shameful, or uncomfortable. Defensive operations may be either adaptive or maladaptive, depending on their severity and consequences.

Emotions: Loosely speaking, emotions are states such as anger, sadness, joy, grief, wonder, and love, and the list can go on almost indefinitely. We call them feelings for they are indeed what we feel when we tune into them. These states are often divided into positive and negative, higher and lower, stable or reactive. As we will see, emotions give us very important feedback about boundary violations, the betrayal and abandonment of the self, and who we really are.

Mental States: Mental states are transitory organizations of perception, emotion, meaning, memory, and intention. Each is anchored in and colored by a particular emotion but further defined by related thoughts and perceptions to form a larger whole. Mental states tend to be learned, self-perpetuating, and recurrent. They can be positive or negative, depending on the emotion, and they color or create much of our personal reality. Sadness, for example, will take us into the associated mental state, which may include sad ideas, perceptions, memories, and expectations of similarly sad times.

Psychological Defenses: When thoughts, feelings, or reality perceptions become too painful, threatening, or personally unacceptable, ego functions are utilized to deny, blur, or distort them. For example, we can forget whatever was distressing us (repression) or convince ourselves that things don't feel so bad (rationalization and denial). Psychological defenses can be adaptive when used to get through difficult or overwhelming situations, or maladaptive when used excessively in ways that obstruct healthy self-contact, problem-solving, or communication.

Unconscious: Those parts of the personality that exist outside of our awareness are said to fall in the unconscious. Consistent with Freudian and Jungian theory respectively, the personal unconscious is made up of forgotten or repressed biographical memories, motivations and conflicts that were buried because of their painful and traumatic nature, and the collective unconscious which consists of archetypes (universal categories and patterns of meaning and perception, and their expression in images and symbols) genetically accumulated over millions of years of mankind's evolutionary experience.

Personality: This is the distinct, discernible, and self-regulating organization of an individual's psychological functioning. It is composed of ego, consciousness, the unconscious, the self (true and false), emotional and defensive response patterns, and the soul. Every personality is a valid, unique, and irreproducible genetic and biographical form, and each constitutes an entire personal universe of experience and meaning. The healthiness of the personality depends on it traumatic history and how caring and aware the ego is with self and others, mind and emotions, soul and God.

Symptoms: When the personality becomes imbalanced, when breakdown or distortion of healthy personality functioning occurs, symptoms arise. Like heat and smoke from an engine low on oil, they tell us that something is wrong. Symptoms are typically comprised of painful emotions, their associated mental states, maladaptive psychological defenses, and self-defeating behavior of one sort or another. Symptoms derive essentially from the mismanagement or wrong alignment of ego, self, emotion, soul, and community.

Psychotherapy: In psychotherapy, the knowledge and principles of human psychology are applied in the service of ameliorating emotional suffering. When integrated into the medical model, psychotherapy becomes a formal process aimed at diagnosing, treating, and curing or alleviating psychological disorders. Like medicine, it is accountable to society and hence regulated by ethical standards and laws. Like every other field of human interest, psychotherapists may be divided into different schools of thought whose philosophies, assumptions, and practices may vary widely (e.g., cognitive, psychodynamic, behavioral, existential, humanistic, transpersonal).

Religious Abuse: Any and every form of religion can be used abusively. Abusers may be clergy, teachers, gurus, parents, or followers. Abuse occurs whenever someone is required to unquestioningly believe and follow somebody else's religion or its tenants. Such abuse is always built upon a rigidly authoritarian and narcissistic power structure that forbids healthy scrutiny with emotional and physical punishment. Obedience is rationalized as God's will, and people are taught that questioning the leadership is tantamount to disobeying God. Guilt, shame, self-doubt, and self-betrayal are also fostered to maintain the abuser's power and manipulation.

Religious Addiction: Religious addiction occurs whenever a religious belief or practice is unconsciously used in an obsessive-compulsive manner to defend against underlying emotional problems. A dysfunctional use of religion, addictive behavior has virtually nothing to do with healthy religion or spirituality, and often arises from earlier religious abuse. Feeling inherently worthless, evil, guilty, or condemned by God, religious addicts pursue rigid ascetic, masochistic, or compulsive religious practices hoping to control their pain or achieve "salvation" from their suffering. Extremely controlling of themselves, they may also seek to control others, forcing them into the same practices and beliefs. Like alcoholism, religious addiction is usually a progressive problem, eventually isolating or alienating the individual from healthy family and friends.

RELIGIOUS AND SPIRITUAL TERMS

Theology: Theology is the study of God, the sacred, and sacred scripture. Its etymological roots are also Greek and make reference to reasons, arguments and discourses about God. In general, theology seeks a logical, cohesive, and ongoing understanding of an established tradition of revelation and faith. Often more intellectual and theoretical, it covers all aspects of the divine, including the nature of the sacred, the dynamics of man's relationship to it, and God's purposes in creation. At its core, of course, theology is an attempt to understand the mystical experience responsible for the religion's very existence.

Church, Sect, and Cult: A church is a formal institutional structure organized around a specific body of religious beliefs. Its institutional functions are 1. to bring worshippers to the divine through ritual, sacrament, ceremony, and celebration, 2. to disseminate the teachings of scripture and practice, and 3. to provide a social forum for the care and guidance of the congregation. The priest, minister, rabbi or other religious leader direct these functions but they are not believed to be actual incarnations of the divine.

A sect is usually smaller than a church and the relationship of its members to the divine is intended to be more personal and direct, rather than under formal clerical direction. It is often a loose, democratic organization with power located in the laity or nominally in a pastor.

DEFINITIONS OF SOUL

"How Do You Define Soul?"

* *"We are not who we think we are. The soul is that part of us the religions refer to as 'I AM.' It is my essence. It is continuous. We are always who we are. The real me. Like how you change all through your life stages, it's what is still the same, unchanged. It can grow or regress. It's like a delicate almost transparent thing that Changes shapes like the color of a rainbow on the skin of a bubble if the light hits it right. It Changes and moves. It is the part of you that just knows. Whether you like it or not, whether you want to acknowledge what it tells you or ignore it, it just knows. It just exists with or without you."*

* *"For me, it's cosmic energy, like a heartbeat of the universe, the Divine essence of an individual. To me it's here (points to the heart region). It's like going inside but its as big as all outdoors. It's like a light...a beam or bursting forth of light, so it's not static. There's momentum involved, a kind of coming forth, tremendous movement. When I touch into that, it's like doors open."*

* *"I'm a little leery of the word...all this religions stuff. The truest part of oneself is the thing that comes to mind, the deepest part. Sometimes when I'm up in the mountains, I feel like I have a connection that's getting to the core of me."*

* *"The part of me that's eternal. Like the idea that the brain is only a tool to make things happen. Where do the ideas for the impulses come from? Whoever I am is not located in my body."*

* *"Your spiritual center. It's really difficult to discuss. Soul is the God in us. You don't connect to it all the time. It's not always visible. There are glimpses but it's not something I am always cognizant of. And it's more noticeable when it's injured. It's injured when we live our life in a way that's not true for us. I think soul is also a connection with one another as well as with God and with the forest, animals, the sky and the wind. Which is why I think it goes on beyond the life span of our body. I don't think it wears out. I think it continues to grow and flourish. The image that comes up is that of light, a centered light. Maybe that's what people see when they die...maybe it's their soul they're drawn to and have a consciousness with after death."*

* *"Your imagination, your inner self. It's like you have two people, your outer person and your inner person, and that's your soul."*

* *"It's this sort of internal part of myself. As an image, it's this round, white, ball-like sphere...incorruptible. Parts of the' body are draped over it, but its beyond time and space. It's the part of yourself that connects to the universe. It's not corruptible by body problems or emotional states and allows connection to the larger reality. It's not some heaven like ethereal realm, it's the living nature rhythms of outside space, the biosphere of life, the life energy of the earth."*

* *"I get tangled up with the religious connotations to it. It's kind of like what a person really is. It's inside the shell. You take the shell with you every place you go, day in and day out. I keep coming up with something that defies what my scientific background says should be. Something*

that defies death, that there's a continuity, a no beginning and no end to what a person is, and you have this like blip hanging off it which is life on earth. It's what encompasses all of it. It's what God created. And you can do various things with it, one of which is coming to earth for an 80 year period. There's a lot before and a lot after and you can hang various lifetimes off it like a clothesline, never beginning and never ending with clothespins on it holding different lifetimes. I see the soul as fully defining what that intelligence (God) is. Here on earth you don't get a full sense of soul. There's more to a soul than you are able to glimpse in an 80 year life span. It's like a Pandora's box or a book. It's like God opens the book of Fred and it's like a ghost or a genie will come out and the genie is like the soul."

* *"Everything! My heart beating, breathing, that's me...the soul. I believe when I die, my soul will go wherever. It's to me like a whisper, very light. It's always there. I think it's more than anything not the angry part of my mind. It's the good part."*

* *"It means a lot to me. It means the receptacle of the spirit. Until you really have felt soul, you can't have a real relationship, you can't have a relationship with the spirit. They go hand in glove. And you can't have a relationship with what really is creative in you and in the planet. A lot of my experience lately has been: this is my personality and this is my soul, and my soul is getting bigger."*

* *"You think of soul as down and wet and moist. Soul is maybe the reality of the psyche, kind of the realm of the emotions. It's darkness as contrasted with spirit which I see as a beckoning with brightness. It's going into the depths as opposed to coming into the light. Soul is what you come into the world with."*

* *"It's the connection between the life force and the personality. So when I think of soul, I have an image of something that trails way back and comes up and has considerable shape in the present. Its tail goes back to the beginning of time. So there's the creation of the universe, the basic organizing principle of the universe. The soul is the stuff of the connection between the organizing principle or the energy from which we all come. But that's only a piece of it because in your lifetime, connecting with that stuff evolves it, develops wisdom in it; becoming dimensional is all part of the form in a lifetime. And the soul is the bridge back into the great energy and organizing principle of the universe. When I am most completely and fully real, I am almost all soul at that moment. Self is the psychological or personality aspect of what forms and soul is the life force in us that just comes with us. The moment we can be totally present with who we are in its deepest way, Soul and self are one."*

* *"I have never understood that word very well. My soul is...I think of my soul as sort of my unconscious. The times I feel like I was in touch with my soul, and it happens quite a bit when I'm in here (therapy), is when something becomes clear to me about the meanings or motives of certain feelings. It's like I'm demonstrating my soul. It's the sum total of all the feelings I've had either conscious or unconscious. I will never forget the day I was at that funeral for my patient. We were standing outside. It was sunny and getting kind of hot. I was fighting back tears. I don't know what my wife said to me, but I feel like I was left just exposed, like I was wearing my soul on my face. I sort of remember snapping back into my soul-less face soon thereafter at this little get together after the funeral."*

* *"It is the inner room or place where I communicate with God, where I am at my essence, where I discover or unite with my essence. It's the expression of who I am and I think who I am is a gift of God, or the Creator, whatever that means. It's the essence within all of us of who we are...united with the universal, the eternal, what makes us part of a commonalty."*

* *"My soul is my being. If I didn't have a soul, I wouldn't be at all. A part of me that makes me what I am, that keeps me being a quiet person, a person that wants to be alone, that needs to be alone, to get in touch with myself, to bring me back to the woman I know that I am. When I'm in touch with my soul, I know that I am content with myself. My soul of course is the spiritual part of me. It's just a figure of a woman that looks like me, talks like me, acts like me, but is not solid. You can see through her and put your hand through her, but she is more real than I am most of the*

time. She is what I keep searching for and she's always there waiting. I guess I'm not looking in the right places. It's also probably the most tender part of me."

* *"I think the soul is just the part of you that kind of...when you die, it kind of breaks into little pieces. The loved ones, each one kind of gets a part. It's a part of their soul that stays with you. It's the thing that gives you life, that gives you happiness. I think it keeps you from being depressed sometimes. You get different things from different people. I think God made you, and to each one he gives a little piece of Him. I don't think that's the heart, it's the soul, a little piece of God is in each one and that's the soul."*

* *"The soul is that part of me that is the repository of those experiences, those emotions and felt sensations that remind me that I am human, thus connected more and more to other humans."*

* *"It is my inner self, gut, the essentials, essence; feeling and being, not thinking; what's honest, real, unencumbered; no bullshit."*

* *"Soul is the spirit outside and within the body, the essence of being outside the physical plane. It is the universal connection to perfection and the foundation of heart and intuition."*

* *"Soul is the essence of our spiritual and moral being, the core of our individual humanity. It's my inner self and it makes the body more than just a creature. And I think the soul is hidden beneath the conscious."*

* *"To me, it's tied to God and it means that even if your body dies, your soul is intact. It's the part that remains and goes to God. It's something you would not want to not have, like sell your soul to the devil. I think a part of it, too, is how you treat other people, because your soul is tied to the religious part. So a soul is the total being. You have a heart and it pumps but the soul is the fiber of the person, and as long as you have your soul, you're pretty good. It's God, Mother Theresa. Those are the images I see...The Virgin Mary...and mothers."*

* *"I've never thought about it. I suppose it means like the essence, that which transcends the body-image. Maybe sort of wispy smoke, nothing with form. I don't know. I think the soul has to do with where a person is with respect to their own spirituality."*

* *"Psyche. It's not some kind of metaphysical principal, but that which is intangibly, essentially you...that inner core, that center which really is you. And from where you can connect with that which is transcendental. If you don't have the first, you can't have the second."*

* *"I think the soul is the essence of what a human being truly is. It's the best part of us, the part that isn't selfish and worldly and competitive. It's the part that has to do with being giving, that shows concern, that can be generous, that is not looking for a material reward for behavior or actions...and it's spiritual."*

PSYCHOSPIRITUAL ISSUES AS HUMAN PROBLEMS

PERSONALITY PROBLEMS

ego: Psychospiritual ego problems may be manifested in:

a. inadequate knowledge: inaccurate understanding of spirituality, failure to recognize spiritual goals and realities, inability to sense and discern spiritual energies or ask meaningful questions.

b. limited ego strength: inability to hold the spiritual dimension in focus amidst life or emotional problems, or being overwhelmed or controlled by emotion, situational problems, or others, precluding conscious participation in the spiritual journey.

c. frankly impaired ego functions: intellect, memory, and reality orientation disorganized, delirious, cloudy, or delusional.

d. limited regressive ability: inability to relax, regress, and transcend ordinary ego functions and beliefs in the service of mystical awareness

self: Psychospiritual self problems may be manifested in:

a. false self: defensive inflation, rigidity, and over-identification with the false self, suppressing true self and its relationship to soul

b. true self: ignorance, betrayal, abandonment, or devaluing of true self and its relation to soul, or control of true self by others obstructing spiritual contact

c. historical trauma: damage, fragmentation, or annihilation of the true self secondary to extreme trauma or abuse, compromising the whole personality and its transpersonal center.

d. death of the self: dissolution of the self in the spiritual journey which can be frightening and disorienting.

soul: Psychospiritual problems involving the soul may be manifested in:

a. impaired connection to soul: limited sensitivity to one's spiritual values, laws, and experience.

b. disconnection from soul (or the conviction that it has been corrupted or stolen): loss of vitality, emptiness, depression, illness, and even death.

spirit: Psychospiritual problems involving spirit may be manifested in:

a. empty or absent relationship to God: inability to feel the presence of God as a real and tangible reality.

b. disconnection from spirit: lack of spontaneity, art, dance, and joy; inability to be touched or moved by the spirit in creative expression.

mystical vision: Psychospiritual problems involving mystical vision may be manifested in:
a. loss of mystical apprehension: lack of wonder and awe for the divine mystery and the sacred as a living reality all around us.
b. inability to see spiritual beauty and wonder in others: permits or encourages us to devalue, reject, and even destroy others without remorse.

consciousness: Psychospiritual problems in consciousness may be manifested in:
a. misunderstanding of specific non-ordinary states of consciousness: out-of-body and mystical experiences, lucid dreaming, expanded consciousness, and ESP.
b. fear of the ultimate nature of consciousness: even gradual transition to cosmic consciousness can be profoundly threatening, confusing, and disorienting to the unprepared.

life stage: Psychospiritual problems with life stages may be manifested in:
a. inability to change stages: resisting the psychospiritual growth tasks in one stage by clinging to those in an earlier stage, or, conversely, trying to accomplish task beyond one's present stage; prevents the transformative work associated with the current stage.
b. failure to shift from the first to the second half of life: inability to accept the defeat of the ego (hero) at midlife prevents the birth and awakening of soul and the spiritual life.
c. resistance to the dissolution of identify and personality in aging: limits the mystical breakthrough associated with aging.
d. fear of death: undermines the great potential for love, transformation, and grace in the end of life transition.

BODY PROBLEMS

illness: Psychospiritual problems involving illness may be manifested in:
disease, psychophysiologic stress symptoms, and accidents often reflect powerful issues and energies denied at the conscious level, forcing them into the body for expression.

feeling: Psychospiritual problems involving feeling may be manifested in:
deadness of body feeling and sensation, reduced awareness of the spiritual energy of physical being, preventing full awareness of our spiritual nature.

vitality: Psychospiritual problems involving vitality may be manifested in:
reduction in body vitality due to serious illness and deadening of feeling.

RELATIONSHIP PROBLEMS

marriage: Psychospiritual problems involving the marriage may be manifested in:
a. conflict: having unconsciously repeated their childhood family experiences in the marital relationship, each struggles unsuccessfully to change the other, until the pain of useless conflict becomes an invitation to journey into soul; if each partner does his or her own psychological work, the inherent codependency of marriage is undone.

b. spiritual partners: when the codependency of marriage is undone, marriage becomes a multifaceted friendship between two truly individuating people, a contract between spiritual beings committed to unconditionally supporting and loving each other's spiritual growth.

c. love: an opportunity for the divine to flow into the world and for us to be filled with God's nature, in this way, marriage enters the sacred realm.

parent-child relationships: Psychospiritual problems with parent-child relationships may be manifested in:

a. conflict: adults must learn to differentiate between self and other (for parents cannot live their children's lives), and between false self, true self, and soul, for their children's true natures cannot be legislated; conflict can bring these distinctions into awareness.

b. missed spiritual friendship: each offspring must find his or her own self and destiny, and to the extent child rearing is done respectfully, parents and children can become friends, supporting each others' spiritual unfolding; when conflict persists instead, such spiritual friendship is never known.

c. the cultivation of souls: child rearing is a spiritual undertaking, literally consisting of the support and cultivation of our children's' souls.

family relationships: Psychospiritual problems in the family may be manifested in:

a. spiritually damaging systems: families organized in chaotic, controlling, paranoid, distant, violent, or other dysfunctional styles of relating crush opportunities for open and loving relationships, the ground of real spirituality.

b. inability to experience family spirituality: families that cannot enter sacred space together miss first and basic experience of spirituality in community.

adult-parent relationships: Psychospiritual problems in adult relationships with their parents may be manifested in:

a. failure to care for aging parents: lingering parent-child conflicts preclude the possibility of adult children becoming spiritual caretakers for their aging parents, robbing both of one of the most important spiritual times in the life span.

b. lack of modeling for spiritually meaning death: when parent-child relationships are blocked, adult children miss the chance to participate in the dying process in a spiritual way that could enhance their own dying.

RELIGIOUS PROBLEMS

abuse: Psychospiritual problems may be manifested in religious abuse when an individual, family, group, or institution use religious precepts and practices to rationalize shaming or controlling others.

addiction: Psychospiritual problems may be manifested in religious addiction when:

a. religious precepts or practices are used to compulsively control, alter, suppress, or avoid personal emotional problems (e.g., low self-esteem, loneliness, guilt, or unrecognized mental disorders).

b. religious precepts or practices are used to avoid interpersonal problems (e.g., intimacy, sexuality, conflict, or rejection).

beliefs: Psychospiritual problems with beliefs may be manifested when one's ideas about religion are inaccurate and self-injurious, that is, when they create excessive guilt, anxiety, or rigid adherence to practices.

teachers: Psychospiritual problems with teachers may be manifested in:
a. over-reliance or dependence on someone else to run one's life.
b. failure to recognize the psychological problems, exploitation, control, or abuse of a teacher, group, or religious institution.

guilt: Psychospiritual problems are often manifested in guilt. - When guilt is a product of religious abuse or erroneous religious beliefs, then it is neurotic and damaging. Guilt may also be legitimate, serving as the experience of appropriate shame when the ambitions or behavior of the false self have injured the true self or another. In neurotic guilt, the judgmental conscience needs modifying to free the true self from injury. Legitimate guilt, on the other hand, requires a religious process, often some form of ritual atonement, to correct.

SPIRITUAL PROBLEMS

spiritual path confusion: Psychospiritual problems with the spiritual path may be manifested in misunderstanding of its stages, tasks, and realities.

spiritual materialism: Problems with spiritual materialism may be manifested when spiritual experiences become objects of misinterpretation, pursuit, fascination, self-inflation, or attachment.

misuse of spiritual techniques: Problems with techniques occur when they become overly important or compulsive, displacing the other activities of a balanced life.

SOCIETAL PROBLEMS

norms: Psychospiritual problems with societal norms occur when the collective rules governing religious behavior become extreme, rigid, or damaging to the self and its healthy emotional, social, and spiritual functioning.

collective beliefs: Psychospiritual problems with collective beliefs of society occur when they become extreme, rigid, or damaging to emotional, social, and spiritual functioning.

VARIETIES OF PSYCHOLOGICAL AND SPIRITUAL HEALING

Contents: Psychological Healing
             Spiritual Healing
             Modern Versions of Ancient Spiritual Practices
             Contributions to Psychospiritual Therapy

PSYCHOLOGICAL HEALING

Psychological healing evolves from the simplest forms of loving contact, and then builds in hope, expectation, and imagination.

TOUCH

The oldest healing action known, gentle and loving touch relieves fear and anxiety. Mothers quickly learn the power of touch in quieting a child's distress. To hold, caress, or stroke another under safe and trusting conditions releases and sooths distress in ways we constantly underestimate, for if we really appreciated its power in this culture, rich and sustained hugging would be a far more common form of contact.

CARING

Touch is one element of caring, mankind's original mode of psychological healing. We care for children, the old and sick, for each other, and for our world. Caring is more then taking care of, it is an attitude communicating love, support, value, security, and commitment that contributes far more than we know to maintaining health and recovering from illness. Scientific studies repeatedly demonstrate that caring from spouse, family, and community not only increases our capacity to recover from illness but is critical to our survival.

HOPE

An extension of touch and caring is hope. When we are without hope, when we feel that getting well is impossible or pointless, then we heal more slowly and die sooner, for the will and energy to live give out.

PLACEBO

Throughout history, healers have known the value of the placebo. In the treatment of pain, for example, study after study demonstrates that a third of people given treatment with the expectation of improvement, will report improvement even when The "medicine" is nothing more than a sugar pill. The placebo effect probably embodies all the preceding healing powers.

RELAXATION AND MEDITATION

Research abounds with evidence for the benefits of relaxation. Mind, emotions, and body all profit from times of deep relaxation. Formal methods of relaxation have proliferated, integrating breath, imagery, music, and bodily sensation. Meditation, practiced simply for its relaxing and centering qualities, is equally potent.

HYPNOSIS

Building on the efficacy of caring, hope, positive expectation, and relaxation, hypnosis weaves in imagination, persuasion, and drama. Mixing these ingredients together explains a good part of the success of the shaman's healing ritual and the physician's bedside manner. When practiced skillfully, hypnosis (formal or informal) allows us to change our subjective experience of physical and emotional symptoms, and to alter our perception and attitude toward life problems.

SPIRITUAL HEALING

With its much longer history and world-wide diversity, there are many more categories, forms, and schools of spiritual healing than psychological, for scientific psychology is a very late arrival in the healing arts. Though their outward appearances may differ across times and cultures, anthropologists and religious scholars cite many common themes and processes. Human beings appeal to the supernatural in the following ways:

SHAMANISM

Shamanic medicine is the oldest form of spiritual healing known. Anthropologists describe the shaman as the tribal specialist who has learned to travel to the spiritual world in order to propitiate, control, or serve the spirits responsible for his patient's problems, and then return with a cure. Entering altered mental states, the shaman is said to leave his body, travel as a soul through space and time to other worlds or other parts of this world, and then acquire "medicine," spirit helpers, or information necessary for healing. Before, during, or after the trance travel, the shaman may dance for hours around the patient, appeal to the spirits or ancestors, perform various rites and rituals, take on his illness, extract negative energies, or use special herbs and fetishes. The dramatics of shamanic healing are often said to be part of its power, instilling hope and evoking non-ordinary states of consciousness in the patient.

SACRED PLACES, FORCES, AND OBJECTS

As old as Shamanism (and usually part of it) is the power of sacred places, objects, and forces. Shrines, historical religious sites, unusual geographic formations, and locations of alleged miracles have all be approached as places of sacred power. From the dawning of history, believers pilgrimage to them hoping to be healed by the sacred power of the site. Churches and temples are felt to be sacred places, for they we built to invoke reverence and connection to the divine. Natural forces may also be viewed as animated by spirits, forces, or other forms of supernatural agency controlling the lives and destinies of men, including earth, plants, animals, fire, air, moon, stars, and sky. The belief that spirits reside in material things and that worshipping them can produce the assistance of these beings (fetishism), is akin to idolatry or the belief that praying to statures or alters somehow reaches the sacred being they represent. Sacred objects such as masks, prayer sticks, medicine bundles, carved figures, or animal parts are similarly felt to protect, hold magic, impart power, heal, or control the forces they represent.

SPIRITUAL TOUCH

Touch is more than simply a physical comfort. Among trained or naturally talented people, it is said to be a channel for healing energies. Nurses, hospice and child-care workers, and psychic healers all describe the power of therapeutic touch in facilitating the body's natural response to illness and creating a conduit of healing spiritual energies. The reception and movement of subtle energies through the fingers is only recently being reappreciated by conventional healers, though not without considerable controvercy.

PRAYER

Closely intertwined with shamanism and the worship of sacred places, processes, and things is prayer. Beseeching the divine to intervene on our behalf is the most ancient form of spiritual healing. Spiritual healing is felt to come from the "other world" and people pray naturally and spontaneously in times of crisis, illness, and misfortune. Praying also helps us come to terms with terrible events as we seek to understand and balance God's will with our own.

FAITH HEALING

Faith healing is very close to shamanic healing in form, function, and origin, and relies heavily on prayer as its mode of operation. It goes by many names today - supernatural healing, divine healing, miraculous healing, ritual healing - and thrives in church revivals, old time camp meetings, televangelism, Pentecostal and Charismatic services, Christian Science, and in the psychotherapy of religion-based practitioners, to name a few. Christian practitioners, for example, believe that illness is an expression of divine will, arising from sin and the "fall of man," and that redemption by Jesus is the required healing. Recalling that Christ's disciples were commissioned to heal the sick, evangelists believe they are fulfilling this promise, serving as vessels or channels of divine energy through individual and group prayer, laying on of hands, and calling for the ill to give themselves over to Christ.

MEDITATION AND CONTEMPLATION

In addition to its obvious physical and psychological value, meditation is found throughout traditions as a means of altering consciousness to reach spiritual planes or states. It may involve devout and continuous reflection on a religious theme, image, or object, or a means of emptying consciousness to know the transcendent essence of mind and reality. Contemplation is similarly a practice of freeing awareness of thoughts and images, and turning inward towards God.

RITUAL

In ritual, we use actions, intentions, and objects in the material world as a symbolic means of aligning or communicating with the sacred or supernatural world. Whether it is a simple prayer, rain dance, rite of passage, religious ceremony, or repetition of a holy event (e.g., the last supper, Buddha's enlightenment), ritual is a symbolic way of momentarily bridging the sacred and profane worlds in order to effect some form of contact, healing, or correction of our relationship to the divine. It is felt that rituals restore or renew man's connection to the sacred world upon which he is totally dependent for survival, direction, and meaning.

SPIRITUAL TEACHERS

There have always been spiritual teachers. Depending on the culture and historical era, they may appear as shaman, guru, sorcerer, cleric, teacher, workshop facilitator, or retreat leader. The teacher's credentials may be formal, for example, the training required to become a priest or rabbi, semi-formal, such as approval or certification from a guru, or informal, consisting of personal spiritual experiences from which an individual creates his own teaching. Some consider their power and expertise to be based on study and training, others feel they are a channel for divine energies, and a few base it on claims of possessing a God-realized nature. A community of practitioners often surrounds the teacher, who prescribes and supervises their spiritual practices and progress.

PSYCHIC COUNSELING

The psychic counselor is said to use extrasensory psychic abilities or divination techniques to peer into the psychological and spiritual bases of an individual's problems. Clairvoyance, astrology, palmistry, crystals, pyramids, past lives, channeling, and reading cards, tea leaves, runes, auras and energy fields may be used in psychic counseling. Though the present names and explanatory models for these techniques may appear to differ from the original shamanic practices, the essential elements are the same throughout history. The psychic counselor may also use psychic energies in healing (e.g., energy field manipulations, laying on of hands).

MODERN VERSIONS OF ANCIENT SPIRITUAL PRACTICES

Medical, anthropological, psychological, social, and spiritual studies suggest that the "active ingredients" among ancient spiritual healing practices include: 1. a mythic-emotional-religious model of cause and effect that is awesome, powerful, and larger than the patient's conventional reality; 2. dramatic, stressful, and heroic healing methods that often involve life and death drama, 3. altered states of consciousness in the healer and patient that allow extraordinary healing efforts in both; 4. the patient's confidence in and surrender to the healer, with positive expectations of recovery; and 5. the activation of the body's own healing processes through the restoration of hope, psychophysiologic arousal, and placebo.

These ancient forms of spiritual healing hide everywhere in current medical and psychological practices. Wherever they occur, they represent the same physical-psycho-social-spiritual processes in ever changing guises, eras, cultures, and mythologies. How many medical "cures" are actually due to these ancient methods is difficult to ascertain, but we can be sure they continue to contribute in active and important ways, including:

* touch, caring, hope, placebo, and even indirect hypnosis (e.g., a nurse's touch, the doctor's bedside manner, the promise of cure, sugar pills, and the use of "treatments" of uncertain scientific basis e.g., herbal treatments, colonics, acupressure, transcutaneous nerve stimulation).
* shaman-like healers, sacred healing spaces, secular variations of faith healing, and the rituals of confession, atonement, and restoration (e.g., counseling and psychotherapy).
* religious practices used in holistic medicine (e.g., yoga, visualization, hypnosis, and meditation).
* the emergency room (costumes, miraculous machines, life-and-death drama, and the mysterious "other world" known as the hospital).
* silent prayer, spiritual teaching, implicit spiritual direction (used naturally by spiritually inclined counselors and psychotherapists)

Deeper still is the religious psyche and its inborn response to crisis. When someone we love becomes seriously ill, and particularly when western medicine's "magic" fails, a voice inside automatically begins to pray: "Please God, heal and protect our loved one." If the illness goes on, we begin to ask for guidance or understanding: "Please God, what is this all about? Have I done something wrong? What do you want from me?" Superstitions emerge, magically linking our loved one's healing with our own behavior, thoughts, or practices. If our personal efforts fail, we reach out for more formal religious help from clergy, prayer services, or rituals of spiritual healing. We sense there is a larger spiritual context to the crisis. It pulls us into its realm for we must leave no stone unturned. In this way, personal crises also return us to ancient, archetypal beliefs and practices.

THE CONTRIBUTIONS TO PSYCHOSPIRITUAL THERAPY

Any and all of the psychological and spiritual healing forms discussed earlier can contribute to or complement spiritually oriented psychotherapy, depending on the practitioner's training, experience, and expertise, and the client's readiness and prepartion. The follow chart provides some examples:

Contributions of Healing Forms to Psychospiritual Therapy

<u>Psychological Healing</u>

touch:
handshake, friendly touch, hugs can communicate deep implicit healing contact; explicit use via therapeutic and energetic touch

caring:
all forms of healing are intensified by the caring attitude

hope:
all forms of healing are further activated by instilling hope

placebo:
simply coming in for treatment can evoke the placebo effect

hypnosis:
guided imagery and suggestion can be used to bring healing images into the wounded psyche (e.g., receiving love or healing from a religious figure) (e.g., Tan, in Shafranske, 1996)

counseling:
prepares the client to begin the psychotherapeutic journey

psychotherapy:
prepares the client to begin the spiritual journey

<u>Spiritual Healing</u>

shamanism:
shamanistic techniques used to create religious trance, altered states, soul travel, soul retrieval as a therapy experience (e.g., Goodman, 1990; Ingerman, 1991; Harner, 1982)

sacred places,
forces, & objects:
used to evoke communion with the immanent divine or in shamanistic fashion to reach the other world, contact guardian spirits or healing energies, for protection, etc. (e.g., Harner, 1982)

prayer:
silent or communal prayer has meaningful effects (Dossey, 1993) and instills greater openness to the divine

faith healing:
healing through the invocation of the spirit's direct action in the client's body, emotions, or life

spiritual teachers:
spiritual teaching, guidance, and even initiation can be a natural part later in the therapeutic process

psychic counseling:
psychic divination as a tentative but rich source of information, and psychic healing as an adjunct

pastoral counseling:
prepares the client for the use of spiritual techniques appropriate to the particular faith, and expand client's openness to larger experiences

spiritual direction:
brings the spirit directly into the therapy contributing to client's immediate awareness, discernment skills, and life decisions

PSYCHOTHERAPY AS VISION QUEST

The ritual nature of psychotherapy can be seen more clearly when we compare it to the Vision Quest, a sacred rite conducted by Native American and other traditional peoples around the world. Often performed at times of passage (e.g., in puberty or later in life), it is a religious quest for spiritual meaning and revelation.

The ritual takes the following form. After a time of preparation and instruction, the individual leaves his family and people to venture out into the wilderness. For many days he is alone in the wild, praying, fasting, meditating, staying up all night, and waiting. Consuming only water, he wanders or searches. As the social, nutritional, and sleep deprivation increase in the vast wilderness, consciousness is opened, altered. He enters a sacred dimension when everything has mythic significance. The world itself changes, becomes subtly alive, one with his mind. Gradually everything takes on meaning, everything speaks to the questor's problem or state of consciousness.

As the days go by, the questor prays for a sacred vision that will serve his life or his people. Hungry and alone, tired, stretched beyond his resources, staying up all night chanting, singing, dancing, and performing sacred rituals, he waits. He poses questions about the purpose of his life and his place in the community, and throws them into the wilderness. Deeply immersed in the cycles of day and night, then and now, life and death, good and evil, failure and success, childhood and old age, emptiness and fullness, he breaks down realizing life itself will all be over too soon. Alone, powerless over his own destiny, he knows that he does not have forever and searches ever more intensely for his sacred vision.

From the fathomless pit of powerlessness and despair, the seeker may eventually be given what he has been seeking. Guardian spirits come in the forms of animals, plants, supernatural figures, ancestors, natural elements or forces, or in dreams or dream-like visions. From these spirits or experiences, he is blessed with special information, a power, a spirit name, and he learns what he must be for his tribe.

The questor returns home bringing his spiritual bounty back to his people. The vision has had personal and tribal importance, so he shares it in dance, song, or story, and the tribe itself is spiritually nourished by its reliving. All benefit when the sacred is touched and brought back. Through the Vision Quest, the Great Spirit teaches his people about creation, and they are thankful. The questor returns changed. He is now more of a spiritual man who knows his sacred gift and purpose more clearly. Through this perilous journey, through this greatest of all tests, he has found his "medicine."

A spiritually oriented psychotherapy is very much like this ancient ritual. In fact, they are made from the same fabric. A seeker, burdened with troubles, his life a desert, knows he must somehow search for the meaning of his suffering. He also knows from his own failure that he alone cannot figure it out, so he looks for an elder, a wise man, a shaman in the garb of the secular therapist, to help him in this search. In time, he learns that the answers are bigger than both of them, and must come from the "other world."

In religious parlance, the "other world" is the place of spirits, ancestors, God, heaven, or hell. In the language of psychotherapy, the "other world" translates to the unconscious which offers its guidance in dreams, daydreams, guided imagery, intuitions, slips of the tongue, free associations, and bodily symptoms or sensations. Thus, the "other world" is constantly revealing itself though we may not understand it.

Psychotherapy is a vision quest built into a modern secular ritual. Its journey begins with desperation and descends into a quagmire of seemingly impossible problems and deep despair. Like the vision quest, it seems as if everything familiar and reassuring is stripped away: illusions, defenses, control, pretense, magical thinking, and secrets. Descending into the underworld of the psyche, the seeker confronts the ancient wounds of childhood, the deep nature of self and soul, and all the parts of himself rejected long ago. In this process, too, all his customary and entrapping states of mind are revealed, and he begins to learn how each contributes to his suffering. Sooner or later, the searcher asks the ultimate questions that inform this search: "Who am I"? Why am I here? What must I do to be released from the self and its chains of illusion? "As therapy proceeds, the boundaries between self and soul, individual and divine, become more and more permeable and the therapy hour itself sometimes seems like a non-ordinary state of consciousness". The psyche grows pregnant with something profound, but it will not be born, yet.

Then, when all the client's resources seem depleted, when there is no place else to hide or turn, something new is born. In the manger of his psychological poverty, the divine is awakened. Its gift may come as a major transformation or, more commonly, in numerous small metamorphoses. The client changes. He is different. A new center has formed and a new life gradually evolves. These gifts of the quest arrive only as a person gives up egocentricity and control, that is, when he is willing to lose it all to find the truth.

As the journey of psychotherapy draws to an end, the client returns to his life with new energies and aspirations. Carried on the wings of divine renewal, he loves anew, builds anew, and has so much now to contribute. What he has learned and how he has changed offers something new and revitalizing to his family and community. In one way or another, he has become a prophet, mentor, elder, shaman, magician, bodhisattva, or enlightened one. Like Prometheus, he has taken fire from the heavens to light the way for humankind through the darkness of ignorance and repression.

The point I wish to emphasize here is that psychotherapy, even in its secular or medicalized form, is a more powerful and profound method of change than most therapists realize. But the power is in the ritual, and the consciousness of the one who guides it. If the therapist has no vision or mythic grasp of this ritual format, then his therapy will be diluted and empty. To return this archetypal power to the art of psychotherapy, the therapist must know the secret ways of the journey, how to honor and petition the Sacred Being in whom the whole transformation takes place, how to replace sterile medical jargon with more potent mythic words, and how to plant the seeds of this great ritual in his client's soul. Then, without preconception, like a midwife, patient and trusting, the therapist will see these seeds bear fruit. As one who has taken both the psychotherapeutic journey and the vision quest, I know first hand the power and the equivalencies of these rituals.

Finally, it should be pointed out that virtually any meaningful and sustained spiritual practice will initiate this transformative processes. Whether it is meditation, fasting, chanting, asceticism, service, daily prayer, mountain climbing, running, or any other activity, if it is performed with genuine desire for higher learning and spiritual transcendence, the same stages apply. Like supervised spiritual practice, the value of an enlightened psychotherapy is that this process of transformation is consciously and intentionally nourished, guided, and protected.

SOME IDEAS ON TAKING A RELIGIOUS AND SPIRITUAL HISTORY

Mental health professionals know a lot about inquiring into the medical, familial, social, educational, and economic backgrounds of their clients, but they rarely think of taking a serious religious and spiritual history. We are finally beginning to recognize, however, that religious and spiritual health can be as important to our clients' emotional adjustment and well-being as any of these other factors, and should, therefore, be assessed. Therapists also need to remember that their clients often appreciate the chance to discuss their religious and spiritual beliefs and experiences. In fact, it is one area they commonly complain is not addressed as fully as they would wish in their psychotherapeutic experience.

To conduct a religious and spiritual history, the areas listed below should be sensitively addressed. Inquiry includes factual information as well as personal feelings, associations and experiences. As with any evaluative procedure, this process involves assessment, evaluation, and recommendations. Keep in mind the distinctions between religion, spirituality, mystical, and non-ordinary experience. Religion refers to the client's institutional beliefs and practices. Spirituality refers to their personal, private and subjectively experienced relationship to the transcendent. Mystical experience consists of a profound and direct contact with the sacred. The term non-ordinary states of consciousness refers to extraordinary experiences that fall outside our everyday reality (e.g., out-of-body experiences). Keep in mind also that the sacred referent should be very flexible, allowing the client to use whatever term he chooses (i.e., God, the transcendent, higher power, supreme being, the spirit world, or a particular figure such as Jesus, Mohammed, Moses, Buddha). For simplicity, this questionnaire will use God as the sacred referent.

ASSESSMENT AREAS AND QUESTIONS

I. Religious Background and Activities:
    A. What religion where you raised in? Which specific denomination? What are some early memories of your religious training?
    B. Was your religious training strict or lenient, intense or relaxed, consistent or sporadic, pleasant or unpleasant?
    C. How religious were your parents?
    D. Did you remain in that religion? If not, why did you change?
    E. Do you currently attend religious services or activities?
    F. What do you get out of your religious activities and affiliation?
    G. Do you feel personally supported by the people in your religion?
    H. Can you turn to your clergy or congregation for help in times of personal need? When was the last time you consulted your clergy?
    I. What religious acts, ceremonies or rituals are most important to you?

II. Religious Beliefs:
A.   Do you have a conception of God? What is it?
B.   Is God personal or impersonal, close or distant, involved or uninvolved, loving or stern, inside or outside?
C.   Do your beliefs about God bring you comfort or distress?
D.   Has your notion of God changed over the years? Recently?
E.   What do you believe God expects from you?
F.   Do you feel God disapproves of the life you have lead?
G.   What are your favorite religious passages, ideas, stories or characters?
H.   What do you expect to happen when you die?
I.   What do you believe about sin, grace, repentance, heaven and hell?

III. Prayer Experience:
A.   Do you pray? How? How often? What is it like to pray? What does prayer mean to you? What do you experience when you pray?
B.   What do you believe happens when you pray?
C.   Do you believe your prayers have been heard or answered?
D.   Do you believe God cares about your prayers?

IV. Spiritual and mystical experiences:
A. Have you had any of the following spiritual or mystical experiences? Do you know anyone who has? What happened?

__religious conversions	__near death experiences
__out of body experiences	__12 step spirituality
__religious dreams	__religious visions or hallucinations
__miracles	__religious heading
__soul loss or possession	__kundalini
__witchcraft	__enlightenment or mystical experiences
__hearing God voice	
__other non-ordinary states of consciousness	__drug induced religious experiences
	__other (describe)

B.   What effect have your spiritual or mystical experiences had on you?
V. Spiritual meaning of life:
A.   What is the spiritual meaning of your life?
B.   What have been the major spiritual stepping stones of your life? How has God worked in your life?
C.   Do you ascribe any spiritual meaning to your current problems?
D.   How does God function in your personal life?

EVALUATION: RESULTS, DIAGNOSIS, RESOURCES, DECISION

I. Assessment Results: Nature of Religious or Spiritual Distress or Dysfunction
    A. Nature of the God Image
        1. Specific Images Used:

a. Friend	g. Creator	m. Redeemer
b. Comforter	h. Holy Spirit	n. Sufferer
c. Creator	i. Judge	o. Lover
d. Mother/Father	j. Unfathomable	p. Dark Night

e. Spouse
f. Provider

k. All Powerful
l. All knowing

2. Pathology of the God Image:
   a. Absence of meaningful God image: meaninglessness, empty, or dead universe
   b. Negative God image: stern, unforgiving, judgmental, perfectionistic, authoritarian, unavailable

B. Specific religious beliefs, involvements, or formal practices that cause or contribute to client's distress or dysfunction.
   1. Guilt, shame, fear, hell, damnation, sin, personal unworthiness
   2. Conflicts between personal beliefs and formal dogma
   3. Bizarre or confusing ideas about religion
   4. Coercion or pressure from religious group

C. Religious beliefs or practices that conflict or interfere with medical or psychotherapeutic procedures.
   1. Disbelief in medical or psychological procedures
   2. Interference from relatives or congregation with client's treatment

D. Pathological Use of Religion:
   1. Magical or autistic thinking
   2. Religiosity
   3. Excessive austerity
   4. Other

E. Misunderstanding of genuine spiritual experiences (e.g., near death, spontaneous mystical experience, religious dreams, synchronous events, religious vision)
   1. Client misinterprets a religious experiences as evidence of craziness
   2. Client's other medical or psychological providers misinterpret his/her religious experience as mental illness.
F. Presence of Concurrent Organic or Psychiatric Disturbance

II. Differential Diagnosis
   A. Basic Questions:
      1. To what extent are client's problems caused or aggravated by their religious background, training, beliefs, or current affiliation?
      2. To what extent is the client pathologically incorporating religious symbols or ideas into their ongoing organic or psychiatric problems?
      3. To what extent are the client's experiences genuinely spiritual rather than manifestations of psychiatric or organic conditions? Are they being misinterpreted?

   B. Differential Diagnosis
      1. Organic vs. functional etiology, or mixed
      2. Psychotic vs. mystical state, or mixed
      3. Adaptive vs. defensive use of religious, spiritual, mystical or other non-ordinary states of consciousness

III. Review of Available Resources
   A. Religious Resources:
      1. Religious community: affiliation, fellowship, emotional support, guidance in times of hardship or crisis. These may also include:
          a. Support groups
          b. Classes
          c. Prayer meetings
          d. Volunteer assistance
      2. Religious professionals: clergy, pastoral counselors, spiritual directors
      3. Religious beliefs: purpose and meaning of life, morality, forgiveness and love, solace in times of hardship or crisis
      4. Religious history: stability, continuity, connection

   B. Spiritual Resources:
      1. Extent to which client feels close to, loved, or known by God
      2. Extent to which client's felt relationship with God provides comfort, hope, meaning, and happiness.
      3. Extent to which prayer and spirituality help client cope with hardship, crisis or illness.

   C. Medical Resources:
      1. Examination
      2. Tests for organic pathology
      3. Treatment: Medication, hospitalization, consultation

   D. Psychological Resources:
      1. Immediate crisis intervention
      2. Short term integration and working through of crisis experience
      3. Long term work on characterologic wounds and/or spiritual journey

   E. Other Resources In Social Environment:
      1. Alternative safe environment during spiritual emergency
      2. Support structure through crisis

   F. Additional Specialized Guidance through Mystical State or Other Non-Ordinary States of Consciousness

   G. Educational Resources: classes, reading, advice

IV. Decision:
   A. Selection and location of resources to meet client needs
   B. Coordination and management of resources over time

BIBLIOGRAPHY

Abbott, Douglas, Berry, Margaret, & Meredith, William. Religious Belief and Practice: A Potential Asset in Helping Families. *Family Relations,* 1990, 39, 443-448.

American Psychiatric Association. *Diagnostic and Statistical manual of Mental Disorders.* Washington, DC: 1994.

American Psychological Association Monitor, Vol. 27, #8, Aug. 1996.

Arterburn, Stephen, & Felton, Jack. *Toxic Faith.* Oliver-Nelson Publishers, Nashville: 1991.

Assagioli, Robert. *Psychosynthesis.* Penguin Books, New York:1976.

Bassett, R. L., Camplin, W., Humphrey, D., Dorr, C., Biggs, S., Distaffen, R., Doxtator, I., Flaherty, M., Hunsberger, P. J., Poage, R., & Thompson, H. Measuring Christian maturity: A comparison of several scales. *Journal of Psychology and Christianity,* 9, 84-93, 1990.

Bergin, Allen. Quoted in *The Family Therapy Networker,* Sept/Oct. 1990.

Bogart, G. The use of meditation in psychotherapy: A review of the literature. *American Journal of Psychotherapy,* July, 1991, 383-412.

Boorstein, Seymour, ed. *Transpersonal Psychotherapy.* State Univ. of New York

Press, Albany: 1996.

Booth, Leo. *When God Becomes a Drug: Breaking the Chains of Religious Addiction & Abuse.* Tarcher/Putnam,1991.

Bottoms, Bette, Shaver, Phillip, Goodman, Gail, & Qin, Jianjian. In the Name of God: A Profile of Religion-Related Child Abuse. In *Religious Influence on Personal and Societal Well-Being.* J. of Social Issues, Vol. 51, #2, Plenum Pub., New York, Summer, 1995.

Buber, Martin. *The Way of Response.* Schocken Books, New York: 1966.

Bucke, Richard. *Cosmic Consciousness: A Study in the Evolution of the Human Mind.* E.P. Dutton, New York: 1923.

Campbell, Joseph. *The Hero with a Thousand Faces.* Bollingen Foundation, Inc., New York: 1949.

Campbell, Joseph. *Myths to Live By.* Bantam: 1972

Campbell, Joseph. *The Power of Myth.* Doubleday, New York: 1988.

Coles, Robert. *The Spiritual Life of Children.* Houghton Mifflin Company, Boston: 1990.

Cox, Harvey. "Christianity" in Sharma, Arvind, ed., *Our Religions.* Harper San Francisco: 1995.

Csikszentmihalyi, M.*Flow: The Psychology of Optimal Experience.* Harper & Row, New York: 1990.

DeJong, G. F., Faulkner, J. E., & Warland, R. H. Dimensions of religiosity reconsidered: Evidence from a cross-cultural study. *Social Forces,* 54, 866-889, 1976.

Deikman, Arthur. *The Observing Self: Mysticism and Psychotherapy.* Beacon Press, Boston: 1982.

Dossey, Larry. *Healing Words: The Power of Prayer and the Practice of Medicine.* HarperSanFrancisco:1993.

Dougherty, Rose Mary. *Group Spiritual Direction.* Paulist Press, New York/Mahwah, NJ: 1995.

Edinger, Edward. *The Christian Archetype: A Jungian Commentary on the Life of Christ.* Inner City Books,1987

Edwards, Tilden. *Spiritual Friend: Reclaiming the Gift of Spiritual Direction.* Paulist Press, New York: 1980.

Eliade, Mircea. *The Sacred and the Profane.* Harcourt Brace, New York: 1961.

Ellison, E. W. Spiritual Well-Being: Conceptualization and measurement. *Journal of Psychology and Theology,* 11, 330-340, 1983.

Feurstein, Georg. *Holy Madness: The Shock Tactics and Radical Teachings of Crazy-Wise Adepts, Holy Fools, and Rascal Gurus.* Paragon House, NY: 1991.

Fowler, James. *Stages of Faith: The Psychology of Human Development and the Quest for Meaning.* Harper San Francisco: 1981.

Fowler, James. Pluralism and Oneness in Religious Experience: William James, Faith-Development Theory, and Clinical Practice. In Shafranske, Edward, ed., *Religion and the Clinical Practice of Psychology,* American Psychological Assn., Washington, D.C.:1996

Gallup, George. *Adventures in Immortality: A Look Beyond the Threshold of Death.* McGraw-Hill, New York: 1982.

Gallup, George, & Castelli, J. *The People's Religion: American Faith in the 90s.* Macmillan, New York: 1989.

Gartner, John. Religious Commitment, Mental Health, and Prosocial Behavior: A Review of the Empirical Literature. In Shafranske, Edward, ed. *Religion and the Clinical Practice of Psychology.* American Psychological Assn., Washington, D.C.: 1996.

Genia, Vicky. *Counseling and Psychotherapy of Religious Clients.* Praeger: 1995.

Goleman, Daniel, & Davidson, Richard, eds. *Consciousness: Brain, States of Awareness, and Mysticism.* Harper & Row: 1979.

Goodman, Felicitas. *Where Spirits Ride the Wind: Trance Journeys and Other Ecstatic Experiences.* Indiana University Press:1990.

Gordon, James. *The Golden Guru: The Strange Journey of Bhagwan Shree Rajneesh.* The Stephen Greene Pressing, Lexington, Massachusetts: 1987)

Gratton, Carolyn. *The Art of Spiritual Guidance.* Crossroad Publishing Co., New York: 1992.

Grof, Christina, & Grof, Stanislav. *The Stormy Search for the Self: A Guide to Personal Growth through Transformational Crisis.* Tarcher/Perigee: 1992

Grof, Stanislav, & Grof, Christina, eds. *Spiritual Emergency: When Personal Transformation Becomes a Crisis.* Jeremy Tarcher, Los Angeles: 1989.

Guggenheim, Bill, & Guggenheim, Judy. *Hello From Heaven.* Bantam Books: 1996.

Halligan, Fredrica & Shea, John, eds. *The Fires of Desire: Erotic Energies and the Spiritual Quest.* Cross Roads, New York: 1992.

Harner, Michael. *The Way of the Shaman.* Bantam Books, New York: 1982.

Hillman, James. *Archetypal Psychology: A Brief Account.* Spring Publications, Dallas: 1981.

Hillman, James. *The Soul's Code: In Search of Character and Calling.* Random House, New York: 1996.

Hunsberger, Bruce. Religion and Prejudice: The Role of Religious Fundamentalism, Quest, and Right-Wing Authoritarianism. In *Religious Influence on Personal and Societal Well-Being.* J. of Social Issues, Vol. 51, #2, Plenum Pub., New York, Summer, 1995.

Huxley, Aldous. *The Perennial Philosophy.* Harper & Brothers, New York:1945.

Ingerman, Sandra. *Soul Retrieval: Mending the Fragmented Self.* Harper San Francisco: 1991.

Jaeckle, Charles, & Clebsch, William. *Pastoral Care in Historical Perspective.* Jason Aronson, New York: 1964.

Jaffe, Lawrence. *Liberating the Heart: Spirituality and Jungian Psychology.* Inner City Books, 1990.

James, William. *The Varieties of Religious Experience: A Study in Human Nature.* The Modern Library, New York: 1936.

Johnson, David & VanVonderen. *The Subtle Power of Spiritual Abuse: Recognizing and Escaping Spiritual Manipulation and False Spiritual Authority Within the Church.* Bethany House Publishers: Minneapolis: 1991.

Johnson, K.D. Theopathology: Concept, assessment, intervention. *The Journal of Pastoral Care,* 45, 244-252.

Jung, Carl. *Modern Man in Search of a Soul*. Harcourt Brace & Company, 1933.

Kabat-Zinn, J., Lipworth, L., Burney R., & Sellers, W. Four-year follow-up of a meditation-based program for the self-regulation of chronic pain: Treatment outcomes and compliance. *Clinical Journal of Pain*, 1986, 2: 159-173.

Kabat-Zinn, J, Massion, A., Kristeller, J., Peterson, L., Fletcher,, K., Pbert, L., Linderking, W., & Santorelli, S. Effectiveness of a meditation-based stress reduction program in the treatments of anxiety disorders. *American Journal of Psychiatry*, 1992, 149: 936-943.

Kass, J. D., Friedman, R., Leserman, J., Zuttermeister, P.C., & Benson, H. Health outcomes and a new index of spiritual experience. *Journal for the Scientific Study of Religion*, 30, 203-211, 1991.

Katz, Steven, ed. *Mysticism and Philosophical Analysis*. Oxford University Press, New York: 1978.

Kelly, Eugene W. *Spirituality and Religion in Counseling and Psychotherapy*. American Counseling Association, Alexandria, VA: 1995.

Larson, Earnie, & Parnegg, Janee. *Recovering Catholics: What To Do When Religion Comes Between You and God*. HarperSanFrancisco:1992.

Lukoff, David, Lu, F. & Turner, R. *"Toward a More Culturally Sensitive DSM-IV: Psycho-religious and Psychospiritual Problems."* Journal of Nervous and Mental Disorders, Vol. 180, 11, 11/92.

Lukoff, David, Lu, F. & Turner, R. "Diagnosis: A Transpersonal Clinical Approach to Religious and Spiritual Problems" In Scotton, B. W., Chinen, Allan, G., & Battistia, John R. (Eds.) *Textbook of Transpersonal Psychiatry and Psychology*. Basic Books, New York: 1996.

Maslow, Abraham. *Toward a Psychology of Being*. D. Van Nostrand, New York: 1968.

May, Gerald. *Simply Sane: The Spirituality of Mental Health*. Crossroads, New York: 1994.

May, Gerald. *Care of Mind, Care of Spirit: A Psychiatrist Explores Spiritual Direction*. Harper San Francisco: 1992.

McKee, Denise D. & Chappel, John N. Spirituality and Medical Practice. *The Journal of Family Practice*, 35, 2, 1992.

Moody, Raymond. *Life After Life*. Mockingbird Books, Atlanta: 1975

Moore, Thomas. *Care of the Soul: A Guide for Cultivating Depth and Sacredness in Everyday Life*. Harper Collins, New York: 1992.

Ormerod, Neil, & Ormerod, Thea. *When Ministers Sin: Sexual Abuse in the Churches*. Millennium Books: 1995.

Oser, F. K. The development of religious judgment. In F. K. Oser & W. G. Scarlett (Eds.), Religious development in childhood and adolescence. *New Directions for Child Development*, 1991, 52, 5-25.

Pargament, Kenneth. Religious Methods of Coping: Resources for the Conservation and Transformation of Significance. In Shafranske, Edward, ed. *Religion and the Clinical Practice of Psychology*. American Psychological Assn., Washington, D.C.: 1996a.

Pargament, Kenneth. In Clay, Rebecca. Psychologists' faith in religion begins to grow. American Psychological Association Monitor, Vol. 27, No. 8., Aug. 1996b.

Peck, Scott. *The Road Less Traveled: A New Psychology of Love, Traditional Values and Spiritual Growth*. Touchstone, New York: 1978.

Peck, Scott. *Further Along the Road Less Traveled: The Unending Journey Toward Spiritual Growth*. Touchstone/Simon &Schuster: 1993.

Perry, John. *The Self in Psychotic Process*. Spring Publications, Dallas: 1953.

Perry, John. Spiritual Emergence and Renewal. In Grof, Staislav and Grof, Christina (ed.).*Spiritual Emergency: When Personal Transformation Becomes a Crisis*. Jeremy Tarcher, Los Angeles, 1989.

Pike, Nelson. *Mystic Union: An Essay in the Phenomenology of Mysticism*. Cornell University Press, Ithaca, 1992.

Ring, Kenneth. *Life at Death: A Scientific Investigation of the Near-Death Experience.* Coware, McCann & Geoghegan, New York: 1980.

Ring, Kenneth. *Heading Toward Omega: In Search of the Meaning of the Near-Death Experience.* William Morrow, New York: 1984.

Rizzuto, A. M. Religious development: A psychoanalytic point of view. In F. K. Oser & W. G. Scarlett (Eds.), Religious development n childhood and adolescence. *New Directions for Child Development,* 1991, 52, 47-60.

Robinson, John. *Death of a Hero, Birth of the Soul: Answering the Call of Midlife.* Tzedakah, Sacramento: 1995; re-released by Council Oak, Spring 1997.

Saliba, John. *Understanding New Religious Movements.* William Eerdmans Publishing Company: 1995.

Sannella, Lee. *The Kundalini Experience.* Integral Publishing, 1992.

Sanford, John. *Ministry Burnout.* Paulist Press, New York: 1982.

Scott-Maxwell, Florida. *The Measure of My Days.* Penguin Books, New York: 1968.

Scotton, Bruce W., Chinen, Allan B., & Battista, John R. *Textbook of Transpersonal Psychiatry and Psychology.* Basic Books (A Division of HarperCollins Publishers), New York: 1996.

Shafranske, Edward, ed. *Religion and the Clinical Practice of Psychology.* American Psychological Assn., Washington, D.C.: 1996.

Simpkinson, Anne. Soul Betrayal. *Common Boundary,* 14, 6, Nov/Dec. 1996.

Spero, M. H. *Religious Objects as Psychological Structures.* University of Chicago Press, Chicago: 1992.

St. John of the Cross (trans. Allison Peers). *Dark Night of the Soul.* Doubleday, New York: 1990

Stace, W.T. *Mysticism and Philosophy.* Tarcher, Los Angeles: 1960.

Steere, David. *Spiritual Presence in Psychotherapy: A Guide for Caregivers.* Brunner/Mazel, Inc. New York: 1997.

Sullivan, Barbara. *Psychotherapy Grounded in the Feminine Principle.* Chiron Publications, Wilmette, Illinois: 1989.

Tan, Siang-Yang. Religion in clinical practice: Implicit and explicit integration. In Shafranske, Edward, ed. *Religion and the Clinical Practice of Psychology* American Psychological Assn., Washington, D.C.: 1996.

Urbanowski, Ferris & Miller, John. Trauma, psychotherapy, and meditation. *Journal of Transpersonal Psychology,* 1996, 28: 31-48.

Underhill, Evelyn. *Mysticism.* New American Library, New York: 1974.

Van Dusen, Wilson. *The Natural Depth in Man.* Swedenborg Foundation, New York: 1981.

Veach, Tracy L. & Chappel, John N. Measuring Spiritual Health: A Preliminary Study. *Substance Abuse,* 13, 139-147, 1992.

Waldfogel, Shimon & Wolpe, Paul Root. Using Awareness of Religious Factors to Enhance Interventions in Consultation-Liaison Psychiatry. *Hospital and Community Psychiatry,* 44, 5, May 1993.

Walsh, Roger. *The Spirit of Shamanism.* Jeremy Tarcher, Los Angeles: 1990.

Watts, Alan. *Psychotherapy East & West.* Ballatine, New York:1961.

Welch, John. *When Gods Die: An Introduction to John of the Cross.* Paulist Press, New York/Mahwah: 1990.

Welwood, John, ed. *The Meeting of the Ways: Explorations in East/West Psychology.* Schocken Books, New York: 1979.

White, John, ed. *The Highest State of Consciousness.* Anchor Books, Garden City, New York: 1972.

White, John, ed. *What is Enlightenment?* Jeremy Tarcher, Los Angeles: 1984.

Witmer, J. M., Sweeney, T. J., & Meyers, J. e. *Wellness Evaluation of Li festyle: The WEL Inventory.* Mind Garden, Palo Alto, CA: 1994.

Z, Phillip. *A Skeptic's Guide to the Twelve Steps.* Harper Collins, New York: 1990.